ZERO CARBON BRITAIN 2030

A NEW ENERGY STRATEGY

The second report of the
Zero Carbon Britain project

Foreword

Forewords and quotes below from:
Professor Graham Parkhurst, Centre for Transport and Society
Sir John Haughton, Former Co-Chair, Intergovernmental Panel on Climate Change
Professor Godfrey Boyle, Open University
Rob Hopkins, Transition Towns Founder
Paul Davies, Wates Living Spaces
Dr Victoria Johnson, new economics foundation
Hugo Spowers, Riversimple.

"As historically the first high-carbon economy to have developed, and today being a significant net importer of carbon-intensive goods, the UK has a particular responsibility to take political and practical leadership in the international process of decarbonisation. ***zero****carbon****britain****2030*** makes an important contribution to the climate change debate. It is pioneering in offering a fully integrated routemap for addressing carbon emissions from the UK perspective, going beyond the most ambitious targets hitherto to propose a 90 percent reduction by 2030 (rather than the 2050 typically discussed), together with 'carbon capture' equivalent to the remaining 10 per cent.

In order to effectively eliminate carbon emissions from British industry, homes, power generation, and transport systems, the report seeks to "power down" high-carbon living by reducing energy demand, so as to facilitate a transfer to fossil-free supply. Importantly, the carbon reduction benefits are placed in the context of wider benefits of 'regime change', including avoiding the spectre of ever more expensive and scarce oil, the opportunities for 'green jobs' and the creation of a more equitable society. New technologies and more efficient design are evaluated as an essential part of the decarbonisation strategy, to be "powered up". Offshore wind and wave energy are identified as having the strongest potential as renewable energy sources, providing most of the fossil-fuel free energy mix by 2030 (and with the latter including no new nuclear capacity).

Although embracing the importance of new technologies, the report does recognise the limits to 'fit and forget' fixes, identifying more radical reform as essential in the agricultural sector, which in the future will focus on 'locking in' carbon in the soil and vegetation, and in spatial and transport planning, to prioritise the needs of people, rather than energy-intense vehicles. These strategic shifts will also need to be accompanied by behaviour and lifestyle changes by citizens, such as more walking and cycling and less meat consumption.

Whilst it is the nature of scenarios that they are rarely followed precisely by actual events, **zero***carbon***britain***2030* has effectively applied a 'backcasting' approach to demonstrate that at least one set of policy options and technical measures exists to eliminate carbon emissions whilst simultaneously enhancing our quality of life. We now need the political leadership, public consensus, and ongoing scientific support to turn possibility into reality."

Professor Graham Parkhurst, Centre for Transport and Society, University of the West of England.

"This new report from the Centre for Alternative Technology is much to be welcomed, coming as it does at the start of a new administration. The goal of peak emissions by 2016 is less than seven years away. Everything necessary to reach that first goal will have to be put in place by the next government – a challenge they must take up with unusual urgency. A year ago in May 2009, a Nobel Laureates Symposium on Climate Change hosted in London by the Prince of Wales had as its title, *The Fierce Urgency of Now*.

One of the few positive outcomes of the Copenhagen Conference in December 2009 was the near-global consensus for a goal of $2°$ C for the maximum rise of global average temperature from its pre-industrial value due to human activities. That is a necessary, but tough target for the world to meet. It will require, for instance, peak global emissions by about 2016. However it was very disappointing that little was accomplished at Copenhagen to set up the actions required for its realization.

Two reasons are often advanced to delay action on climate change. The first is to present climate change as a longer-term issue and argue that of more immediate concern are big issues like world poverty. That may appear to be the case until it is realised that the plight of the world's poor will become enormously worse unless strong action to curb climate change is taken now. The second is to suggest the financial crisis must have top priority and action on climate change will have to wait. That again may seem good sense until it is realised that there is much to be gained if both crises are tackled together. Also, many studies, for instance those by the International Energy Agency[1] (IEA, 2008), demonstrate that necessary action is affordable; increased investment in the short term is balanced by savings that accrue in the longer term.

This report presents detailed information and argument to demonstrate that zero emissions by 2030 is within reach – given appropriate commitment, dedication and effort on the part of government, industry, NGOs and the public at large. In calling for a common sense of purpose, not just nationally but internationally too, it points out the benefits to society – its health, social welfare and sustainability – that will result from the pursuit of such a goal. May I urge you to study carefully its arguments and its findings."

Sir John Houghton, Former Co-Chair of the Intergovernmental Panel on Climate Change.

"Since their pioneering *Low Energy Strategy for the UK* in 1977, the Centre for Alternative Technology has been pointing the way towards a sustainable energy future for Britain. Now the CAT researchers have done it again. Their new **zero**carbon**britain**2030 report, building on the analysis in the first Zero Carbon Britain report in 2007, describes in detail how the UK could make the transition to a zero carbon society as early as 2030. CAT's integrated approach involves "powering-down" (reducing energy wastage) and "powering-up" (deploying renewable energies), combined with lifestyle and land use changes. It demonstrates that the UK economy could be 100% powered by renewables – if we can muster the political will to make it happen. And if we do, the Britain of 2030 will be a greener, cleaner, fairer place. ZCB2030's proposals are more radical than those of the UK Government, which envisages a much slower 80% reduction in carbon emissions by 2050. But even if they don't yet agree with all of its conclusions, ZCB2030 should be essential reading for politicians, policymakers, researchers and anyone else interested in positive responses to the challenges of climate change and energy security."
Godfrey Boyle, Professor of Renewable Energy, Open University.

"The first *zerocarbonbritain* report, published in June 2007, was an extraordinary document. Although aspects of a zero carbon Britain were missing from it, such as food and farming and behaviour change, it was an audaciously bold and desperately needed framing of a key concept – how the UK could move to being a zero carbon economy over 20 years. Rather than come up with endless reasons why this seemingly impossible task couldn't be done, the default political response to climate change at the time, it set out a bold vision for a lower-energy future. It was a visionary and inspired project, as well as a prototype for a larger and more detailed follow-up. It is that follow-up, **zero**carbon**britain**2030, that you now hold in your hands.

With Government still in denial about peak oil, with the scale of the changes necessitated to have the best possible chances of avoiding catastrophic climate change leading some to deem them impossible, and others to retreat into a rejection of the science, ZCB2030 is a breath of fresh air. We stand at an unprecedented crossroads, making choices now that will profoundly affect the future. What ZCB2030 does brilliantly is to argue that the approach of powering down (reducing demand) and powering up (building a new, zero carbon energy infrastructure) is not a hair shirt, survivalist rejection of modernity, rather it is the logical, achievable next step forward for the people of these islands. It is a move towards entrepreneurship, resilience, connectedness and stability. It offers a return to scale, a bringing home of the impacts of our actions, and a shift to a world that we can hand on to our grandchildren with relief and pride, and with a twinkle in our eyes.

Bringing together much of current thinking on energy, food, climate change, economics and the psychology of engaging people in such a monumental undertaking, it argues its case patiently and clearly. In the Transition movement, we often ask the question, 'what would it feel like, look like, smell like, sound like, if you woke up in 2030 and we had successfully managed this transition?' ZCB2030 offers a very tangible taste of such a world, of energy-efficient homes, with less need to travel and highly efficient public transport for when we do need to, more localised food production and a more seasonal diet, of energy production owned and managed by the communities it serves. For many of you reading this report, some of these things will already be an integral part of your lives. In all the time that I taught gardening and permaculture, nobody ever came back to me and said that their quality of life had been diminished by acquiring those skills. Likewise, the societal shift in this direction will be a collective journey, a collective undertaking, and one that offers an increase in our quality of life, rather than a decrease.

Inevitably with a work going against the status quo in such a fundamental way, such as ZCB2030, questions arise, such as whether, in the light of the UK's recent economic turmoils and declining levels of surplus net energy, we can actually afford to implement the new infrastructure set out here? Will there be sufficient economic slack to allow us to resource this? One thing is certain, that the transition set out here is the clearest, best researched and most attractive option that is currently on the table, and we are beholden to work out how to make it, or something that has built on it, happen. ZCB2030 also offers a national framework, within which communities can begin to design their own approaches, their own 'Zero Carbon [insert name of settlement in question] Plans'. Some are now starting to do this, offering a fascinating synergy of top down and bottom up thinking. Indeed the Totnes Energy Descent Action Plan, which I was involved in, drew heavily on *zerocarbonbritain* for its energy section.

ZCB2030 deserves several reads through, packed as it is with information and links. Now that we have it, what can we do to bring it into reality? We can spread it around, enthuse about it far and wide, badger and lobby our elected local and national representatives with it, and at the local level, use it to underpin our thinking about where we see our communities going. Whether we choose to see the changes compelled by peak oil and climate change as a disaster, or as an historic opportunity to, as Thomas Paine put it, 'build the world anew', is up to us. For me, the vision of the future that ZCB2030 sets out is a powerful attractant, one that is increasingly inspiring and motivating individuals and communities across the country to do their bit to bring it about.

The generation that lived through the War had a vital life mission, survival. The next generation had the strong mission that they wanted their children to have happier and richer lives than they had. For the last couple of generations though, we have rather been treading water, without a collective mission. ZCB2030 offers that, a call to arms, the opportunity to undertake a great work that generations hence will tell tales about and celebrate in song. I, for one, am profoundly grateful for the effort and thinking that has gone into this remarkable piece of work, and I look forward to the day when we can look back to it, not as another report that grew dusty on a shelf, but as a key contribution to the society-wide discussion so urgently needed in the move towards

the remarkable, timely, selfless and compassionate shift that the people of these islands made in response to the challenges faced."
Rob Hopkins, Founder of Transition Towns.

"As a contractor involved in the construction and refurbishment of buildings in the UK, we understand that most of the technical solutions required to deliver the vision set out in this report exist today and are tried and tested products and solutions. It is our belief that this undertaking represents the biggest economic opportunity our nation has witnessed since the industrial revolution, we have the opportunity to rebuild our economy and create huge employment. However in order for this to happen we need not to focus on the technical barriers but the financial one s, in order to unlock this opportunity we require new ways of valuing property, and new and innovative financial models. We need to understand that we can no longer separate the capital cost of works from the running costs of buildings, to deliver a zero carbon Britain we need to start planning for the long term and be prepared to make difficult decisions today that will benefit our future."
Paul Davies, Wates Living Spaces.

"This report clearly shows that the Great Transition to a zero carbon Britain is not only the most pressing challenge of our time, it is also entirely possible. The solutions needed to create a low-carbon and high well-being future for all exist, what has been missing to date, is the political will to implement them".
Dr Victoria Johnson, Senior Researcher, Climate Change and Energy Programme, nef (the new economics foundation).

"This important report both acknowledges the scale of change required andrecognisesthat the various issues cannot be addressed independently. My work is in the transport sector and I have for long argued that we cannot make sensible decisions about transport policy independently of energy policy in the wider sense, so the systemic analysis in this report is to be welcomed. Furthermore, contemporary debate, and investment, revolves around technology and what incremental reduction of impacts it is realistic to expect from our commercial system. In contrast, this report loudly proclaims a goal and then develops a strategy to get there. Less unsustainable is still not sustainable – yet there appears to be a subconscious delusion that it is more reasonable to contest nature's laws than stem the ever-burgeoning transport requirement that the market has the 'right' to demand!

A step change in the environmental burden imposed by transport is required, and this requires a step change in solutions. We need a synthesis of multiple technical solutions rather than the one-size-fits-all approach that the versatility of the internal combustion engine has allowed us. The criterion by which we match technical solutions to specific niches will be energy efficiency, thedominant metric that we must pursue, anddifferent solutions are more efficient in different niches. Therefore, a complex mix of almost all the fuels and powertrains that have been proposed have a role to play, with the exception of the proposals in the 50's for family cars powered by nukes! This makes it more realistic to meet demand because a) the aggregated energy demand is lower and b) the demand is spread over all renewable energy sources and energy vectors; whilst potential on greening the electricity grid is substantial, the last thing we can afford is to impose the entirety of transport demand on the grid as well.

But this report does not just dwell on the technologies. Technology does have a vital role to play but, although necessary, it is not sufficient. In this report, CAT have tackled the whole of the particularly knotty problem of decarbonising this area of human activity – Power Down before we conclude how much we need to Power Up, reduce demand *as well as* focus on efficiency and develop renewable strategies to meet our needs. There is a great temptation to look to technology for solutions when the principle barriers to sustainable transport are not technical but to do with the inertia in the highly mature systems that we have developed. These systems have been remarkably effective at achieving what they were intended to achieve, enabling cheap travel, but they were forged in an area when the constraints of today were simply not on the radar, so it is hardly surprising that the systems that we have inherited are no longer fit for purpose. Highlighting an example in the report, we recognise that we need to wring the maximum utility out of every unit of resource we use and yet wecontinue to sell vehicles rather than a transport service. This rewards the opposite of what we are trying to achieve, the maximisation of resource consumption rather than the minimisation, obsolescence and high-running costs rather than longevity and low-running costs; issues such as these are not a matter of technology butpeople, politics and business."

Hugo Spowers, Riversimple

Endnotes

[1]IEA (2008), Energy Technology Perspectives, IEA/OECD

Reviewers, seminar participants and additional contributors by chapter

The contributors to this project have done so in relation to their own particular areas of expertise. Many have only worked on one chapter of the report, therefore an individuals listing here should not be interpreted as an endorsement of the entire report. An array of forewords is provided from academia, industry and community involvement organisations. The forewords also span engineering, science and business backgrounds.

Executive summary
Kim Bryan, Alex Randall.

Climate science
Godfrey Boyle, Shaun Chamberlin, Peter Harper, Richard Hawkins, Bruce Heagerty, Sir John Houghton, Tim Jenkins, Ilkka Leinonen, Valerie Livina, Mark Maslin, Ranyl Rhydwen, Jeff Ridley, Stephen Stretton, Mike Thompson, Chris Vernon, David Wasdell.

Energy security
Shaun Chamberlin, Sir John Houghton, Larry Hughes, Tobi Kellner, Ilkka Leinonen, Valerie Livina, Damian Randle, Ranyl Rhydwen, Chris Vernon.

The built environment
Paul Allen, Pat Borer, Godfrey Boyle, Jamie Bull, Tom Chance, Paul Davies, Jonathan Essex, Paul Fleming, Peter Harper, Maria Hawton-Mead, Tobi Kellner, James Livingstone, David Thorpe, Chris Twinn, Simon Tucker, Sara Turnbull, Tom Woolley.

Transport
Godfrey Boyle, Roger Geffen, Gavin Harper, David Infield, Peter Lipman, Kelvin Mason, Veronique Meunier, Tariq Muneer, Tobi Kellner, Graham Parkhurst, Damian Randle, James Skinner, Hugo Spowers, Alan Storkey, Samantha Tharne.

Land use and agriculture
Paul Allen, Godfrey Boyle, Grace Crabb, Chris Dixon, Robert Evans, Mariska Evelein, Simon Fairlie, Clive Faulkner, Martin Fitton, Michael Fullen, Andy Goldring, David Hood, Julie Ingram, James Macduff, Michael Macleod, Alan McDonald, George Monbiot, Ken Neal, Elena Perez-Minana, Clare Rhydwen, Deepak Rughani, Saran Sohi, Chloe Ward, Martin Wolfe, Dominic Woolf, Marcus Zipperlen.

Renewables
Jo Abbess, Paul Allen, Godfrey Boyle, Jamie Bull, Arthur Butler, Ian Fairlie, Gavin Harper, Peter Harper, David Hood, Tobi Kellner, Bill Langley, Siobhan Luikham, Walt Patterson, Stephen Stretton, Gerry Wolff.

Microgrids
Paul Allen, Godfrey Boyle, Jamie Bull, Arthur Butler, Rob Gwillim, Gavin Harper, David Hood, Billy Langley, Walt Patterson, Gerry Wolff, Stephen Stretton.

Policy and economics
Paul Allen, Godfrey Boyle, Shaun Chamberlin, Richard Douthwaite, Peter Harper, Tanya Hawkes, Colin Hines, Tim-Helweg Larson, Roger Levett, Johnathan Neale, Molly Scott-Cato, Stephen Stretton, Josie Wexler.

Employment
Tobi Kellner, Viki Johnson, Andrew Simms, Leonie Green, Martin Kemp, Godfrey Boyle, Molly Scott Cato, Kathleen Hewlett, Ed White, Jeremy Leggett, Anne Pettifor, Matt Crossman

The Centre for Alternative Technology and the *zerocarbonbritain2030* team would like to extend their deepest gratitude to all those who have contributed to this project, the vast majority of whom have received no financial reward.

Authorship and acknowledgements

Throughout 2009 a series of research seminars and public events brought together a wide audience to co-create a vision for a sustainable future. A vision for **zero**carbon**britain**2030.

Please note that those who have contributed to, or reviewed **zero**carbon**britain**2030 may not necessarily agree with everything contained within it.

Executive editor: Martin Kemp

Authors by chapter:

Executive summary Contributing authors: Martin Kemp, Josie Wexler.

Introduction Contributing authors: Paul Allen, Martin Kemp, Josie Wexler.

Climate science Lead author: Josie Wexler; Contributing author: Henning Dräger.

The energy security context Lead author: Josie Wexler; Contributing authors: Martin Kemp, Paul Allen, Henning Dräger.

Equity Lead author: Siobhan Luikham; Contributing author: Joseph Walker.

The built environment Lead author: Sadhbh Ní Hógáin; Contributing author: Martin Kemp.

Transport Lead author: Christopher Mason; Contributing authors: Martin Kemp, Samantha Tharne, Josie Wexler, Joseph Walker.

Motivation and behavioural change Lead author: Siobhan Luikham; Contributing authors: Sam Saville, Amy Dartington, Alex Randall, Martin Kemp.

Land use and agriculture Lead author: Peter Harper; Contributing authors: Josie Wexler, Martin Kemp, Elena Perez-Minana.

Renewables Lead author: George Gregory; Contributing authors: Henning Dräger, Bruce Heagerty, Martin Kemp, Trevor Marshall, John Shanks, Mikko Simula, Josie Wexler, Heather White.

Microgrids Lead author: Jaise Kuriakose; Contributing author: Martin Kemp.

Policy and economics Lead author: Paul Reynolds; Contributing authors: Martin Kemp, Siobhan Luikham.

Employment Lead author: Victoria Johnson; Contributing authors: Daniela Platsch, Karen Schucan-Bird, Andrew Simms.

Residual emissions Lead author: Josie Wexler; Contributing author: Martin Kemp.

Summing up zerocarbonbritain2030 Lead author: Josie Wexler; Contributing author: Martin Kemp.

The *zerocarbonbritain2030* team

Project Director: Paul Allen, **Research Director**: Martin Kemp, **Research Coordinator**: Josie Wexler, **Project Administrator**: Siobhan Luikham, **Energy Modelling**: John Barton, Jamie Bull, Martin Kemp **Publisher**: Allan Shepherd, **Copy Editing**: Fred Foxon, Siobhan Luikham, Helene Oakley, Josie Wexler, Bruce Heagerty, Richard Hampton **Design and Desktop Publishing**: Graham Preston, Annika Lundqvist, Richard Hawkins, Elena Perez-Minana, Esther Tew.

The steering group: Paul Allen, Kim Bryan, Peter Harper, Tanya Hawkes, Tobi Kellner, Martin Kemp, Deirdre Raffan, Alex Randall, Deborah Sale, Mike Thompson, Josie Wexler.

Organisational acknowledgements

Please note that contributors' involvement is often in a niche area. **zero**carbon**britain**2030 is very broad; listing here does not necessarily entail agreement with everything contained within the report. Most contributors have done so without any payment, therefore further demonstrating their commitment to the field of sustainability.

We would like to extend our sincere thanks to our funders and partner organisations for their support.

Funding from

Esmee Fairbairn Foundation, Carnegie UK Trust, William A Cadbury Trust, Waterloo Trust, Simon Gibson Charitable Trust, The W F Southall Trust, The Marmot Charitable Trust and The Gunter Charitable Trust.

Many thanks also to all our individual private donors whose anonymity is respected and support greatly appreciated.

Centre for Alternative Technology, 2010

Published by CAT Publications, a division of
the Centre for Alternative Technology Charity Limited; a company limited by guarantee
Charity no. 265239; Company no. 1090006, registered in Wales
Registered office: Llwyngwern, Machynlleth, Powys

First published in the United Kingdom, 2010
© Centre for Alternative Technology, 2010

ISBN 978-1-902175-61-4

1 2 3 4 5 6 7 8 9 10

The details are provided in good faith and believed to be correct at the time of writing, however no responsibility is taken for any errors.
Our publications are updated regularly; please let us know of any amendments or additions which you think may be useful for future editions.

Printed with vegetable-based inks on recycled paper and bound in the UK by Cambrian Printers.
Cambrian Printers have been independently accredited with FSC and PEFC chain of custody certification,
ISO 14001 concerned with environmental management and Green Dragon Standard 5 awarded by Arena Network
Cambrian Printers, Aberystwyth 01970 627111.

Mixed Sources
Product group from well-managed
forests and recycled wood or fiber
www.fsc.org Cert no. TT-COC-2200
© 1996 Forest Stewardship Council

Contents

" Effort and courage are not enough without purpose and direction "

John F. Kennedy

executivesummary ●

Executive summary

Introduction

zero_carbon_**britain**_2030_ is a fully integrated solution to climate change. It examines how we can meet our electricity and heating requirements through efficient service provision, while still decreasing carbon dioxide, methane, nitrous oxide and other emissions.

The report starts by examining the current "context" in the Climate science and Energy Security chapters. It then moves on to how we can "PowerDown" heat and electricity demand largely through new technology, efficient design and behaviour change. Land offers tremendous potential not only to decrease emissions but also to sequester residual emissions. We then move on to how we can "PowerUp" through the use of renewable technology and finally we examine the policy that can help bring this about and the job creation that will come with it.

Context

CLIMATE SCIENCE

- Since the Industrial Revolution humans have been adding significantly to the greenhouse gas blanket that surrounds the Earth. Established physical principles suggest that this should raise the Earth's temperature. In the century that has passed since this warming was first predicted, the average surface of the globe has warmed by about 0.8°C. A multitude of different lines of evidence have confirmed that emissions of human origin are the primary cause of this warming. These include measurements of incoming and outgoing radiation, the lack of any plausible alternative explanation and distinctive "fingerprints" that identify the warming as caused by an enhanced greenhouse effect (Intergovernmental Panel on Climate Change [IPCC], 2007).

- Future warming has been estimated based on a sound scientific understanding of physical systems and feedbacks as well as the study of past temperature changes. Using these methods, the IPCC (2007) estimates a warming of between 1.1 and 6.4°C over pre-industrial temperatures for the coming century, depending on how much we emit, exactly how sensitive the climate is to greenhouse gases and how the natural carbon cycle responds to the increasing CO_2 and temperatures. This warming is expected to have profoundly negative impacts on many people and ecosystems, particularly those that are already vulnerable.

- More than 100 countries have adopted a

target limit of 2°C of warming relative to pre-industrial temperatures. To exceed this would have very dangerous consequences for many people. A study by Meinshausen *et al*. (2009) suggests that to have a 70% chance of staying below 2°C it will be necessary for global greenhouse gas emissions to peak before 2020, be cut by 50% by 2050 and approach zero before 2100. To provide an 84% chance, a 72% global cut by 2050 would be required. Other studies have suggested broadly similar figures (Allen *et al*., 2009; Weaver *et al*., 2007). If the world was to converge on equal per capita emissions by 2050, global cuts of this magnitude would require a per capita cut in the UK of 92% or 86% from 1990 levels by 2050.

- As the required global cut is severe, such a scenario would require poor countries to also make cuts by 2050. The long industrialised countries hold the historical responsibility for climate change and possess far greater resources to invest in low carbon technologies. The UK should therefore take on a greater share of the burden and cut emissions faster in order to allow the majority world a longer time period to decarbonise. Furthermore, because imported goods account for about a third of our emissions (Helm *et al*., 2007) deeper domestic cuts are required in order to compensate for foreign emissions produced on our behalf.
- In conclusion it is recommended that in the UK we should aim to reduce our greenhouse gas emissions to zero as fast as possible. In this report we adopt 2030 as our target year. Because warming is ultimately caused by cumulative emissions over time, we should also keep the quantity of greenhouse gases emitted during the transition phase as low as possible.

ENERGY SECURITY

- The UK is currently undergoing two major changes in relation to its use of energy. Firstly, North Sea oil and gas production is in terminal decline. In 2005 we became a net energy importer for the first time in 25 years (Oil & Gas UK, 2009). Secondly, more than a third of current electricity generation capacity is due to be retired over the next two decades (Department of Trade and Industry [DTI], 2007). Both of these factors make this a critical time to assess our energy system.
- Non-renewable fossil fuels clearly cannot last forever. In particular, serious concerns have been raised over the future of the global oil supply. Over 95% of the oil currently in production is "conventional" oil which is easy to extract (Méjean *et al*., 2008). Non-negotiable physical constraints influence the speed at which such oil can be pumped, and output from a single well (or aggregated over a whole region) inevitably rises to a peak and then declines (Sorrell *et al*., 2009). The point at which the global peak production rate is reached is generally referred to as "peak oil". Despite a

wide variety of estimates concerning its timing, a growing number of calculations suggest that it is likely to occur somewhere between the present day and 2031 (Greene *et al.*, 2006; International Energy Agency [IEA], 2008; Sorrell *et al.*, 2009; Vernon, 2009).

- If a shortage of oil occurs the price will rise until some customers are priced out of the market. As prices rise, more expensive extraction technology and unconventional oils can become economic, slowing the decline in production but at the expense of higher production costs. The overall effect is rising prices, but the shape of the rise is hard to predict.
- High oil prices have serious effects on wider society. The prices of all fuels are linked to a degree (Nuclear Energy Agency [NEA], 1998). There are good reasons to believe that a peak in oil production will not lead to a smooth painless transition into a post-oil world unless conscious intervention is employed (Hirsch *et al.*, 2005; Sorrell *et al.*, 2009).
- To keep global temperatures within 2°C of pre-industrial temperatures, cumulative CO_2 emissions must be kept below the amount that would be produced from burning the remaining proven economically recoverable fossil fuel reserves (Schmidt & Archer, 2009). Therefore fossil fuel depletion is unlikely to adequately solve climate change for us. However, it provides a further incentive to invest in alternatives to a fossil fuel-based infrastructure.

- In conclusion, there is good reason to believe that conventional oil may soon be reaching its production peak and it would be advisable for this reason alone to reduce the oil dependence of our society and transport system. Furthermore, because there are good reasons to expect significant future volatility in international fuel prices, a renewable electricity generation infrastructure which has no ongoing fuel cost is likely to give us a more stable and secure electricity system.

EQUITY

- As touched on in the Climate science chapter, historic responsibility for climate change is not equal between countries globally. Long industrialised nations such as the UK are more responsible for our changing climate than less industrialised nations. Neither are the implications of climate change distributed equally. Often those least responsible for emissions are those most vulnerable to a changing climate. Therefore it is clear that climate change is also a question of equality.
- A comprehensive national and international decarbonisation strategy offers the opportunity to address many social as well as environmental ills. In combination with wider efforts to restructure our economic and financial system and re-evaluate the core values held by society, we can create a decarbonised, fairer world for ourselves, the environment and future generations.

PowerDown

There is huge potential to decrease energy demand without decreasing the services that are provided. In **zero**carbon**britain**2030, energy demand is decreased by over 50%.

The report looks in detail at how energy demand can be decreased from buildings, transport and land use. The Final Accounts examine this at a higher level, referring to the National Emissions Directory, to make sure all sectors are covered.

THE BUILT ENVIRONMENT

Current emissions

- The domestic sector accounts for 28% of total British energy demand (Department of Energy and Climate Change [DECC], 2009). It is responsible for approximately 30% of Britain's total emissions (Department for the Environment, Farming and Rural Affairs [Defra], 2001; DTI, 2003; Power, 2008). Over half of domestic carbon emissions are from space heating (53% in 2005), while one fifth comes from heating water. The remainder comprises of appliances (16%), lighting (6%) and cooking (5%) (Department of Communities and Local Government [DCLG], 2007).
- Non-domestic buildings account for 25% of the country's carbon emissions. Non-domestic buildings emit over 100 million tonnes (Mt) of CO_2 per year.
- The total embodied carbon of construction materials for domestic and non-domestic buildings added up to approximately 70 million tonnes of CO_2 in 2003: 13% of the total UK reported carbon emissions (Lazarus, 2005).

Current policies

- Under the Strategy for Sustainable Construction, new domestic buildings and schools in the UK have to be "zero carbon" in use from 2016. Public buildings must comply by 2018 and other non-domestic buildings by 2019.
- There is a range of legislation governing the construction industry covering issues such as sustainability, energy efficiency and carbon emissions. The key statutory and voluntary legislation is as follows:
  - The Code for Sustainable Homes;
  - Part L of the Building Regulations;
  - Standard Assessment Procedure (SAP);
  - Merton Rule; and
  - Energy Performance Certificates.

Decreasing demand

- By making thermal comfort the goal rather than focusing on heating a building to a certain temperature, there are many options for decreasing energy demand.
- The four key ways to decrease space heating demand are:
- Improve the insulation or fabric of buildings;
- Decrease draughts;
- Decrease the heat demand through:
  - Good 'passive' design to increase natural heat gains,

- Decrease area requiring heat,
- Decrease the thermostat/air temperature,
- Thermal comfort can be maintained through good design resulting in warmer surfaces and less drafts.
- Improving the efficiency of heating technology.
- The target for domestic houses should be a 70% reduction in space heating energy demand as a whole with variation depending on building type.

Refurbishment

- In Britain in 2005 there were over 9 million un-insulated cavity walls and 6.3 million lofts with little or no insulation (DCLG, 2007).
- The priority for refurbishment is clear: a demand reduction for space heating while maintaining thermal comfort. This can be achieved through design and energy efficiency measures, most notably an increase in insulation. These standards should be written into a Code for Sustainable High-Performance Refurbishment.
- A "whole house" approach is necessary. This means designing a strategy for the house rather than seeking incremental reactive improvement.

Embodied energy

- The embodied energy of a material or product refers to the total primary energy consumed during the resource extraction, transportation, manufacturing and fabrication of that item (Hammond & Jones, 2008). It is a measure of the quantity of non-renewable energy per unit of material.
- While current practice often focuses on energy "in use", material selection should take into account the embodied energy of materials in determining preferred choice.

Sequestration

- Natural materials such as wood and straw absorb CO_2 from the atmosphere. This stored carbon could be locked away in building materials resulting in a carbon saving i.e. a "net negative". Therefore the mass sustainable refurbishment of current buildings can also act as a carbon store.
- The materials used for this carbon sequestration include grown and recycled materials.
- This one process has three benefits: it saves carbon; it reduces the cost; and it locks carbon in the building.

Recommendations

- The largest decrease in emissions from building stock will come from refurbishment. A Code for Sustainable High-Performance Refurbishment is required to ensure this is done to a high level and avoid it being done twice. This should include the use of natural materials were possible to lock away carbon.
- Building codes for both domestic and non-domestic buildings should provide a clear definition of "zero carbon", and include a

consideration of the energy, emissions and sequestration potential of construction.

- A clear framework for building design should be drawn up, allowing for different routes to zero carbon buildings.
- A further step for such codes would be to incorporate them into European legislation to create a set of European Sustainability Standards. This would help develop consistency in the "green industry". It can be developed with consideration of the local environment and changes in climate throughout Europe. This standard could be based on an energy demand per m^2 or per building.
- Enforcement of regulations, codes and standards is crucial (Grigg, 2004). Legislative backing could take the form of sustainability or low carbon inspectors. Inspection would be without prior warning; with legal responsibility devolving upon the organisation's directors.
- Substantial education is needed to ensure that people appreciate not only the benefits of low carbon homes, but also the ways in which their own choices and actions can influence the effectiveness of the end result (Osami & O'Reilly, 2009). Action can be achieved through education, marketing and legislation.

TRANSPORT

The current situation

- The transport sector currently accounts for around 29% of UK greenhouse gas emissions, including the UK's share of international aviation and shipping. The largest share (about 40%) of these emissions is from private cars. In terms of distance, the largest share is from medium and long distance trips.

Fuel switching

- Electric vehicles produce about 50% less CO_2 compared to petrol or diesel vehicles under the current grid mix (King, 2008) and this will decrease to near zero as the electricity network is decarbonised. Running the entire UK car and taxi fleet on electricity would require a quantity equal to 16% of current electricity demand (E4Tech, 2007). However, with use of smart charging, electric cars should require little or no additional electricity production capacity because cars could be set to charge when demand is low, such as during the night. Batteries may be charged in garages, allowing vehicle owners to simply swap flat batteries. Improvements in battery technology are expected in the future, and concerns about supply limits on raw materials are unfounded. In the *zerocarbonbritain2030* scenario, all transport modes that can be electrified are electrified, including all private cars and trains.
- Hydrogen is able to store more energy for less weight than batteries and it can be created from zero carbon electricity using electrolysis. However, this process requires twice the energy of using batteries (King, 2008). Because of this, hydrogen is limited in the *zerocarbonbritain2030* scenario to several

significant niche markets where large amounts of power are required or stopping to exchange batteries is difficult, including buses and some goods vehicles.

- Biofuels have been the subject of considerable controversy due to doubts about their overall greenhouse gas balance and their impact on land use change and food prices. "Second generation" biofuels, made from lignocellulosic feedstock such as wood or grasses, may be less problematic because such biofuels tend to have better greenhouse gas balances and the feedstock can be grown on a wider variety of land types. We use some lignocellulosic biofuels in the **zero**carbon**britain**2030 scenario to power the sectors for which there is currently no alternative to liquid hydrocarbon fuels: aviation, shipping, some heavy goods vehicles and some farm machinery. 1.67 million hectares of land in Great Britain is devoted to producing the feedstock. We assume a corresponding reduction in meat consumption, so that there will be no net increase in land use.

Changes to vehicles

- "Lightweighting" could offer efficiency gains of up to 10%, at a cost of £250–500 per vehicle, while low-rolling resistance tyres and improved aerodynamics could give potential efficiency savings of 2–4% each (King, 2008).
- The CO_2 emissions produced in manufacturing during the replacement of the entire car stock in the UK would be between 90 and 150 million tonnes – roughly equivalent to a year's worth of carbon emissions from all transport operations in the UK. It takes over a decade for the entire national car stock to be replaced and so vehicle replacement will have to begin rapidly to be complete by 2030 (King, 2008).

New business models

- The transport modal shifts in **zero**carbon**britain**2030 are generally away from the private car.
- The economics of car use are simplified by moving the upfront costs of car purchase, insurance, and taxation to a system where drivers pay for each mile driven. This would make public transport costs more easily comparable with car costs, and would show that public transport is often a more cost-effective solution. With increased use, public transport provision can improve service and decrease prices.
- Pay-per-hour car clubs and pay-as-you-drive insurance has been shown to cut trips by approximately 25%. At present, vehicle purchasers want durability, reliability and fuel efficiency. Producers however simply seek increased sales. If cars were leased and priced per mile, then incentives for durability would devolve on the leasing company. If that leasing company is also the producer, then it is also able to ensure build quality and durability rather then simply request it.

Behavioural change

- In the ***zero****carbon****britain****2030* scenario an absolute reduction in transit is required. Passenger kilometres travelled domestically decrease by 20%, spread evenly across all modes. Domestic aviation is eliminated and international aviation decreases by two thirds due to limits on biofuel supply. Some short-haul flights can be replaced with trains and ships but an absolute reduction in transit is also likely to be required.
- Aviation is always a challenge for sustainability. Fiscal policy (air passenger duty) is already being implemented in this area. In ***zero****carbon****britain****2030*, aviation has been looked at in depth. The exact future mix of services will be dependent on the priorities of individuals. In this scenario it is anticipated that aviation will be around a third of current levels.
- We expect the average occupancy rate of cars, vans and taxis to increase from the current 1.6 (Department for Transport [DfT], 2009) to 2.
- The modal shift towards public transport is quantified in Table ES.1.
- To facilitate this behaviour change, societal changes will be required. It will also be necessary to adapt town planning to minimise distances and maximise opportunities for walking, cycling and public transport.

Conclusion

- By combining modal shift, increased vehicle occupancy, wider technology improvements and fuel switching, we are able to provide the required services while decreasing transport energy demand by 63% from 2008 levels. The remaining energy requirement is supplied predominantly with electricity, supplemented with some hydrogen and biofuel.

MOTIVATION AND BEHAVIOURAL CHANGE

- In ***zero****carbon****britain****2030*, a huge array of measures will be implemented in each sector to address climate change. Many of these are policy driven, however individuals and communities must also play an active part in decarbonisation. The public can do this by accepting, supporting and indeed calling for the positive change that climate science shows is necessary.
- Change is challenging. But good communications can limit anxiety towards change, and can inspire action.
- How do we best change behaviour; and to what extent is a change in attitudes required? Social marketing theory suggests that government and NGOs must develop communication strategies focused on the audiences they want to reach, rather than the problem they want to solve. This can be achieved by the promotion of a series of entertaining, tangible and achievable action experiences. Reaching out to those not traditionally engaged with "green" or "ethical" issues can foster new social norms and encourage the widespread adoption of new

Table ES.1 Transport today and in ZCB2030		
Transport mode	**Current (2007)**	**ZCB2030 scenario**
Walk	4.89	10.00
Pedal cycle	0.47	3.00
Electric bike	0.00	0.12
Rail	6.86	14.00
Coach	0.88	10.00
London bus/train	1.09	1.30
Local bus/train	3.85	5.00
Motorbike	0.70	2.10
Electric scooter	0.00	0.35
Car, van & taxi	80.16	54.13
UK aviation	1.11	0.17

Percentage of domestic passenger kilometres travelled by mode of travel today, 2007, and in the ZCB2030 scenario.
Significant reductions in the use of cars, vans and taxis are expected by 2030, with corresponding increases in the use of local transport and walking and cycling.
Source: Data for current (2007) based on statistics from DfT (2008).

behaviours across society.

- A simultaneous process of challenging extrinsic values in society, as recommended by identity campaigning proponents, must take place. Social marketing tools are vital, but communicators should consider the long-term ramifications of multiple individual appeals to existing values relating to wealth and social status. Programmes to help draw out intrinsic values using fun, participatory methodologies amongst important role models and norm leaders may be one way of amalgamating lessons from the social marketing and identity campaigning approaches. Supporting local programmes which attempt to achieve specific behavioural objectives but also foster intrinsic, community-oriented values, is another way.

LAND USE AND AGRICULTURE

The current situation

- The current land mass of Great Britain is made up of about 11.2 million hectares of grassland, which is primarily used for grazing livestock; about 4.87 million hectares of arable crops, of which 2.1 million are used for growing livestock feed; 3.24 million hectares of woodland; and 3.28 million hectares of urban land.
- Greenhouse gas emissions from the land use and agriculture sector are made up of nitrous oxide (N_2O), methane (CH_4) and carbon dioxide (CO_2). Methane is produced primarily by livestock in their digestive processes, and from manure. N_2O is released when nitrogen is

added to the soil, either as mineral fertiliser or nitrogen-fixing crops. The bulk of it (60%) comes from fertilised grazed grassland and manure handling and relatively little from arable cropland (15%) (Brown & Jarvis, 2001). Carbon dioxide is produced from tilled or disturbed soils and from the energy used in agriculture.

Methodology: background assumptions

- In the **zero**carbon**britain**2030 scenario we accept 15% of our food needs as imports from the EU, and about 7.5% from the tropics, but apart from this our food needs must be met domestically. This restriction is to enable the creation of the scenario. Apart from this small amount of trade, the landmass of mainland UK has been treated as a separate entity.
- Energy used in agriculture is assumed to be decarbonised - this is dealt with in other chapters. The effect is to reduce the greenhouse gas intensities of land use products by approximately 20% for livestock and about 45% for crops.

Strategy

- Preserving carbon reservoirs has been given high priority. Soil stores a lot of carbon, particularly in peat-lands and to a lesser extent in grasslands. This carbon can be released if the land is disturbed or converted to tilled arable land. In order to avoid this there is no new arable land in the scenario, and peat-lands are especially protected. Woodlands are another reservoir, and in the **zero**carbon**britain**2030

scenario existing woodlands are preserved and carefully managed.

- Switching from products with high greenhouse gas and land intensities to those with lower intensities enables us to achieve two goals; we reduce greenhouse gas emissions from agriculture and at the same time release land for other uses. The greenhouse gas and land intensity of different products can be seen in Figure ES.1 for our 2030 scenario. Livestock products, particularly those from sheep and cows, have much greater land and greenhouse gas intensities than plant products.
- Using the released grassland to grow biomass for energy allows us to supply the demand for storable solid, liquid and gas fuels in other sectors. For these we use energy silage from forage-type grasses, short rotation woody crops and miscanthus. These are perennial crops and so growing them on grassland need not cause a loss of soil carbon. They are also low nitrogen users and hence the emissions from growing them are very low.
- In addition, using some of the released grassland to grow biomass for carbon sequestration allows us to sequester enough carbon to cover the residual emissions from all sectors.
- Some technical changes in land management also allow us to reduce greenhouse gas emissions and increase carbon sequestration. More organic matter is incorporated into soils than is current normal practice, and nitrogen is handled better to reduce N_2O release.

Fig. ES.1 Greenhouse gas and land intensity of different products

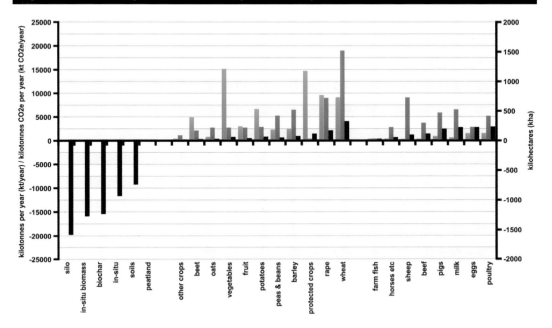

Greenhouse gas and land intensity of different products can be seen in Figure ES.1 for our 2030 scenario.
Livestock products, particularly those from sheep and cows, have much greater land and greenhouse gas intensities than plant products.

Products produced

• In the ***zerocarbonbritain2030*** scenario abundant food for the population is produced but livestock products are reduced to 20-30% of their present quantity. Cow and sheep stocks in particular are much reduced. The levels of egg, poultry and pig-meat production are only a little lower than today because they use little land and we can feed them on high-yielding crop products and food wastes. Plant protein is greatly increased; at the moment the ratio of meat to plant protein is about

55:45, and in the scenario it is to 34:66. This proportion of livestock products matches recommendations for optimum dietary health. Essentially the livestock sector switches from quantity to quality production.

• In the ***zerocarbonbritain2030*** scenario over 70 million tonnes of biomass for energy is produced. This is used in the following ways: 16 million tonnes for biogas (bio-synthetic gas), mainly used to back up the electricity grid; 18 million tonnes of woody biomass for CHP; and 27 million tonnes to create kerosene, petrol and diesel using the Fischer-Tropsch process to power those parts of the transport sector for which there is currently no alternative to liquid fuels.

Carbon sequestration

- After appropriate management changes, land can remove CO_2 from the air and sequester it in soil or above-ground biomass. Carbon can also be sequestered in products. Although neither of these can accumulate carbon indefinitely, they can provide us with a "window" of around 20-30 years, after which other methods of sequestering carbon may be available. These might include deeper soil sequestration or new technologies.
- After food needs have been met, 43% of the remaining "productive non-food" land is dedicated to growing biomass for carbon sequestration. Carbon is also sequestered in soils through best practice management, encouraged though financial incentives. Below are the final figures for carbon sequestration in zerocarbonbritain2030, adjusted for uncertainty.
- About 10 million tonnes of CO_2e per year is sequestered in long lasting biomass products such as buildings and other wood products.
- About 23 million tonnes of CO_2e per year is sequestered in engineered biomass silos.
- Carbon management of existing woodland is improved and 1.37 million hectares of new woodland is planted. This increases CO_2e stored in-situ in standing timber by an estimated 12 million tonnes a year (Read et al., 2009).
- A soil sink of around 9 million tonnes CO_2e per year is achieved through best practice on all soil types (Brainard et al., 2003; Klumpp, 2009; Weiske, 2007; Worrall et al., 2003).
- 4.3 million tonnes of biochar a year is created and incorporated into soils (Sohi et al., 2010) providing sequestration of around 14 million tonnes per year. Biochar is charcoal that is used as an agricultural amendment. It cannot easily be broken down by decomposers and so may have potential as a more permanent net negative process.

Conclusion

In the scenario a healthy diet is provided for the population on only 29% of the land currently used for food production, supplemented by low-carbon imports. It provides a much higher degree of food security than at present. Total greenhouse gas emissions from agriculture are reduced to a fifth of their current quantity, leaving a total of 17 million tonnes of CO_2e. Meanwhile the sector provides enough biomass to fulfil the fuel needs of the other sectors and to sequester carbon at a rate of 67 million tonnes of CO_2e year. These "negative emissions" match the residual emissions from other sectors to meet the scenario's ultimate goal, of a zero carbon Britain.

PowerUp

RENEWABLES

- The Renewables chapter combines leading research and modelling on renewable heat and electricity to create one integrated energy model to meet the needs of the **zero**carbon**britain**2030 scenario. As our basis, we use the UK Energy Research Council's (UKERC, 2009) £18 million research into electricity scenarios and integrate this with the work of NERA Economic Consulting and AEA (2009) for DECC on heat, and work from the National Grid (2009) on biogas, as well as further specialised research from an array of academic sources. With this, we create a vision of how the energy system could look like in 2030.

- The Renewables chapter also brings together data from our other chapters. Data on heat demand comes from our chapter on The Built Environment; data on increased electrical requirements come from our Transport chapter; and data on the available biomass from the Land Use and Agriculture chapter. As the integration between these sectors increased so did the potential number of solutions. For the purpose of this report we are showing just one of these routes.

- Since *zerocarbonbritain: an alternative energy strategy* (*zerocarbonbritain*, 2007) was

---

Fig. ES.2 Delivered energy provision in ZCB2030

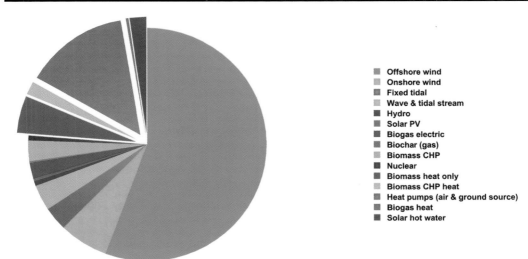

Legend:
- Offshore wind
- Onshore wind
- Fixed tidal
- Wave & tidal stream
- Hydro
- Solar PV
- Biogas electric
- Biochar (gas)
- Biomass CHP
- Nuclear
- Biomass heat only
- Biomass CHP heat
- Heat pumps (air & ground source)
- Biogas heat
- Solar hot water

Delivered energy provision for heat and electricity, by source (%), in ZCB2030.
Segments displaying heat sources are pulled out from main pie chart.

published, there has been a lot more research demonstrating the potential of renewables. Jacobson and Delucchi (2009) demonstrate that 100% of the world's energy needs can be met from renewables by 2030, and the European Energy Agency (EEA, 2009) has found that the economically competitive potential of wind generation in Europe is seven times that of projected electrical demand in 2030. Renewables and sustainable biomass can power Britain without the need for fossil fuels and nuclear power.

- The breakdown of the sources of electricity and heat production in the *zerocarbonbritain2030* scenario is shown in Figure ES.1. This shows a large proportion of delivered energy being from wind, especially offshore wind.
- Offshore wind is a tremendous resource for the UK. In *zerocarbonbritain2030*, this provides 615TWh per year from 195GW of generation capacity. There are several questions this raises, for example over embodied energy, resource use, balancing the grid, skills, and economics.
- The energy required to make something is referred to as its embodied energy. To calculate the energy return on energy invested (EROEI) of a renewable energy source the embodied energy can be compared to the energy it generates through its lifetime. The EROEI for wind is higher than other renewables. A 5MW turbine can give a return of approximately 28:1 (see Lenzen & Munksgaard, 2002) which can be compared to photovoltaics (PV), where some of the highest calculated ratios, based on US weather, are about

10:1 (U.S. Department of Energy [US DoE], 2004). Many of the measures outlined in other chapters of this report, such as the rapid move towards electric transport, will further improve the EROEI of wind turbines.

- The core resource requirements for installing 195GW of offshore wind are steel and concrete. The embodied energy of these materials would be 115TWh. There will also be a varying degree of processing and maintenance, depending on the details of the turbines installed and where they are installed, plus operations and maintenance. There have been concerns raised about offshore wind's steel requirements (Mackay, 2008). The UK currently uses 13.5 million tonnes of steel per annum (The Manufacturers' Organisation [EEF], 2009), therefore in 2013 offshore wind would be using 0.6% of current annual UK steel and in its peak year it would require 10.4% of current demand. This is an achievable quantity and will clearly not be a barrier, especially with construction and automation moving away from steel.
- The UK steel market specialises in high-quality steel, including steel designed for the manufacture of wind turbines. However, the largest UK steel producer, Corus, was forced to indefinitely mothball a number of UK production sites from January 2010 due to broken contracts, resulting in the loss of about 1,700 UK jobs (Corus, 2009). The development of wind power in the UK has the potential to ease the decline of the UK steel industry in the medium-term and, over the long-term, it has the potential to contribute to its

growth as we export our technology.

- One of the challenges of a renewables and biomass scenario is the balancing of variable supply with variable demand. This can be addressed on both the supply and the demand side. On the demand side, there are lots of services that do not need to run at an exact time but can rather be run within a range of times. This flexibility can be used to "re-time loads" on the grid, making management easier. While there is flexibility during the day, the big area of potential is moving demand overnight. Electric cars, for example, may charge at night. This also minimises the need for additional grid capacity, therefore decreasing the cost of the infrastructure and final electricity pricing. On the supply side, some biogas is used as additional dispatchable generation to back up the grid.

- The **zero**carbon**britain**2030 scenario has been successfully tested with the "Future Energy Scenario Assessment" FESA energy modelling software. This combines weather and demand data to test if there is enough dispatchable generation to manage the variable base supply of renewable electricity with the variable demand.

- Even after a decrease of energy demand of over 55% on current (2008) levels, electricity demand will roughly double because of the partial electrification of the transport and heat sectors. However, required increases to the electricity infrastructure can be minimised through balancing measures such as demand side management.

- The development of offshore wind resources and an EU grid may also be utilised to ease electricity distribution in the UK from North to South.

- Using data on the capital, operations and management costs of power generation technologies (European Commission, 2008) we find that onshore wind has similar capital costs to coal but without the fuel requirements. The capital cost of coal with CCS is similar to the cost of offshore wind, but has substantial running costs that offshore wind does not possess, and this is before adding in any carbon cost. The cost per kWh for customers will be dependent on a range of factors including the policy mechanisms in place, the ownership of the generation, the capacity factors of the generation and future fuel costs.

- There are various different mechanisms in place to reward people for producing renewable electricity which include: Renewable Obligation Certificates (ROCs), Levy Exemption Certificates (LECs), the Climate Change Levy, feed-in tariffs (FITs), as well as Use of System electricity grid charges, the Transmission Use of System (TNUoS), Distribution Use of System (DNUoS) and Balancing Services Use of System (BSUoS) charges. The major policies on the electricity side are the Renewable Obligation Certificates and feed-in tariffs. Levy Exemption Certificates (LECs) are a way of integrating these policies with the Climate Change Levy.

- A sustainable, secure, efficient Britain can be powered without relying on fossil fuels or nuclear power.

MICROGRIDS AND DISTRIBUTED GENERATION

- Distributed generation tends to occur when the energy source and the consumer are located close together, limiting transmission and distribution losses (Institute of Engineering and Technology [IET], 2006).
- Distributed renewables are part of the solution to decarbonise the UK energy infrastructure, society and economy. Smaller-scale renewables are generally more expensive, and have a higher embodied energy than large-scale renewables. However, they increase the total potential of sustainable generation of the UK and help increase efficiency and decrease demand where they are deployed.
- Minimising losses in the system is a delicate balance; one of the key areas is a balance between transmission losses and storage losses. Distributed generation and Microgrids can save on transmission losses and must be carefully designed to ensure that storage and the losses associated are minimised.
- Microgrids can be used in niche applications to assist distributed generation and help manage the variability of the transmission grid.

Framework

POLICY AND ECONOMICS

The challenges we face are unprecedented. We need strong decisive action now to rewire our economy to ensure that the dual problems of climate change and energy security can be tackled. Fortunately, as detailed, in other chapters of this report in making such a transition there is much potential for creating jobs (Bird, 2009; Jungjohann & Jahnke, 2009; Forrest & Wallace, 2010), increasing energy security and improving livelihoods (Abdallah et al., 2009). A world without fossil fuels can be better in many ways. However, achieving such a transition will not be easy and will require drastic policy interventions at both the international and national level.

International policy frameworks

- At the international level, the crucial first step is to sign a global agreement aimed at reducing temperature rise to below 2°C, and setting a cumulative carbon budget that provides us with a sufficiently high chance of meeting this goal. The exact policy mechanism could come later but ensuring that all countries are on board with this overarching target is critical to changing the direction of the global economy. Another key step is achieving global agreements on ending deforestation, and assuring funding for research and development and an adaptation fund for those hardest hit by climate change. Doing so could reduce the risks of climate change significantly.
- A key decision then needs to be taken over which of three road maps should be taken.

Road map 1: One-price-for-all

• The first road map sees an international agreement as an opportunity to solve the fundamental problem that carbon is not priced properly, and to design a global system which ensures that the true cost of fossil fuels is explicitly included in the pricing mechanism everywhere in the world. It can be seen as a one-price-for-all solution at a global level and could be based on several global scheme proposals such as Cap & Share, Kyoto2 or a globalised, harmonised carbon tax. The existence of a global framework will mean a slightly reduced role for national governments who will no longer have to design a policy mechanism to price carbon. Instead, they will have to design a range of policies to complement the global agreement, balancing the winners and losers from such a scheme and ensuring that the transition to the new agreement is as smooth and as painless as possible.

Road map 2: An international framework with national action initiatives

• The second route is far more focused at the national or regional level with an international agreement providing a general framework that allocates the carbon cuts required by each country, but allows national governments to decide which is the best policy solution for pricing carbon and for achieving these cuts. The framework is there to bind countries together and ensure that all are working towards a common purpose, but does not define or impose one particular policy solution. A key decision in such a framework approach is how the cuts required are allocated between countries and across time, with Contraction & Convergence (C&C) the most commonly-known method.

• The various global one-price-for-all policies may seem desirable, but appear unlikely to be implemented in the near future. An international agreement based upon an international framework is therefore preferable. Such an agreement would provide flexibility, both between countries and over time, and allows different policies to be tried and tested in different regions and circumstances, while at the same time binding countries together and ensuring that all are working towards a common goal.

Road map 3: Regional carbon pricing schemes

• Another possible road map, and one that looks more likely after Copenhagen, is for countries who wish to decarbonise rapidly to forego a global framework – aimed either at an internationally-harmonised carbon pricing mechanism or at determining national carbon budgets – and rather to join together into blocs with other like-minded countries.

• These blocs would then set a common cap,

reduction targets and rules, and use border adjustment taxes and rebates to prevent unfair competition from countries with laxer carbon reduction targets. Powerful blocs could adopt a particular policy for determining carbon budgets or prices within the bloc, and could also include an international redistribution mechanism to benefit poorer nations. This could create a large trade bloc, incentivising other nations to join so as not to be excluded by the border adjustment tax (Douthwaite, 2009).

National policy frameworks

- At the national level, and assuming that no international carbon pricing scheme is implemented, the UK should complement the European Union's Emissions Trading System (EU ETS) and the CRC Energy Efficiency Scheme by introducing a scheme aimed at reducing emissions further. Cap & Share, TEQs and carbon tax schemes all provide viable proposals and the answer may actually lie in combining a firm cap with a tax scheme to provide a certain environmental outcome with a guaranteed floor price for investors. Over time such a scheme may develop and encapsulate the whole economy with the EU ETS actually feeding into it.
- It is also clear that simply internalising the price of carbon will not solve all our problems (Green New Deal Group, 2008; WWF, 2009). We are "locked" into the present technologies and processes and more targeted interventions

are required to put the economy on a more sustainable trajectory. A Green New Deal is needed to provide the investment required in large-scale renewable energy technologies and energy efficiency improvements. Public money should be used as a guarantor, and innovative financial arrangements have to be developed, in order to harness the private sector funds necessary to finance such an enormous investment programme.

- At the same time, we need to develop new and better policy support mechanisms in the renewable electricity and renewable heat sectors. The electricity sector offers an opportunity for rapid decarbonisation in many areas and, with the right policy support, we could go some way to achieving this goal. The new banding of the renewable obligation and Feed-in Tariff for renewable capacity under 5MW will lead to increased investment in renewable generation. In the heat sector, the innovative Renewable Heat Incentive (RHI) currently out for consultation aims to make Britain world-leading in renewable heat. This is projected to bring 78TWh of renewable heat online by 2020 saving 17Mt of CO_2 (NERA Economic Consulting 2009). Combined with policies aimed at tackling skills shortages and non-market barriers, these should provide a fair incentive for the nascent renewable heat industry to develop rapidly.
- Furthermore there is significant potential for smart meters to allow variable pricing to drive both, shifts in, and reductions in, the

demand profile. Finally, we need to ensure that the most vulnerable elements of society are supported and protected during the transition, in particular that an increase in fossil fuel prices is accompanied with a comprehensive retrofitting campaign to reduce the dangers of fuel poverty.

- The challenge rests on the Government to implement change and individuals to demonstrate willingness for change. The policy solutions are there. We can achieve such a transition; such a path is possible. We just have to have the courage to take it.

EMPLOYMENT

- Shifting to a zero carbon Britain could provide significant economic benefits to the UK in increased employment, and therefore increased tax revenues.
- Counting just the number of "jobs" ignores the difference in duration between jobs. Therefore "job years" is used. While development takes more than a year, looking at the installations in a year and the "job years" this creates gives a good indication of the employment in that year.

Table ES.2 Industrial, waste and residual emissions

Source	% of 2007 quantity remaining in ZCB2030	Residual emissions (million tonnes CO_2e)
Industrial combustion	0	0
Landfill	22%	4.2
Other waste	100%	2.4
Cement production	10%	0.6
High greenhouse gas potential greenhouse gases	10%	2.4
Lime production	300%	3.1
Iron and steel production non-combustion emissions	100%	6.8
Nitric and adipic acid production	3%	0.08
Other chemical processes	100%	4.4
Emissions from disused coal mines	100%	1.2
Land converted to settlements	70%	4.0

Industrial, waste and residual emissions in ZCB2030, compared to 2007 (million tonnes CO_2e).
Source: Based on data for 2007 from Jackson et al. (2009) and MacCarthy et al. (2010).

- The peak year for offshore wind development starts in 2022 and is set as 17GW. The direct and indirect job years based on installations in 2022 is 291,270. The same year has 1.45GW of onshore wind deployed which is 22,229 job years. Therefore over 300,000 could be employed in wind power alone by 2030.
- The total deployment of wind power in the UK as envisaged in *zerocarbonbritain2030* would deliver over 3.4 million job years.
- The transition to a low carbon economy will inevitably undermine jobs in other areas. Employment in carbon-intensive industries such as oil and gas, iron, steel, aluminium, cement and lime are already at risk from carbon pricing. However, the UK's oil and gas industry is also at risk from peak production in the UK's indigenous reserves, and the increased mechanisation of labour. Evidence suggests that green jobs in energy, construction, transport and agriculture should more than compensate for this, although these may not emerge in the same geographical locations.

Table ES.3 The greenhouse gas emissions balance sheet for ZCB2030	
	Million tonnes CO_2e
Great Britain: Total emissions in 2007 (including international aviation and shipping split 50/50 between the countries travelled between)	**637**
Residual emissions in ZCB2030: Industry, waste and disused coal mines	**30**
Residual emissions in ZCB2030: Land use and agriculture sector	**17**
Residual emissions in ZCB2030: Miscellaneous and other sectors	**20**
Residual emissions: Grand total	**67**
Percentage of 2007 emissions remaining	**10%**
Carbon sequestration	**- 67**
Net emissions: Final total	**Zero**

Total British greenhouse gas emissions, 2007, and residual emissions and sequestration, 2030, under ZCB2030 (million tonnes CO_2e).

Conclusions

RESIDUAL EMISSIONS

• While electricity has been addressed in detail, the industrial and waste sectors still currently constitute around 24% of total British emissions. Many of these emissions can be reduced, and a summary of the reductions that we estimate can be made is given in Table ES.2.

THE FINAL EMISSIONS BALANCE SHEET

The final emissions balance sheet under the **zero**carbon**britain**2030 scenario is shown in Table ES.3.

The value of **zero**carbon**britain**2030 reaches far beyond emissions; a bold national endeavour will provide a plethora of economic, environmental and social benefits, including a common sense of purpose.

The actions taken will bring about a far brighter future, revitalise communities, renew British industry and provide a sustainable economy.

References

Abdallah, S. *et al*. (2009) The Happy Planet Index 2.0: Why good lives don't have to cost the Earth, London: nef.

Allen, M. *et al*. (2009) "Warming caused by cumulative carbon emissions towards the trillionth tonne", *Nature*, 458(7242), pp.1163-1166.

Bird, J. (2009) *Green jobs: Prospects for creating jobs from offshore wind in the UK*, London: Institute for Public Policy Research (ippr).

Brainard J, A. Lovett & I. Bateman (2003) *Social & Environmental Benefits of Forestry: Phase 2: Carbon Sequestration Benefits Of Woodland*, Report to Forestry Commission, Centre for Social and Economic Research on the Global Environment, School of Environmental Sciences, University of East Anglia. Available at: http://www.forestry.gov.uk/website/pdf.nsf/pdf/carbonseqrep0603.pdf/$FILE/carbonseqrep0603.pdf [Live: March 2010].

Brown, L. & S. Jarvis (2001) "Estimation of Nitrous Oxide Emissions from UK Agriculture", IGER Innovations. Available at: http://www.aber.ac.uk/en/media/chapter_10.pdf [Live: March 2010].

Corus (2009) "Broken contract leads to mothball of Teesside plant", press release 04 December 2009. Available at: http://www.corusgroup.com/en/news/news/2009_tcp_mothball [Live: March 2010].

Department of Energy and Climate Change (DECC) (2009a) *Digest of United Kingdom Energy Statistics 2009*, London: The Stationery Office (TSO).

Department for Communities and Local Government (DCLG) (2007a) *Building a Greener Future: policy statement*, July 2007, Wetherby: Communities and Local Government Publications.

DCLG (2007b) *English House Condition Survey 2005, Annual Report: decent homes and decent places*, Wetherby: Communities and Local Government Publications.

Department for the Environment, Farming and Rural Affairs (Defra) (2001) *Digest of Environmental Statistics*, London: Her Majesty's Stationery Office (HMSO).

Department for Transport (DfT) (2008) *National Travel Survey 2007*, Transport Statistics Bulletin, London: DfT.

DfT (2009) *National Travel Survey 2008*, Transport Statistics Bulletin, London: DfT.

Department of Trade and Industry (DTI) (2003) Energy white paper: our energy future – creating a low *carbon* economy, Norwich: TSO.

DTI (2007) *Meeting the Energy Challenge: A White Paper on Energy*, London: The Stationery Office.

Douthwaite, R. (2009) "Cap & Share", presentation given to the **zero**carbon**britain**2030 Policy, Actions & Economics seminar, 30 September 2009 [unpublished].

European Commission (EC) (2008) "Energy Sources, Production Costs and Performance of Technologies for Power Generation, Heating and Transport", Commission Staff Working Document accompanying the

Communication From the Commission To the European Parliament, the Council, the European Economic and Social Committee and the Committee of the Regions, Commission of the European Communities. Available at: http://ec.europa.eu/energy/strategies/2008/doc/2008_11_ser2/strategic_energy_review_wd_cost_performance.pdf [Live: March 2010].

European Environment Agency (EEA) (2009) *Europe's onshore and offshore wind energy potential: An assessment of environmental and economic constraints*, Technical report 6/2009. Luxembourg: EC.

Forrest, N & J. Wallace (2010) "The Employment Potential of Scotland's Hydro Resources", Nick Forrest Associates, September 2009. Available at: http://www.scotland.gov.uk/Resource/Doc/299322/0093327.pdf [Live: March 2010].

Greene, D.L., J.L. Hopson & J. Li (2006) "Have we run out of oil yet? Oil peaking analysis from an optimist's perspective", *Energy Policy*, 34(5), pp. 515-531.

Green New Deal Group (2008) A Green New Deal: Joined up policies to solve the triple crunch of the credit crisis, climate change & high oil prices, London: nef.

Grigg, P. (2004) Assessment of energy efficiency impact *of Building Regulations compliance*, report for the Energy Savings Trust and Energy Efficiency Partnership for Homes, Client Report No 219683, 10 November 2004, Watford: Building Research Establishment.

Hammond, G. & C. Jones (2008) "Inventory of Carbon and Energy", Version 1.6a, Sustainable Research Team, Department of Mechanical Engineering, University of Bath, UK.

Helm, D., R. Smale & J. Phillips (2007) "Too Good To Be True? The UK's Climate Change Record", Dieter Helm CBE [online]. Available at: http://www.dieterhelm.co.uk/sites/default/files/Carbon_record_2007.pdf [Live: March 2010].

Institute of Engineering and Technology (IET) (2006) "Distributed Generation: A Factfile provided by the Institute of Engineering and Technology". Available at: www.theiet.org/factfiles/energy/distributed-generation.cfm?type=pdf [Live: March 2010].

International Energy Agency (IEA) (2008) *World Energy Outlook 2008*, Paris: Organisation for Economic Development/IEA.

Jacobson, M.Z. & M.A. Delucchi (2009) "A Path to Sustainable Energy by 2030", *Scientific American*, November 2009.

Jackson, J. et al. (2009) "Greenhouse Gas Inventories for England, Scotland, Wales and Northern Ireland: 1990-2007", AEAT/ENV/R/2873 Issue 1. Available at: http://www.naei.org.uk/reports.php [Live: March 2010].

Jungjohann, A. & B. Jahnke (2009) *Europe: Creating new jobs with renewable energies*, 19 May 2009, Heinrich Böll Stiftung. Available at: http://www.boell.org/downloads/Creating_Green_New_Jobs_with_Renewable_Energies1.pdf [Live: March 2010].

King, J. (2008) *The King Review of low-carbon cars Part II: recommendations for action*, March 2008, London: HMSO.

Klumpp, K. *et al.* (2009) "Grazing triggers soil carbon loss by altering plant roots and their control on soil microbial community", Journal of Ecology, 97 (5), pp. 876-885.

Lazarus, N. (2005) "Potential for reducing the environmental impact of construction materials", commissioned by Bioregional Development Group, January 2005. Available at: http://www.bioregional.com/files/publications/Z-squaredImpactMaterials_Jan05.pdf [Live: March 2010].

Lenzen, M. & J. Munksgaard (2002) "Energy and CO_2 life-cycle analyses of wind turbines—review and applications", *Renewable Energy*, 26(3), pp. 339-362.

MacCarthy, J. *et al.* (2010) "UK Greenhouse Gas Inventory, 1990 to 2008: Annual Report for submission under the Framework Convention on Climate Change", AEAT/ENV/R/2978 30/04/2010. Available at: http://www.naei.org.uk/reports.php [Live: April 2010].

Mackay D. (2009) *Sustainable Energy – without the hot air*, Cambridge: UIT Cambridge Ltd.

Manufactuers' Organisation (EEF) (2009) "UK Steel: Key Statistics 2009, EEF. Available at: http://www.eef.org.uk/NR/rdonlyres/B1210239-A3C3-472D-B1E5-A48DBFBCF306/15206/UKSteelKeyStatistics2009.pdf [Live: March 2010].

Meinshausen, M. *et al.* (2009) "Greenhouse-gas emission targets for limiting global warming to 2 °C", Nature, 458(7242), pp. 1158-1162.

Méjean, A. & C. Hope (2008) *Modelling the costs of non-conventional oil: A case study of Canadian bitumen*, Cambridge Working Papers in Economics 0810, Faculty of Economics, University of Cambridge.

National Grid (2009) "The potential for renewable gas in the UK", January 2009. Available at: http://www.nationalgrid.com/NR/rdonlyres/9122AEBA-5E50-43CA-81E5-8FD98C2CA4EC/32182/renewablegasWPfinal1.pdf [Live: March 2010].

NERA Economic Consulting & AEA (2009) "The UK Supply Curve for Renewable Heat", Study for the Department of Energy and Climate Change, July 2009, URN 09D/689. Available at: http://www.nera.com/image/PUB_Renewable_Heat_July2009.pdf [Live: March 2010].

Nuclear Energy Agency & International Energy Agency (1998): *Projected costs of generating electricity: Update 1998*, Paris: Organisation for Economic Co-operation and Development (OECD).

Oil and Gas UK (2004) "Gas - The UK's Fuel of Choice", Oil and Gas UK [online]. Available at: http://www.oilandgas.org.uk/issues/gas/ [Live: January 2010].

Osami, M. & A. O'Reilly (2009) "Feasibility of zero carbon homes in England by 2016: A house builder's perspective", *Building & Environment*, 44(9), pp. 1917–1924.

Power, A. (2008) "Does demolition or refurbishment of old and inefficient homes help to increase our environmental, social and economic viability?", *Energy Policy*, 36(12), pp. 4487-4501.

Read D. J. *et al.* (eds) (2009) *Combating climate change – a role for UK forests: The synthesis report. An assessment of the potential of the UK's trees and woodlands to mitigate and adapt to climate change. The synthesis report*, Edinburgh: TSO.

Schmidt, G. & D. Archer (2009) "Climate change: Too much of a bad thing" Nature, 458(7242), pp.1117-1118.

Sohi S. P. *et al.* (2010) "A review of biochar and its use & function in soil", *Advances in Agronomy*, 105, pp. 47-82.

Sorrell, S. *et al.* (2009) *Global Oil Depletion: An assessment of the evidence for a near-term peak in global oil production*, London: UK Energy Research Centre.

UK Energy Research Centre (UKERC) (2009) *Making the transition to a secure low-carbon energy system, synthesis report*, London: UKERC.

U.S. Department of Energy [US DoE] (2004) "What is the energy payback for PV?", PV FAQs, The National Renewable Energy Laboratory. Available at: http://www.nrel.gov/docs/fy04osti/35489.pdf [Live: March 2010].

Vernon, C. (2009) "Peak oil", presentation given to the *zerocarbonbritain2030* Carbon Crunch seminar, 31 March 2009 [unpublished].

Weaver, A.J. *et al.* (2007) "Long term climate implications of 2050 emission reduction targets", *Geophysical Research Letters*, 34, L19703.

Weiske, A. (2007) "Potential for carbon sequestration in European agriculture, Impact of Environmental Agreements On The Cap", final version 16 February 2007, specific targeted research project no. SSPE-CT-2004-503604. Available at: http://www.ieep.eu/publications/pdfs/meacap/D10a_appendix_carbon_sequestration.pdf [Live: March 2010].

Worrall, F. *et al.* (2003) "Carbon budget for a British upland peat catchment", *The Science of the Total Environment*, 312(1), pp. 133-146.

WWF (2009) *Blueprint Germany: A Strategy for a Climate Safe Germany*, Berlin: WWF.

Zero carbon Britain (2007) *zerocarbonbritain: an alternative energy strategy*, Machynlleth: Centre for Alternative Technology.

Figure sources

ES.1 Copyright (2010) *zerocarbonbritain2030*.

ES.2 Copyright (2010) *zerocarbonbritain2030*.

" Without concerted action now, the world will be faced with temperature increases far in excess of 2°C, with unthinkable impacts "

Robert Watson,

Former Chair of the Intergovernmental Panel on Climate Change; Strategic Director for the Tyndall Centre at the University of East Anglia; and Chief Scientific Advisor for the UK Department for Environment, Food and Rural Affairs.

introduction

Introduction

zerocarbonbritain2030 is a fully integrated solution to climate change in the UK. It examines how we can meet our electricity and heating requirements through efficient service provision, while still decreasing carbon dioxide, methane, nitrous oxide and other emissions.

The report starts by examining the current "context" in the Climate science and Energy security chapters. It then moves on to how we can "PowerDown" heat and electricity demand largely through new technology, efficient design and behaviour change. Land offers tremendous potential not only to decrease emissions but also to sequester residual emissions. We then move on to how we can "PowerUp" through the use of renewable technology and finally we examine the policy that can help bring this about and the job creation that will come with it.

All human societies have had to face challenges of one sort or another. But in today's world, the scale and scope of those challenges is perhaps greater than any faced before. Heating, electricity and land use must now be confronted. There is a common solution to a changing climate, the failing economy, diminishing fossil fuel reserves and rising energy prices. Time is now pressing for all countries to rise to these challenges in a manner commensurate with the scale and immediacy of the threat.

zerocarbonbritain2030 explores how Britain can respond to the challenge of climate change in an energy secure, timely and humane way. It shows that many potential solutions already exist and are in operation, ready for wider application. In addition, it shows that making

the necessary transition to a low carbon future would not only stimulate the economy and create jobs, it would also provide greater security, autonomy and an enriched quality of life.

zerocarbonbritain2030 is the result of a long process of developing alternatives to our current unsustainable use of natural resources. Founded in 1973, the Centre for Alternative Technology first published *An Alternative Energy Strategy for the United Kingdom* in 1977 (Todd & Alty, 1997).

Thirty years later, the first zero carbon Britain report, *zerocarbonbritain: an alternative energy strategy*, was produced (Helweg-Larson & Bull, 2007), in response to the scientific evidence on both climate change and energy security, which revealed a situation even more urgent than had been anticipated. That report began to outline how Britain could decrease its energy demand by around 50%, and then go on to meet this reduced demand through indigenous renewable reserves.

That report looked at the renewable resources in Britain as a geographical unit. Now, *zerocarbonbritain2030* considers how Britain can play its part within a wider, global solution. It still has Britain as its focus, but also considers how the people and businesses within it can also take a global lead in fulfilling international obligations to deliver climate and energy security. With that in mind, there is now a chapter on Motivation and behavioural change.

The scope is also widened through an extensive examination of food and farming practices within the Land use and agriculture chapter. This looks at both the potential to reduce emissions and the potential to use the land to sequester carbon, balancing out any residual emissions.

The focus is on policy, but it also includes roles for all sectors of society, such as individuals and businesses. It aims to stimulate debate and build consensus over this new and challenging terrain, signposting where the path is clear, and highlighting places where there is still uncertainty and where research is required.

The current economic situation presents a substantial opportunity. This new report highlights how, by taking the necessary action now, economies can be revitalised, employment created and a secure dividend created to repay the investment, through the value of the energy saved or generated.

As our Climate science chapter demonstrates, there are a range of serious physical and economic impacts that would result from inaction. Dealing with such a challenge requires a degree of urgency that is lacking currently. This report illustrates a potential scenario for meeting the necessary scale and speed of the challenge.

Much excellent work in this area has been published over the past few years. This report aims to synthesise and draw together work done by different expert groups. Through developing a common, coherent vision, *zerocarbonbritain2030* offers a process for integrating detailed knowledge and experience from a wide range of disciplines into a single framework that can clearly and effectively be articulated to promote urgent action across all sectors of society.

The concepts explored in the first *zerocarbonbritain* report have been updated and strengthened through additional input from external experts and organisations. Careful analysis explodes some of the many myths that have grown up in this area, such as that renewable technologies use more energy in their construction than they supply, or that there is one magic bullet that would negate the need for major reductions in energy demand and use of natural resources.

The report is divided into five sections:
- The **Context** section presents the evidence

on which the report is based: the science behind why we need to change our path, how much needs to be done, and how quickly. An introduction is given to the issues of climate change and energy security. The climate science, energy security, carbon budgeting and equity considerations highlight the need for rapid reductions in Britain.

• The **PowerDown** section evaluates how Britain's energy demand can be decreased, looking in depth at two key sectors: the built environment, and transport. Buildings are a key component in dealing with energy and climate problems, and the importance of their role is often underestimated. The report shows that it is possible to drastically reduce energy demand through a "deep refurbishment" of existing buildings, and highlights the need for a code for high performance sustainable refurbishment including the use of natural materials to lock carbon in buildings.

The report then goes on to consider transport, and shows how the sector can be decarbonised through the use of several technologies, particularly the electrification of transport and reduction in vehicle body weight, as well as through modal shifts to public and human-powered transport.

To complement these sector studies, a chapter on motivation and behavioural change examines how to best motivate individuals and how individual action plays an active role in decarbonisation, by accepting, supporting and indeed calling for the positive change that the

climate science shows is necessary. This chapter discusses current personal barriers to action and introduces several strategies to overcome them, including social marketing, identity campaigning and community-led carbon management and energy reduction schemes.

• The **PowerUp** section discusses Britain's strategic renewable energy reserves. The Renewables chapter highlights the potential for renewables in the UK and then considers what could be realised by 2030. The *zerocarbonbritain2030* scenario combines an array of research from experts in the field, including from the UK Energy Research Council, the National Grid and others, into one scenario. Renewable sources of heat and electricity can reliably meet demand through a mixture of smart demand management, back-up generation, storage facilities and connection with neighbouring countries. The *zerocarbonbritain2030* scenario has also been tested using weather data and half hourly demand profiles to ensure that there is enough flexibility in the system to efficiently meet Britain's electricity needs.

To supplement the core scenario there is a chapter on microgrids which highlights some of the uses of distributed generation especially when combined at a local level to meet local needs and improve resilience.

• The **Land use** section considers emissions from land and agriculture and the potential of the land for carbon sequestration. It identifies the emissions originating from land use, how these can be reduced, the change in diet that will be required, and the land-based products available to assist decarbonisation and sequestration. The new diet, which includes reduced meat consumption, is healthier than the current diet. The chapter even highlights many of the potential uses for land-based products and the selection chosen for **zero**carbon**britain**2030. The land has the unique property that, under the right management, it can actually become a net sink for greenhouse gases.

• The **Policy and economics** section examines the legislation and incentives that would be required to make it all happen and the job creation that would come with it. It also examines how environmental considerations must change the ways in which society views fundamental issues, most crucially its sense of direction and purpose in the 21st Century.

It is of no benefit to play down the scale of the challenge. What is required is an overhaul of how energy and fossil fuels are obtained and used. However, in a time of rising unemployment and falling social cohesion, such a challenge may be precisely what is needed. Many of the jobs created would be secure, and of enduring value. They would build the infrastructure, cultivate the knowledge and skills, and develop the enterprises that would be in increasing international demand over the decades to follow.

The report concludes that, with its excellent natural resources and high level of environmental awareness, Britain has the opportunity to rise from its current position to be an international leader in one of the key issues of the age. As we progress down that road and successes become visible, public enthusiasm and engagement with the process will grow.

Choosing the future

When considering the vision of a sustainable future outlined in **zero**carbon**britain**2030, a natural response is to compare it to the recent

Tar sands, Canada.
Source: Rezac/Greenpeace.

past. However, the unsustainability of society's recent trajectory clearly cannot continue. A more appropriate comparison would therefore be with other possible visions of the future.

The Climate Change Bill included an 80% reduction in CO_2 emissions by 2050, compared

Photovoltaic roof – the Centre for Alternative Technology.
Source: Centre for Alternative Technology.

to 1990 levels. The future will not be a mirror of the past and will not be "business as usual".

For example in the short term, climate change could be accelerated through the growing use of unconventional fossil fuels.

The energy return on energy invested (EROEI) is the ratio of the amount of usable energy acquired from an energy resource to the amount of energy expended to obtain it.

In the USA, conventional oil gave an EROEI of over 100:1 in 1930; by 1970, that had fallen to 30:1, and by 2000 had fallen to around 18:1 (Hall, 2008). The extraction of unconventional oils can give a ratio as low as 3:1.

Such increasing inefficiencies are the consequence of inertia maintaining current systems rather than switching to new technologies. The exploitation of the Canadian tar sands arises from the slow development and adoption of new energy sources such as renewables.

As an indication of scale, the Canadian tar sands development currently emit around 36 million tonnes of CO_2 per annum, even before factoring in the considerable additional emissions caused by the removal of forest cover (Greenpeace, 2009). This is about the same as Norway's total emissions in 2006. The process has devastating impacts on the boreal forest, which is completely stripped during surface mining. It has substantial health impacts on the local population, polluting both water and food supplies.

The drive to exploit unconventional oils is one of the many results of inaction. Its costs are financial, social and environmental. As this report highlights, however, there is another way forward. Rather than allowing inertia to drive business as usual, renewables can power a sustainable future.

Consumption or production

Anthropogenic climate change is caused by the consumption of natural resources. The international agreements created to control CO_2 levels are, however, based on countries' territorial emissions – that is, emissions from the production of goods and services within that country. Thus, if China produces goods for export to the UK, the emissions associated with their production are counted as China's own, not the UK's.

This grossly distorts the picture, especially at a time when UK consumption is increasing, while production is decreasing. It has been estimated that on the basis of consumption rather than territorial production, the UK's emissions would have risen by 19% rather than falling by 15% between 1990 and 2007 (Helm et al., 2007).

In aiming to avoid more than 2°C warming, Britain has the potential to take a global lead in fair accounting, by ensuring that the embodied energy and carbon of its imports are also included.

Currently, emissions from imports are generally ignored in energy and carbon modelling. This fits neatly with other nationally-based accounting procedures, and also simplifies the modelling process. A consumption basis would put huge additional demands on creating a workable model and be dependent on a number of assumptions due to the limited availability of data. Perhaps most significantly however, basing models on consumption rather than production would make the challenge of decarbonisation harder due to the much higher baseline that it provides.

Due to the embodied carbon in imports, and for financial reasons, simply reducing the level of imports can help ensure we fit within a fair carbon budget. We must therefore examine ways to reduce imports and ensure that the remaining imports have minimal carbon content.

With policy to promote spending on capital (UK based renewables) rather than goods, and an increasing focus on the quality of goods, the demand for goods will decrease. Where appropriate, increased localisation of production can also be encouraged, therefore further reducing imports.

Another possible mechanism for reducing the export of carbon emissions abroad is to levy taxes to account for the embodied carbon in imported goods.

These taxes would prevent imports from countries with lower environmental standards becoming more cost competitive. They would also generate revenue, which could be ring-fenced and used to finance decarbonisation projects abroad, compensating for the imported emissions. In the absence of an international agreement this seems the most sensible suggestion.

One candidate for such overseas investment would be the Desertec project to supply renewable energy from concentrated solar power farms located in Southern Europe and North Africa. This would help international adaptation and decrease the embodied carbon in imports.

References

Greenpeace (2009) *"Stop the Tar Sands"*, Greenpeace Canada. Available at http://www.greenpeace.org/canada/en/campaigns/tarsands/ [Live: March 2010].

Hall, C.A.S. (2008) "Provisional Results from EROI Assessments", The Oil Drum. Available at http://www.theoildrum.com/node/3810 [Live: March 2010].

Helm, D., R. Smale & J. Phillips (2007) "Too Good To Be True? The UK's Climate Change Record", Dieter Helm CBE [online]. Available at: http://www.dieterhelm.co.uk/sites/default/files/Carbon_record_2007.pdf [Live: March 2010].

Helweg-Larson, T. & J. Bull (2007) *zerocarbonbritain: an alternative energy strategy*, Machynlleth: Centre for Alternative Technology.

Todd, R.W. & C.J.N. Alty (eds) (1977) *An Alternative Energy Strategy for the United Kingdom*, Machynlleth: National Centre for Alternative Technology.

Figure sources

Rezac/Greenpeace.

Centre for Alternative Technology.

" One ought never to turn one's back on a threatened danger and try to run away from it. If you do that, you will double the danger. But if you meet it promptly and without flinching, you will reduce the danger by half "

Winston Churchill

Chapter 1
Climate science

Introduction

The threat of climate change is one of the three key reasons – alongside energy security and global equity – behind the current pressing need for society to alter the ways in which energy is produced and used. Those same reasons underlie the more general need for a radical overhaul of the way in which humanity relates to and uses all of our planetary resources and systems, including the land, the oceans and the atmosphere. If we do not change our current course, the consequences will include species extinctions, mass migration and acute disruption to human societies all over the world.

This chapter presents a summary of the scientific predictions in the area of climate change, and the reasoning on which those predictions are based. Building on this, the final section discusses the quantity of greenhouse gases that the UK can afford to emit over the next few decades, based on the current level of scientific knowledge and understanding.

Evidence of climate change

It has been known since the 19th Century that greenhouse gases such as carbon dioxide (CO_2)

Fig. 1.1 Rising annual global average temperatures

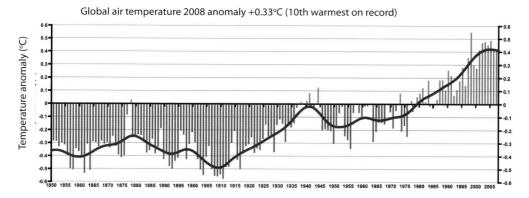

Global air temperature 2008 anomaly +0.33°C (10th warmest on record)

Global average air temperatures (°C), 1850–2008.
All data is shown as the difference in global mean air temperature relative to the period 1961 to 1990 (the temperature change relative to a reference temperature is referred to as the temperature 'anomaly'). The purple line demonstrates smoothed trend. This graph illustrates the rise in global temperature that has occurred over the past 150 years.
Source: Based on data from the Climatic Research Unit, UEA (2009).

Fig. 1.2 Northern hemisphere long-term temperature changes

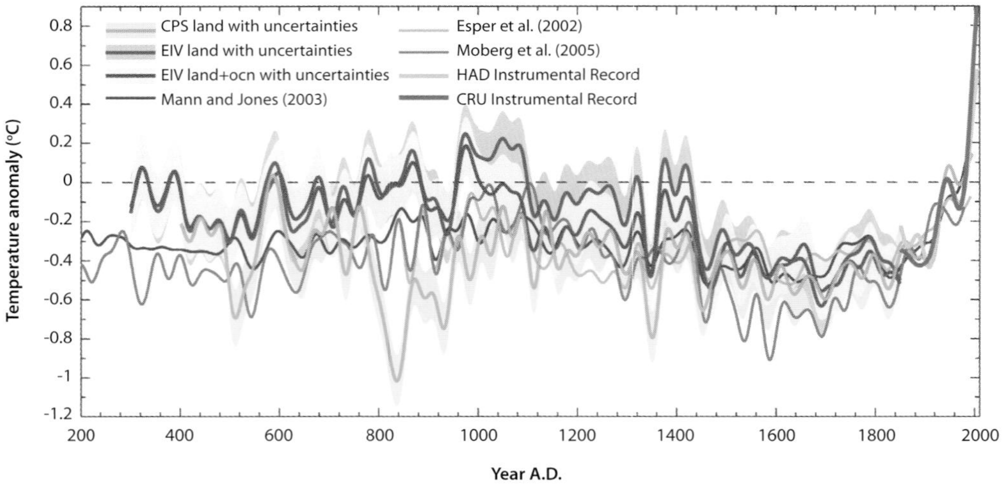

Northern hemisphere temperature reconstructions (°C), 200–2000.

All data are shown as the difference (anomaly) in global mean air temperature relative to the period 1961 to 1990. Composite land and land plus ocean temperature reconstructions are estimated at 95% confidence intervals. Temperature has been calculated from averages of thermometer readings since the 1800s. This graph demonstrates that the scale of global mean temperature increases over the last 150 years is unprecedented within the last 2000 years.

Temperatures since the 1800s are calculated from thermometer readings. Temperatures prior to the 1800s are calculated using temperature "proxies" including tree rings, coral, stalagmites, glaciers, icebergs and boreholes. The climate affects their pattern of growth.

Source: Mann et al. (2008).

and water vapour trap incoming solar radiation and prevent it from leaving the Earth, keeping the planet at a hospitable temperature for life (Fourier, 1824; Tyndall, 1859). Without them, the average temperature of the Earth would be some 20°–30° colder (Houghton, 2009).

At the end of the 19th Century, the Swedish physicist Svante Arrhenius (1896) reasoned that adding to the greenhouse gas blanket through burning fossil fuels would raise the

Earth's temperature. He suggested that this warming might be amplified because, as temperature increased, the air would hold more water vapour. In addition, the melting of ice would expose darker surfaces which would absorb more radiation. Arrhenius produced quantitative estimates of the warming that might occur.

Since Arrhenius's time the Earth has experienced a global average surface warming of about 0.8°C (see Figures 1.1 and 1.2). This warming has not merely been seen in thermometer readings, but also in a multitude of changes to the natural world, including diminishing ice cover, altered plant and animal behaviour and changing seasonal patterns (Intergovernmental Panel on Climate Change, [IPCC], 2007a). Data for the oceans, atmosphere, land and ice since 1950 has been analysed and it has been calculated that the entire earth system has been accumulating heat at a rate of about 6×10^{21} Joules per year (Murphy *et al.*, 2009).

Meanwhile, climate science has progressed immensely and a large number of different lines of evidence have confirmed that the build up of anthropogenic (of human origin) greenhouse gases is the significant cause. This has led to a scientific consensus so strong that no dissenting view is held by any scientific body of national or international standing.

A small selection of these lines of evidence are presented below:

• There is no convincing alternative explanation. Incoming solar radiation has been measured for decades and has not changed significantly, especially during the last 30 years. The trigger for the warming at the ends of previous ice ages is believed to be the Milankovitch cycles (changes in the Earth's orbit that occur regularly in a pattern scanning about 100,000 years), but the next such trigger is not expected for another 30,000 years. The natural effects alone would have produced a slight global cooling over

Fig. 1.3 Global temperature changes and climate models

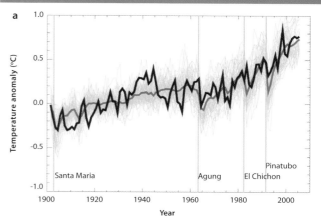

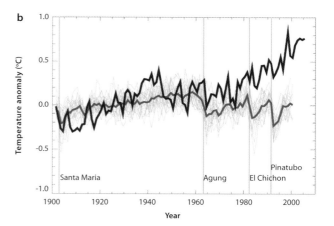

Comparison of global mean surface temperatures changes (°C), 1900–2008, from observations (black) and model simulations forced with (a) both anthropogenic and natural forcings and (b) natural forcings only.

All data are shown as the difference (anomaly) in global mean temperature relative to the period 1901 to 1950. The wide coloured band is made up of different model outputs and the central coloured line is their average. Vertical grey lines indicate the timing of major volcanic events. The comparison demonstrates that model simulations of natural forcings alone do not correlate with actual temperature observations over the last 150 years. However, model simulations of natural forcings and anthropogenic forcings together correlate extremely well with the record of temperature change.
Source: IPCC (2007).

the past 30 years (IPCC, 2007a).

- While the lower atmosphere is warming, the upper atmosphere is cooling (Olsen *et al.*, 2007). This effect cannot be explained without invoking the build-up of greenhouse gases (IPCC, 2007a).

- Unlike warming caused by other heating agents, an enhanced greenhouse effect should lead to greater warming at the poles – again, precisely what is observed (ibid.).

- The tropopause is the altitude at which the air stops cooling as height increases. Over the past few decades, the altitude of the tropopause has been rising. This is another observed "fingerprint" pointing to the presence of an enhanced greenhouse effect (Santer *et al.*, 2003).

- The greenhouse gases all absorb particular wavelengths within the infrared spectrum. When satellite data was examined in 2000, it was found that the quantity of radiation leaving the Earth in the wavelengths absorbed by CO_2 had fallen over several decades, as had that in the wavelengths absorbed by the other greenhouse gases (Harries, 2001).

- The atmospheric levels of all greenhouse gases have been traced back over time using ice core samples. They are found to have remained stable for thousands of years until about 200 years ago when they began to increase rapidly (IPCC, 2007a). The source of the new CO_2 can be established because carbon exists in different isotopic forms. By measuring the proportions of those different isotopes, the source of the carbon can be identified (Newton & Bottrell, 2007). The isotopic fingerprint of the atmospheric CO_2 shows an increasing proportion coming from fossil fuels, rather than from natural sources (Houghton, 2009).

- Factors that disturb the Earth's energy balance and initiate a temperature rise or fall are known as "forcings". Models which incorporate both the natural and the anthropogenic forcings reproduce past temperature profiles very well (see Figure 1.3). They have also accurately simulated more detailed changes such as regional temperature patterns, the variations of warming at different depths in the oceans and the changes that have followed volcanic eruptions. These models correctly predicted the climatic changes that occurred between 1988 and the present day (Mann & Kump, 2008).

CO_2 is not the only greenhouse gas emitted due to human activity. Because it is the main one, other greenhouse gases such as nitrous oxide and methane are often translated into "CO_2 equivalent" (CO_2e) on the basis of how much warming they are estimated to cause compared to CO_2.

Human activity also emits aerosols – small particles that have a net cooling effect by preventing sunlight reaching the Earth. Coincidentally, the cooling effect of aerosols is currently roughly balancing the warming effect of humanity's non-CO_2 greenhouse gases. Hence in warming terms, the total CO_2 equivalent level is approximately the same as the CO_2 level, which is about 385ppm (parts per million), having risen from 280ppm in pre-industrial times.

Over the next few decades, aerosol emissions are likely to decline, due to clean air legislation and because reducing CO_2 emissions through cuts in fossil fuel use will lower aerosol emissions at the same time. Unlike CO_2, aerosols have a short atmospheric life because they are "washed out" by rain. In consequence, over the next few decades the warming effect of the current level of greenhouse gases will increase, and the CO_2 and CO_2 equivalent levels will diverge (Houghton, 2009).

Predictions of the future

CLIMATE SENSITIVITY & FEEDBACKS

An increase in greenhouse gases creates an imbalance between the energy entering and the energy leaving the earth, called a forcing. This causes the Earth to become hotter, and as the temperature rises, it loses more energy to space. Eventually a new equilibrium is reached where energy input and output are in balance at a higher temperature.

"Climate sensitivity" is a measure used to predict the temperature response to a given forcing. It refers to the expected warming that would result from a doubling of the equivalent CO_2 concentration from its pre-industrial level of 280ppm, assuming the CO_2 level is then held constant until the Earth reaches its new equilibrium temperature. It would take centuries to fully reach this new equilibrium, but most of the warming occurs within decades (IPCC, 2007a).

If it were possible to double the amount of atmospheric CO_2 while keeping everything else unchanged, the Earth would warm by about 1.2°C before reaching its new equilibrium (Houghton, 2009). This figure is relatively easy to calculate from the physics of radiative heat transfer theory. However when atmospheric CO_2 is doubled, everything else does *not* remain the same. This is because of feedbacks which are either positive, amplifying the warming, or negative, decreasing it. On the timescales of interest to humanity, they are overwhelmingly positive (IPCC, 2007a).

The most important feedback is water vapour. This is a powerful greenhouse gas, but adding it directly to the atmosphere does not have much effect because it quickly rains out again. This places water vapour in a separate category to the greenhouse gases which make up the "CO_2 equivalent" level. However, because warmer air holds more water vapour, it creates a positive feedback which approximately doubles the warming that would occur had the water vapour level stayed constant (Dessler *et al.*, 2008; Houghton, 2009).

Some of the increased water vapour will

Fig. 1.4 Probability estimates of equilibrium climate sensitivity

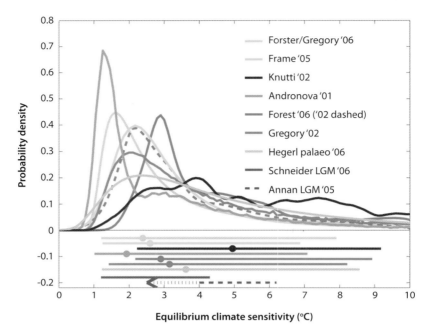

Comparison of different estimates of probability density (or relative likelihood) of equilibrium climate sensitivity (°C).
The bars below the main graph show the respective 5 to 95% probability ranges; the dots show the median estimate. The probability density functions are based on instrumental data from various authors listed in the legend. Based on this, Earth's equilibrium climate sensitivity is most likely to be between 2°C and 4.5°C.
Source: IPCC (2007).

also condense to form clouds, increasing the net cloud cover. Clouds create both positive and negative feedbacks. Some trap heat in the atmosphere, causing warming, while others reflect solar radiation back into space, causing cooling. The estimated net effect of clouds varies between models (Ringer *et al.*, 2007; IPCC, 2007a).

A third important feedback is caused by melting snow and sea ice. As snow and ice melt,

the land and sea that are exposed reflect less radiation, absorbing a greater proportion of the sun's heat. Once more, this creates a positive feedback (Hall, 2004).

The overall effect of these and other feedbacks have been calculated using models which incorporate the circulation of the atmosphere and oceans, cloud formation, sea ice and the other elements of the climate system.

A different approach to estimating the climate sensitivity has been to start from observational data. These include evidence from short-term cooling following volcanic eruptions; the changes during the ice age cycles; the climate at the Last Glacial Maximum (21,000 years ago); the temperature and CO_2 records over the past 150 years; and data from the deep past, tens of millions of years ago, and from the Little Ice Age between 1645 to 1715.

Based on all this work, the Intergovernmental Panel on Climate Change estimates climate sensitivity at between 2°C and 4.5°C, with a best guess of 3°C. The probability of a sensitivity higher than 3°C is greater than one that is lower, and climate sensitivities less than 1.5°C can effectively be ruled out. Climate sensitivities higher than 4.5°C are considered less likely but cannot be totally ruled out (IPCC, 2007a).

CARBON CYCLE FEEDBACKS AND CLOGGING SINKS

Climate sensitivity describes the global mean temperature response to the level of CO_2 in the atmosphere. But on its own this is insufficient to determine the temperature response to our emissions of greenhouse gases, because the quantity that we emit is not the same as the quantity that ends up in the atmosphere.

At present only about half of the emitted CO_2 ends up in the atmosphere because the Earth's ecosystems, such as the oceans and plants, act as carbon sinks (IPCC, 2007a). Predictions of the effects of continued CO_2 emissions are worsened by the fact that as CO_2 concentrations and temperatures rise, the ability of some of those sinks to keep absorbing our emissions is likely to decline. Furthermore, some ecosystems are themselves predicted to start giving out more greenhouse gases as temperatures and CO_2 concentrations rise (Cox et al., 2006).

The responses of the carbon cycle to rises in CO_2 levels or to temperature are referred to as "carbon cycle feedbacks". Many of these feedbacks have only recently started to be incorporated into models (IPCC, 2007a). They include:

The oceans

- **Warmer oceans**: As oceans warm, they absorb less CO_2 (gas solubility decreases with increasing temperature) (ibid.).

  positive feedback

- **Ocean acidification**: As levels of atmospheric CO_2 rise, more is dissolved in the oceans, increasing their acidity. More acidic water reduces the ability of plankton and corals to form shells. Much of the oceanic food chain depends on plankton, making this an extremely serious issue in itself. Declining shell weights have already been observed for several species (Moy et al., 2009; De'ath et al., 2009). It also acts as both a positive and a negative feedback on climate change.

  positive and negative feedback

- **Slower ocean circulation**: Another possible effect of climate change is to reduce the circulation of global ocean currents. This would reduce the biological productivity of the ocean and its ability to absorb CO_2 (IPCC, 2007a).

  positive feedback

On land

- **Increased soil respiration**: Soil contains microorganisms that convert carbon in the soil into CO_2 as they respire. The growth and respiration rates of these microorganisms increase with temperature, which is why soils in hot areas like Africa contain less carbon than soils in colder areas (IPCC, 2007a).

  positive feedback

- **Change in plant uptake and sequestration of CO_2**: More CO_2 in the air can lead to increased plant growth, in turn allowing plants to take up more CO_2 from the atmosphere. However, above a certain level this ceases to aid growth which instead becomes restricted by other factors such as access to water and nutrients. Furthermore, ecosystems struggle to cope with rapid climate changes (IPCC, 2007a). Ecosystems such as forests are reservoirs of carbon, and should they reduce or die off, the carbon they store would be returned to the atmosphere (ibid.).

  positive and negative feedback

When models including some of these feedbacks are run, both the calculated CO_2 level and the ensuing warming are increased. While there is uncertainty about the magnitude of the effect, current understanding indicates that the net feedback from the carbon cycle will be positive and that it will increase as temperatures rise.

Models predict that, by the end of the 21st Century, the additional CO_2 from the biosphere feedbacks, land and sea, will lead to an additional warming of between 0.1°C and 1.5°C compared to the case where climate change has no impact on the carbon cycle (IPCC, 2007a).

PREDICTED TEMPERATURE RISES FOR THE COMING CENTURY

The mechanisms and feedbacks described in the preceding sections have been incorporated into estimates of likely temperature rises over the coming century.

The IPCC (2007a) uses various emissions scenarios to make forecasts based on different assumptions of population growth, economic growth and international cooperation. Mean estimates for temperature rises this centruy under these scenarios are presented in Figure 1.5.

The IPCC's highest emissions scenario is called A1FI (fossil-intensive). Until the global economic recession, the growth rate of global emissions was exceeding that of the A1FI scenario (Raupach, 2007; Anderson & Bows, 2008).

Fig. 1.5 Predicted climate change scenarios to 2100

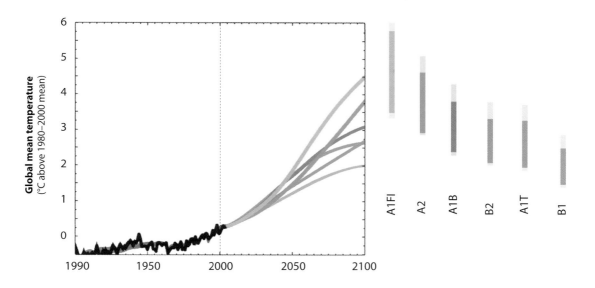

Predicted global temperature increases (°C) to 2100 under each IPCC emissions scenario.
The coloured lines within the graph show the mean temperature estimates for each of the IPCC's six emissions scenarios. Probability ranges are indicated for each scenario to the right of the graph. The darker shaded area for each represents the mean ±1 standard deviation given mid-range carbon cycle assumptions. The lighter shaded area for each depicts the change in this uncertainty range if carbon cycle feedbacks are assumed to be lower or higher than in the medium setting. Each emissions scenario is based on different projected rates of future population growth, international economic and political convergence, and technological change. Current patterns correlate most closely with the high A1FI emissions scenario.
Source: Amended from IPCC (2007).

Impacts

Warming the planet by several degrees takes us into uncharted territory. A temperature rise of 4–6°C would be similar to the difference between our current climate and the depths of the last ice age (Allison *et al.*, 2009).

It is very hard to predict what might happen with such a high degree of warming. Many of the specific predictions that are available refer to fairly moderate temperature rises of 1–3°C,

which may give a misleadingly mild impression of the ultimate impacts. A great deal of uncertainty surrounds the impacts of the larger increases.

At higher temperatures, it is likely that climate change will affect everyone. However, the impacts will not be spread equally. Climate change is also an issue of justice and equity, because while it is the rich world that is primarily responsible for the emissions, the

Box 1.1 Some unknowns and controversies

Methane, permafrost & the fire inside the ice

There are several carbon cycle feedbacks that have not yet been modelled, and are therefore not included in any estimates of likely temperature rises. This means that all the current predictions of temperature rise might be underestimates (Cox *et al.*, 2000; IPCC, 2007a, Jones *et al.*, 2009).

One of these is the possibility of methane or CO_2 releases from permafrost. Permafrost is ground that is permanently frozen, located mainly across Siberia and other northern regions. It contains a huge carbon store – almost twice that in the atmosphere – created from long-dead organisms preserved in the frozen conditions (Schuur *et al.*, 2009). If the permafrost thaws, as it is now starting to do, the carbon can start to be released, either as CO_2 or as methane (Åkerman and Johansson, 2008; Allison *et al.*, 2009; Jin *et al.*, 2008). Methane is about 25 times as powerful a greenhouse gas as CO_2 over a 100-year period (US Climate Change Science Program, 2008).

The likely magnitude of any positive feedback from melting permafrost is not yet known (Archer, 2007; Schuur *et al.*, 2009; Jones *et al.*, 2009). After about a decade of stability, methane levels in the atmosphere have recently risen. It is unknown as yet where this methane originates from (Allison *et al.*, 2009).

There is an even greater store of methane hydrates at the bottom of the oceans (crystals of methane and water). It has been suggested that should the surrounding ocean warm sufficiently, these hydrates could melt and be released into the atmosphere (US Climate Change Science Program, 2008). However, most of this hydrate is hundreds of metres below the ocean floor and will be insulated from the effects of climate change for millennia (ibid.). It is currently considered unlikely that any significant release of methane from ocean hydrates will happen this century (Allison *et al.*, 2009).

impacts will fall most heavily on the poor. This is firstly because of a lack of resources to adapt, and secondly because it is predicted that many of the most serious impacts will hit regions which are already vulnerable through poverty. Some of the specific predicted impacts are:

Water

Climate change threatens fresh water supplies due to:

- Altered rainfall patterns, with dry regions becoming drier and wet regions wetter, and rainfall patterns becoming more variable and less predictable (IPCC, 2007b).

- The contamination of groundwater sources with salt as sea levels rise (ibid.).
- Diminishing meltwater from glaciers, which currently supply water to more than one sixth of the world's population, although this will first increase as the glaciers melt (ibid.).

After a warming of around 2°C, 1 to 2 billion people are predicted to face increased water shortages (IPCC, 2007b).

One of the most disturbing forecasts to date suggests that the proportion of the land surface in extreme drought could increase from 1% in the present to 30% by the end of the century, under one of the high emissions scenarios which the IPCC associates with up to 5.4°C of warming (Burke *et al.*, 2006; IPCC, 2007b).

Food production and human health

A temperature rise of up to 2–3°C is predicted to lead to the redistribution of the world's food production potential from low to high latitude countries (IPCC, 2007b). As it is principally low latitude countries that are poor and economically dependent on agriculture, this is likely to increase global hunger and inequality.

Responding to new growing conditions by adopting new crop varieties or species requires expertise and significant capital outlay. In the absence of adaptive measures, production from the rain-fed agriculture practiced by the poor is predicted to be reduced by up to 50% in some African countries, by as early as 2020 (ibid.).

Above 2 or 3°C of warming the total global food production potential is predicted to decline (ibid.). Additionally, as a result of reductions in freshwater availability in the tropics, diarrhoeal disease is projected to increase, and infectious disease could also increase (Costello *et al.*, 2009; IPCC, 2007b).

Ecosystems

Ecosystems are adapted to particular environmental conditions and struggle to cope with rapid change. Species are already observed shifting towards the poles or to higher altitudes, but their ability to migrate is limited (Pitelka, 1997; Chen *et al.*, 2009). The IPCC (2007b) suggests that 20–30% of species are likely to

be committed to extinction after rises of 2–3°C. Certain particular areas of very high biodiversity, such as coral reefs, are directly threatened by even low levels of warming.

After a 4°C rise, up to 70% of species will be at risk (ibid.). At higher temperatures, the possibilities become more uncertain, but also more dire. There is evidence that large rises in temperature that took place in the deep past led to mass extinction events (Mayhew *et al.*, 2008).

Sea level rise

Over the past 100 years global average sea level has risen by about 12–22cm, and the rate has been increasing (IPCC, 2007b).

In its last assessment report, the IPCC (ibid.) predicted a global sea level rise by 2100 of 18–59cm, plus an additional contribution from observed ice sheet processes that were not well understood, for which they estimated 17cm. Many of these processes are still not well understood but more recent estimates have suggested higher figures and generated estimates of between 0.5 and 2 metres for total sea level rise this century (Pfeffer, *et al.*, 2008; Rahmstorf, 2007; Grinsted *et al.*, 2009).

Sea level rise is something that is committed to long before it happens. The oceans take a long time to heat up, and ice sheets take a long time to melt. Because of this the rise in the longer term will be higher than these figures, as the processes will continue long after the end of the present century.

Half of humanity lives in coastal zones, and the

lowest lying areas are some of the most fertile and densely populated on Earth (Houghton, 2009). The human effects of sea level rise are therefore likely to be significant.

Migration, violence and disasters

Higher temperatures will lead to increased forest fires and flooding, and may increase the power of other extreme weather events such as hurricanes and tropical storms (IPCC, 2007b). Estimates of the number of people who may be uprooted due to climate change by 2050 (i.e. at comparatively low temperature rises of around 1.5–2°C) are in the order of hundreds of millions (Warner *et al.*, 2009).

Many commentators have argued that the reduction in human security caused by changing climate trends and increased extreme weather events, could also lead to violent conflict, particularly in fragile societies (see Homer-Dixon, 1994; Baechler, 1998). The United Nations Environment Programme (UNEP, 2009) claims that the long drought in the Sudan has been one of the major contributing factors underlying the war in Darfur. While it is difficult to attribute any particular event to climate change, it makes droughts like the one in the Sudan more likely to occur.

THRESHOLDS AND TIPPING POINTS

The Earth contains many systems that may undergo abrupt changes after a certain threshold is reached. There may also be thresholds that, when crossed, lead to significant changes, even if those changes occur slowly. A description of the scientific understanding of such "tipping points" was provided by Mitchell *et al.*, (2006), the IPCC (2007a) and later expanded on by Lenton *et al.* (2008). They include:

Ice sheets

The two major ice sheets endangered by climate change are those of Greenland and the West Antarctic. If the Greenland ice sheet melted entirely, it would raise the sea level by about 7 metres. The West Antarctic ice sheet would add a further 5 metres (Oppenheimer & Alley, 2005).

If temperatures above a certain level are sustained in the long term, total melting of the ice sheets becomes inevitable even if the process takes a long time to complete (IPCC, 2007b). The IPCC estimates that the Greenland ice sheet will be committed to melting after global average warming of 1.9 to 4.6°C. It could not derive a similar estimate for the West Antarctic ice sheet as its disintegration depends on its poorly understood interaction with the surrounding ocean.

Ice sheets do not melt overnight. The IPCC (ibid.) suggest that it would take more than 1000 years for the Greenland ice sheet to melt in its entirety. For the West Antarctic ice sheet it states that "present understanding is insufficient for a prediction of the possible speed" (IPCC, 2007c). If the ice sheets start melting rapidly, dramatic sea level rise will occur long before they melt entirely.

Once the ice sheet becomes thinner, temperatures in the region can increase, speeding the melting and causing rain to fall rather than snow. Hence it is believed that once melting has taken place, it may be irreversible (IPCC, 2007a). Despite this, there may be stable states where part of the ice sheet will remain if temperatures return to those similar to the present day (Ridley *et al.*, 2009).

Forests

The Amazon rainforest is an interdependent system which recycles a large fraction of its rainfall. Many models suggest that the Amazon will almost totally collapse after about 4°C of warming, being replaced with savannah within a few decades (Betts *et al.*, 2004). New work suggests that the Amazon could become committed to die off even at lower temperatures (Jones *et al.*, 2009). Other forests in northern latitudes such as those of Canada and Scandinavia, could also die off. Studies suggest a threshold of around 3°C for this, although this is highly uncertain (ibid.).

Forests are large reservoirs of carbon. If they die off or are destroyed, this carbon is returned to the atmosphere, acting as a positive feedback mechanism. The trees of the Amazon contain a quantity of carbon equivalent to about 9 to 14 years of current global annual human-induced carbon emissions (Nepstad, 2007). The collapse of parts of the Amazon is one of the things responsible for the significant extra warming

predicted by some carbon cycle feedback models (Betts *et al.*, 2008; Jones *et al.*, 2009).

Ocean circulation

Ocean currents are another area associated with the possibility of abrupt changes beyond a certain threshold. The Atlantic part of the global thermohaline circulation, commonly known as the Gulf Stream, is predicted to weaken over the next century as a result of climate change. The prospect of a very rapid change in ocean currents is considered possible, although a complete switch off is regarded as extremely unlikely (IPCC, 2007b).

Arctic summer sea ice

When sea ice melts, the darker ocean surface is exposed. This absorbs more radiation, amplifying the warming and causing more melting. All models show a trend of declining Arctic ice cover as temperatures increase. Some show abrupt losses of parts of the Arctic summer sea ice that are irreversible (Holland *et al.*, 2006), but other models show that it is possible for the Arctic to recover from such events (Lenton *et al.*, 2008). In recent years Arctic summer sea ice has declined faster than was predicted by models (Allison *et al.*, 2009).

How much can we afford to emit?

One thing that seems clear is that as temperatures rise the risks increase dramatically. The likely impacts themselves become stronger and the

Box 1.2 Some unknowns and controversies

Long-term climate sensitivity

In general, climate sensitivity has been calculated using feedbacks that act moderately quickly, such as water vapour levels and melting sea ice. Things that do not change significantly in the short term, such as ice sheet cover or ocean circulation, have been assumed to be fixed.

Recent work has suggested that in the longer term climate sensitivity could be significantly higher due to slow feedbacks such as changes in the Earth's reflectivity that occur when ice sheets melt. James Hansen (head of NASA's Goddard Institute for Space Studies) used paleoclimate data from the deep past to arrive at an estimate of 6°C. Hansen *et al.* (2008) argue that these slow feedbacks may begin to come into play on timescales as short as centuries or less.

More recently Lunt *et al.* (2009) used paleodata from a different period in the past to suggest an estimate for the long-term climate sensitivity. Their estimate is less than Hansen's but still 30–50% more than the IPCC's estimate of sensitivity based on fast feedbacks alone.

Hansen *et al.* (2008) use paleoclimate data to further suggest that if CO_2 levels are maintained at or above their current level for long enough, they risk triggering processes that will lead eventually to the melting of most of the ice on the Earth and a very large temperature and sea level rise. To guard against this possibility they suggest a global target of 350ppm CO_2 equivalent, significantly below the current level.

The arguments and conclusions of Hansen and colleagues in this area are controversial within the climate science community (Annan, 2008; Connolley, 2008; Allen, 2009).

probability increases that some of those changes will themselves trigger an escalation of the warming process, leading to yet more impacts.

More than 100 countries have adopted a target limit of 2°C relative to pre-industrial levels (Meinshausen *et al.*, 2009). A 2°C rise cannot probably be considered "safe". As described above, the impacts of even this amount of warming are severe. With an increase of 2°C, the Earth would probably be hotter than it has been for millions of years (Schmidt & Archer, 2009). An alliance of small island states and Least Developed Countries has called for the target to be 1.5°C (Alliance of Small Island States [AOSIS],

2009). However 2°C has been considered the upper limit on an acceptable level of risk, and it is imperative that this target, at least, is not exceeded.

CALCULATING A GLOBAL EMISSION'S BUDGET BASED ON 2°C

Many analyses have assessed the probability of exceeding different threshold temperatures after various emissions cuts (House *et al.*, 2008; Allen et al., 2009; Meinshausen *et al.*, 2009). The analysis performed recently by Meinshausen *et al.*, (2009) was aimed specifically at limiting warming to below 2°C.

Because CO_2 has a long atmospheric lifetime, the total cumulative amount of CO_2 emitted into the atmosphere is what is important for the climate, not the rate at which it is released (Allen et al., 2009). Meinshausen et al. (2009) calculate that limiting cumulative CO_2e emissions over the 2000–2050 period to 1,000Gt (gigatonnes) CO_2 yields a 75% probability of warming staying under 2°C. Known emissions in the period 2000–2006 were 234Gt CO_2e, hence this would leave less than 766 gigatonnes for release between 2007 and 2050.

There are only a limited range of plausible emissions trajectories that can be followed between now and 2050 if we are to stay within any set cumulative budget. Because of this, emissions in 2050 are quite a good indicator of the amount likely to be released in the intervening years. Meinshausen et al. (2009) estimate that we will have about a 70% chance of staying under 2°C if global emissions are cut by 50% from 1990 levels by 2050; as long as emissions have peaked before 2020, continue to be cut after 2050 and approach zero before 2100. If the same pattern is followed but with a cut of 72% by 2050 instead, we have an 84% chance of staying under 2°C. Global emissions in 1990 were about 36 billion tonnes CO_2e per year (Committee on Climate Change [CCC], 2008). Therefore a 50% global cut entails that annual global emissions will need to be cut to 18 billion tonnes and a 72% cut would require them to fall to 10 billion tonnes.

Meinshausen et al. (2009) also assess greenhouse gas emissions in 2020. They conclude that while emissions in 2020 are a less reliable indicator of temperature rise than emissions in 2050, they do provide some indication. They calculate that we have around a 79% chance of staying under 2°C if CO_2e emissions are 30 billion tonnes in 2020, around a 63% chance if they are 40 billion tonnes, and a 26% chance if they are 50 billion tonnes. CO_2e emissions in 2007 were 48.1 billion tonnes (CCC, 2008), and so this suggests that emissions must peak and start to fall at a time significantly before 2020 if we are to have a good chance of avoiding a 2°C rise in temperature. This is confirmed by other analyses (Met Office, 2009).

A plethora of different methods have been proposed for dividing emissions budgets and cuts between nations. These are discussed in the Policy and economics chapter. The starting point for such a discussion must be the vastly uneven current distribution of greenhouse gas emissions, as is shown in Figure 1.6.

To stabilise the climate at any temperature requires emissions to eventually trend towards zero in the long term (Matthews & Caldeira, 2008). Because of this, dividing the carbon budget is not a matter of deciding how much different countries must decarbonise, but at what speed. Given the huge disparity of starting points, it would clearly be unjust to suggest that everyone should cut at the same speed. The rich, long-industrialised countries have far more to cut than the majority world.

TOWARDS A UK EMISSIONS BUDGET

If the world were to converge on equal per capita emissions by 2050 and assuming the global population in 2050 will reach about 9.2 billion (CCC, 2008), the suggested 2050 budget of 18 or 10 billion tonnes would give an annual personal allowance of about 1.96 or 1.10 tonnes of CO_2e per year. UK emissions in 1990 were 797 million tonnes of CO_2e (ibid.) and the population was 57 million (Ross, 2007). Therefore to cut to

Fig. 1.6 International contributions to climate change

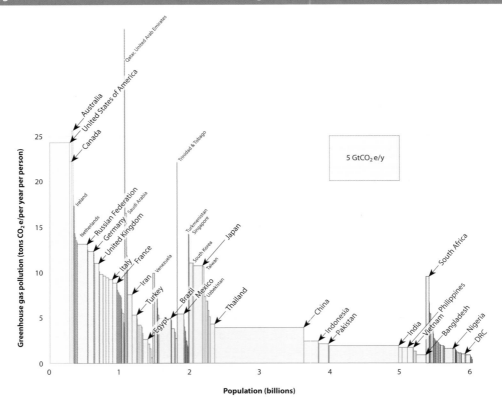

Greenhouse gas emissions (CO_2e) by nation and per capita for nations (2000).
The vertical axis shows greenhouse gas emissions per capita for each nation in 2000. The horizontal axis shows the population size of each nation. The total area of the graph covered by each nation represents its total greenhouse gas emissions, per year. Some countries with large populations such as China and India do produce a significant proportion of the world's greenhouse gas emissions. However, this graph clearly demonstrates the enormous difference in per capita greenhouse gas emissions across the world, and shows that many wealthy nations with relatively small populations also emit a significant proportion of total greenhouse gas emissions because their per capita emission levels are so high.
Source: Mackay (2009).

the personal allowance associated with an 84% chance of avoiding 2 degrees of warming would require a per capita cut in the UK of 92% from 1990 levels. The personal allowance associated with a 70% chance would require a per capita cut of 86%.

However, there are several reasons why cuts in the UK should be deeper. The first reason relates to how national emission totals are calculated. The standard accounting method is to attribute emissions to countries on a geographical basis, i.e. where those emissions are produced. But goods are often consumed in a different country from that in which they were manufactured. The effect of this accounting is therefore to downplay the emissions associated with consuming goods, and to give the impression that moving manufacturing to poor countries is lowering greenhouse gas emissions, when in fact it may be raising them.

This is a significant issue. Helm *et al.* (2007) calculated that if emissions were allocated to countries on the basis of consumption rather than production, it would increase the UK's total emissions by a massive 50%, meaning that we have outsourced a third of our emissions. Designing policies to deal with this is difficult, as the UK has limited control over how goods are made in China. However, until this issue has been addressed it suggests that a genuine equality in per capita emissions by 2050 would require deeper domestic cuts than those suggested above, in order to compensate for foreign emissions produced on the UK's behalf.

The second reason for deeper 2050 cuts in the UK becomes clear when the size of the 2050 per capita allowance of 1 or 2 tonnes is examined. Few countries currently emit as little as 1 or 2 tonnes per capita. The average per capita emissions in the portion of the world deemed too poor to be required to make cuts under the Kyoto Protocol is 4.2 tonnes of CO_2 equivalent per year (IPCC, 2007d). Average per capita emissions in Mozambique are about 1.7 tonnes, and in Malawi around 3 tonnes (Baumert *et al.*, 2005). If such low targets are to be achieved, it is not only rich countries that will have to make cuts by 2050. Poor countries will have to as well.

Long-industrialised countries possess infrastructure and wealth achieved by burning fossil fuel over the past 100 years. They now have the resources to invest in low carbon technologies for the future. The majority of countries do not. Historical responsibility for climate change rests overwhelmingly on the long industrialised world, while it is the majority world that will be hit the hardest by the consequences. Those who have already spent so much of the global carbon budget should therefore allow others to now have their share. In historical terms, the UK's emissions are the second highest in the world, and only just below those of the United States (Mackay, 2009).

This is not merely a matter of justice. It is neither politically nor technically possible to demand that countries that are already poor and have neither the infrastructure nor the funds to invest in low carbon technologies cut their emissions anyway. To have a good prospect of remaining below 2°C of warming, rich countries will initially have to reduce their emissions below the level that they demand of poor countries.

Finally, there are some reasons why it may be wise to regard the conclusions of Meinshausen *et al.* (2009) as conservative. The UK government's Committee on Climate Change (2008) predicts that trajectories leading to a 50% global cut by 2050 would result in greater cumulative emissions over the period than Meinshausen allows, which would generate more warming. Furthermore, it should be noted that Meinshausen *et al.* assume that global emissions cuts will continue after 2050. If cuts do not continue on their path towards zero after 2050 then emissions before 2050 must be lower in order to avoid a 2°C rise.

Weaver *et al.* (2007) modelled the warming that would occur if greenhouse gas emissions were cut by different percentages by 2050 and then held constant. They found that all scenarios involving less than a 60% global reduction by 2050 culminated in more than a 2°C rise this century. Even when emissions were stabilised at 90% below present levels at 2050, the 2°C threshold was eventually broken. Clearly it will not be easy for emissions from the whole globe to approach zero.

If we wish to avoid a 2°C rise in temperature, there is no time to lose in cutting our emissions as fast as possible.

Recommendations

It is recommended that the UK must develop an emissions budget that:
• is based on a high probability of avoiding an upper limit of 2°C warming;
• is based on good accounting;
• apportions a fair portion of a global budget to the UK.

In light of the analysis presented in this section, it is recommended that the UK must:
• aim for as close to a 100% cut as possible. This should be done as fast as possible. In this report, we have chosen 2030 as the target date;
• keep the quantity of greenhouse gases emitted during the transition phase as low as possible.

References

Åkerman, H.J. & M. Johansson (2008) "Thawing permafrost and thicker active layers in sub-arctic Sweden", *Permafrost and Periglacial Processes*, 19(3), pp. 279–292.

Allen, M. (2009) "Planetary boundaries: Tangible targets are critical", *Nature Reports Climate Change*, October 2009, 3, pp. 114–115.

Allen, M. *et al.* (2009) "Warming caused by cumulative carbon emissions towards the trillionth tonne", *Nature*, 458(7242), pp.1163–1166.

Alliance of Small Island States (AOSIS) (2009) "AOSIS Climate Change Summit", AOSIS [online]. Available at: http://www.sidsnet.org/aosis/summit2009.html [Live: March 2010].

Allison, I. *et al.* (2009) *The Copenhagen Diagnosis, 2009: Updating the World on the Latest Climate Science*, Sydney: The University of New South Wales Climate Change Research Centre (CCRC).

Anderson, K. & A. Bows (2008) "Reframing the climate change challenge in light of post-2000 emission trends", *Philosophical Transactions of the Royal Society A*,

366(1882), pp. 3863–3882.

Annan, J. (2006) "Can we believe in high climate sensitivity?", James' Empty Blog [online]. Available at: http://julesandjames.blogspot.com/2006/09/can–we–believe–in–high–climate.html [Live: March 2010].

Archer, D. (2007) "Methane hydrate stability and anthropogenic climate change", *Biogeosciences*, 4(4), pp. 521–544.

Arrhenius, S. (1896) "On the Influence of Carbonic Acid in the Air upon the Temperature of the Ground" *Philosophical Magazine and Journal of Science*, 5(41), pp. 237–276.

Baechler, G. (1998) "Why environmental transformation causes violence: a synthesis", Environmental Change and Security Project Report (4), pp. 24–44.

Baumert, K.A., T. Herzog & J. Pershing (2005) *Navigating the Numbers: Greenhouse Gas Data and International Climate Policy*, Washington: World Resources Institute.

Betts, R.A. *et al.* (2004) "The role of ecosystem-atmosphere interactions in simulated Amazonian precipitation decrease and forest dieback under global climate warming", *Theoretical and Applied Climatology*, 78, pp. 157–175.

Betts, R., M. Sanderson & S. Woodward (2008) "Effects of large-scale Amazon forest degradation on climate and air quality through fluxes of carbon dioxide, water, energy, mineral dust and isoprene", *Philosophical Transactions of the Royal Society of London B: Biological Sciences*, 363(1498), pp. 1873–1880.

Burke, E.J., S.J. Brown & N. Christidis (2006) "Modelling the Recent Evolution of Global Drought and Projections for the Twenty-First Century with the Hadley Centre Climate Model", *Journal of Hydrometeorology*, 7(5), pp. 1113–1125.

Chen, I. *et al.* (2009) "Elevation increases in moth assemblages over 42 years on a tropical mountain", *Proceedings of the National Academy of Sciences*, 106(5), pp. 1479–1483.

Committee on Climate Change (CCC) (2008) *Building a low-carbon economy – the UK's contribution to tackling climate change*, London: The Stationery Office.

Connolley, W.M. (2008) "He's at it again", STOAT: Taking science by the throat [online]. Available at: http://scienceblogs.com/stoat/2008/03/hes_at_it_again.php [Live: March 2010].

Costello, A. *et al.* (2009) "Managing the health effects of climate change", *Lancet*, 373, pp. 1693–1733.

Cox, P.M. *et al.* (2000) "Acceleration of global warming due to carbon-cycle feedbacks in a coupled climate model", *Nature*, 408(6809), pp. 184–187.

Cox, P.M. *et al.* (2006) "Conditions for sink-to-source transitions and runaway feedbacks from the land carbon cycle", in Schnellnhuber, H.J. (ed.) (2006) *Avoiding dangerous climate change*. Cambridge: Cambridge University Press, pp. 155–161.

De'ath, G., J. M. Lough & K.E. Fabricius (2009) "Declining Coral Calcification on the Great Barrier Reef", *Science*, 323(5910), pp. 116–119.

Dessler, A.E., Z. Zhang & P. Yang (2008) "Water-vapor climate feedback inferred from climate fluctuations, 2003–2008", Geophysical Research Letters, 35, L20704.

Fourier, J. (1824) "General Remarks on the Temperature of the Terrestrial Globe and Planetary Spaces", *Annales de chimie et de physique*, 27, pp. 136–167.

Grinsted, A., J.C. Moore & S. Jevrejeva (2009) "Reconstructing sea level from paleo and projected temperatures 200 to 2100 AD", *Climate Dynamics*, 34(4), pp. 461–472.

Hall, A. (2004) "The Role of Surface Albedo Feedback in Climate", *Journal of Climate*, 17(7), pp. 1550–1568.

Hansen, J. *et al.* (2008) "Target atmospheric CO_2: Where should humanity aim?", *The Open Atmospheric Science Journal*, 2, pp. 217–231.

Harries, J.E. *et al.* (2001) "Increases in greenhouse forcing inferred from the outgoing longwave radiation spectra of the Earth in 1970 and 1997", *Nature*, 410(6826), pp. 355–357.

Helm, D., R. Smale & J. Phillips (2007) "Too Good To Be True? The UK's Climate Change Record", Dieter Helm CBE [online]. Available at: http://www.dieterhelm.co.uk/sites/default/files/Carbon_record_2007.pdf [Live: March 2010].

Holland, M.M., C.M. Bitz, & B. Tremblay (2006) "Future abrupt reductions in the summer Arctic sea ice", *Geophysical Research Letters*, 33, L23503.

Homer-Dixon, T. (1994) "Environmental Scarcities and Violent Conflict: Evidence from Cases", *International Security*, 19(1), pp. 1–40.

Houghton, J. (2009) *Global Warming: The Complete Briefing*, Fourth Edition, Cambridge: Cambridge University Press.

House, J.I. *et al.* (2008) "What do recent advances in quantifying climate and carbon cycle uncertainties mean for climate policy?", *Environmental Research Letters*, 3(4), 044002.

Intergovernmental Panel on Climate Change (IPCC) (2007a) *Climate Change 2007: The Physical Science Basis. Contribution of Working Group I to the Fourth Assessment Report of the Intergovernmental Panel on Climate Change, 2007,* Cambridge: Cambridge University Press.

IPCC (2007b) *Climate Change 2007: Impacts, Adaptation and Vulnerability. Contribution of Working Group II to the Fourth Assessment Report of the Intergovernmental Panel on Climate Change, 2007,* Cambridge: Cambridge University Press.

IPCC (2007c) *Climate Change 2007: Synthesis Report. Contribution of Working Groups I, II and III to the Fourth Assessment Report of the Intergovernmental Panel on Climate Change,* Geneva: IPCC.

IPCC (2007d) *Climate Change 2007: Mitigation of Climate Change. Contribution of Working Group III to the Fourth Assessment Report of the Intergovernmental Panel on Climate Change, 2007,* Cambridge: Cambridge University Press.

Jin, H. *et al.* (2008) "Changes in permafrost environments along the Qinghai–Tibet engineering corridor induced by anthropogenic activities and climate warming", *Cold Regions Science and Technology,* 53(3), pp. 317–333.

Jones, C. *et al.* (2009)"Committed terrestrial ecosystem changes due to climate change", *Nature Geoscience,* 2(7), pp. 484–487.

Lenton, T.M. *et al.* (2008) "Tipping elements in the Earth's climate system", *Proceedings of the National Academy of Sciences,* 105(6), pp. 1786–1793.

Lunt, D.J. *et al.* (2010) "Earth system sensitivity inferred from Pliocene modelling and data", *Nature Geoscience*, 3(1), 60–64.

Mackay, D. (2009). *Sustainable energy: without the hot air,* Cambridge: UIT Cambridge.

Mann, M.E. & L.R. Kump (2008) *Dire Predictions: Understanding Global Warming,* London: Dorling Kindersley.

Matthews, H.D. & Caldeira, K. (2008) "Stabilizing climate requires near-zero emissions", *Geophysical Research Letters,* 35, L04705.

Mayhew, P.J., G.B. Jenkins, & T.G. Benton (2008) "A long-term association between global temperature and biodiversity, origination and extinction in the fossil record", *Proceedings of the Royal Society B: Biological Sciences,* 275(1630), pp. 47–53.

Meinshausen, M. *et al.* (2009) "Greenhouse-gas emission targets for limiting global warming to 2°C", *Nature,* 458(7242), pp. 1158–1162.

Met Office (2009) *Science: Driving our Response to Climate Change,* Exeter, Devon: Met Office.

Mitchell, J.F. *et al.* (2006) "Extreme events due to human-induced climate change", *Philosophical Transactions of the Royal Society A: Mathematical, Physical and Engineering Sciences,* 364(1845), pp. 2117–2133.

Moy, A.D. *et al.* (2009) "Reduced calcification in modern Southern Ocean planktonic foraminifera", *Nature Geoscience,* 2(4), pp. 276–280.

Murphy, D.M. *et al.* (2009) "An observationally based energy balance for the Earth since 1950", *Journal of Geophysical Research Atmospheres,* 114, D17107.

Nepstad, D.C. (2007)*The Amazon's Vicious Cycles: Drought and Fire in the Greenhouse, Ecological and Climatic Tipping Points of the World's Largest Tropical Rainforest, and Practical Preventive Measures*, a report to the WWF, Gland: WWF International.

Newton, R. & S. Bottrell (2007) "Stable isotopes of carbon and sulphur as indicators of environmental change: past and present", *Journal of the Geological Society*, 164(4), pp. 691–708.

Olsen, M.A., M.R. Schoeberl & J.E. Nielsen (2007) "Response of stratospheric circulation and stratosphere-troposphere exchange to changing sea surface temperatures", *Journal of Geophysical Research Atmospheres*, 112, D16104.

Oppenheimer, M. & R.B. Alley (2005) "Ice sheets, global warming, and article 2 of the UNFCCC", *Climatic Change*, 68(3), pp. 257–267.

Pfeffer, W.T., J.T. Harper & S. O'Neel (2008) "Kinematic Constraints on Glacier Contributions to 21st-Century Sea-Level Rise", *Science*, 321(5894), pp. 1340–1343.

Pitelka, L.F. (1997) "Plant migration and climate change", *American Scientist*, 85(5), pp. 464–473.

Rahmstorf, S. (2007) A Semi-Empirical Approach to Projecting Future Sea-Level Rise, *Science*, 315(5810), pp. 368–370.

Raupach M.R. *et al.* (2007) "Global and regional drivers of accelerating CO2 emissions", Proceedings of the National Academy of Sciences, 104(24), pp. 10288–10293.

Ridley, J. *et al.* (2009) "Thresholds for irreversible decline of the Greenland ice sheet", *Climate Dynamics*, 33.

Ringer, M.A. *et al.* (2006) "Global mean cloud feedbacks

in idealized climate change experiments", *Geophysical Research Letters*, 33(7), L07718.

Ross, G. (2007) "The Great Population Scare British Demographic Projections, 1956–75", Radstats Journal, 95 [online]. Available at: www.radstats.org.uk/no095/Ross95.pdf [Live: March 2010].

Santer, B.D. *et al*. (2003) "Behavior of tropopause height and atmospheric temperature in models, reanalyses, and observations: Decadal changes", *Journal of Geophysical Research Atmospheres*, 108, D14002.

Schmidt, G. & D. Archer (2009) "Climate change: Too much of a bad thing" *Nature*, 458(7242), pp.1117–1118.

Schuur, E.A.G. *et al*. (2009) "The effect of permafrost thaw on old carbon release and net carbon exchange from tundra", *Nature*, 459(7246), pp. 556–559.

Tyndall, J. (1859) "Note on the Transmission of Radiant Heat through Gaseous Bodies", *Proceedings of the Royal Society of London*, 10, pp. 37–39.

U.S. Climate Change Science Program (2008) *Abrupt Climate Change: Final Report, Synthesis and Assessment Product 3.4.*, December 2008, Washington DC: U.S. Climate Change Science Program.

United Nations Environment Programme [UNEP] (2009) *From Conflict to Peacebuilding: The Role of Natural Resources and the Environment*, Nairobi: UNEP.

Warner, K. *et al*. (2009) *In Search of Shelter: Mapping the Effects of Climate Change on Human Migration and Displacement*, London: CARE International.

Weaver, A.J. *et al*. (2007) Long term climate implications of 2050 emission reduction targets. *Geophysical Research Letters*, 34, L19703.

Figure sources

Copyright (2010) ***zero*carbon*britain*2030**. Based on data from the Climatic Research Unit, University of East Anglia (2009). Data available from: http://www.cru.uea.ac.uk/cru/data/temperature/#datdow. Dataset source: Brohan, P., J.J. Kennedy, I. Harris, S.F.B. Tett and P.D. Jones (2006) "Uncertainty estimates in regional and global observed temperature changes: a new dataset from 1850", *Journal of Geophysical Research*, 111, D12106.

Mann, M. E., Z. Zhang, M. K. Hughes, R. S. Bradley, S. K. Miller, S. Rutherford and F. Ni (2008) "Proxy-Based Reconstructions of Hemispheric and Global Surface Temperature Variations over the Past Two Millennia", *Proceedings of the National Academy of Sciences*, 105, pp. 13252–13257, Supporting Information (Fig. S15, p. 21). Copyright (2008) National Academy of Sciences, USA.

Intergovernmental Panel on Climate Change (IPCC) (2007) *Climate Change 2007: The Physical Science Basis. Working Group I Contribution to the Fourth Assessment Report of the Intergovernmental Panel on Climate Change*, Cambridge: Cambridge University Press (Figure 9.5, p. 684).

IPCC (2007) *Climate Change 2007: The Physical Science Basis. Working Group I Contribution to the Fourth Assessment Report of the Intergovernmental Panel on Climate Change*, Cambridge: Cambridge University Press (Figure 9.20, p. 720).

Amended from IPCC (2007) *Climate Change 2007: The Physical Science Basis. Working Group I Contribution to the Fourth Assessment Report of the Intergovernmental Panel on Climate Change*, Cambridge: Cambridge University Press (Figure 10.26, p. 803).

Mackay, D. (2009) *Sustainable Energy – without the hot air*, Cambridge: UIT Cambridge Ltd, www.uit.co.uk/sustainable. Also available free to download for non-commercial use from www.withouthotair.com.

Chapter 2
The energy security context

Introduction

A secure energy supply is one that is able to deliver the energy services we require in a reliable manner and at an affordable price. The security of our supply of energy is affected by a multitude of areas including technology, infrastructure, policy, geology and trade.

This chapter examines some of the issues affecting the UK energy system and its security.

It details several aspects of our domestic energy system that are currently undergoing major changes. It then addresses global energy security, with a focus on oil. Finally, the relationship between energy security and climate change is discussed.

The chapter concludes by highlighting the common solutions to the problems of global energy insecurity, and climate change.

Fig. 2.1 UK energy production and consumption

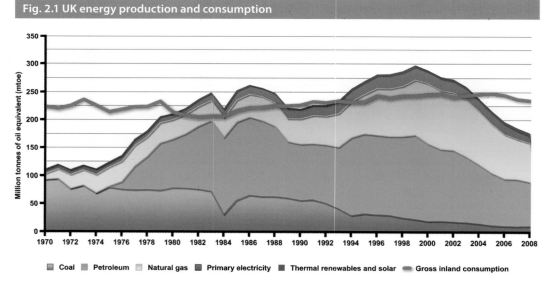

Coal ▪ Petroleum ▪ Natural gas ▪ Primary electricity ▪ Thermal renewables and solar ▪ Gross inland consumption

UK energy production by energy type and gross inland consumption (million tonnes of oil equivalent), 1970-2008.
"Primary electricity" includes nuclear and natural flow hydro electricity but excludes output from pumped storage stations. From 1988, it also includes generation from wind farms. Production of "thermal renewables and solar" has only been recorded since 1988. It includes solar and geothermal heat, solid renewable sources (wood, waste, etc.), and gaseous renewable sources (landfill gas and sewage gas). Since 2004, the UK has returned to being a net importer of energy. Source: Based on data from DECC (2009).

Fig. 2.2 UK North Sea oil production

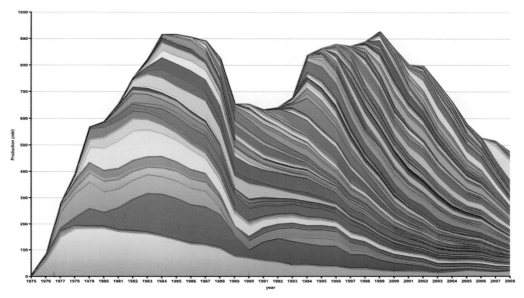

Oil production on the UK continental shelf (megabarrels), by oilfield, 1977–2008.
Different colours represent production from different oilfields. UK oil extraction has declined significantly since 1999 (the peak year of production).
Source: Sorrell et al. (2009).

UK energy security:

UK ENERGY PRODUCTION AND IMPORTS

In 2005 the UK again became a net energy importer, as shown in Figure 2.1. The principal reason for this is the decline in North Sea oil and gas production. Britain has been extracting gas from the North Sea since 1967 and oil since 1975. The basin is now "mature" (Oil & Gas UK, 2009).

North Sea oil production reached its peak in 1999. It had experienced a previous peak and decline in the mid 1980s (see Figure 2.2). This was caused by the decline of several giant fields; the oil price crash of 1986, which led to postponement of new investment and exploration; and the Piper Alpha disaster and subsequent remedial safety work. The 1999 peak can be seen to be attributed to the exhaustion of exciting fields and the inability of newly producing fields to make up the shortfall. Oil production from the North Sea is now in

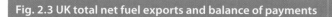

Fig. 2.3 UK total net fuel exports and balance of payments

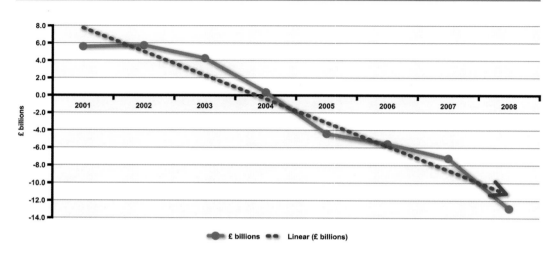

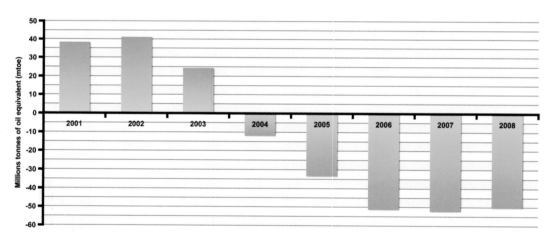

UK total net fuel exports, 2001–2008, based on (a) a balance of payments basis (£ billions) and (b) a quantity basis (million tonnes of oil equivalent).
In 2004, the UK became a net-importer of fuel. Due to rates of currency exchange, the UK only became a net-importer of fuel on a balance of payments basis in 2005. However since then, the balance of payments for fuel has continued to decline, even though the quantity of net exports (imports) has for the last three years been relatively stagnant.
Source: Based on data from DECC (2009).

terminal decline (Sorrell *et al.*, 2009).

The picture with regard to gas is very similar. UK gas production peaked in 2000, and is now declining at approximately 5% per annum (Department of Energy and Climate Change [DECC], 2009). If the UK continues to rely on gas for many of its energy services it will increasingly have to import it from Norway, the Netherlands, the former Soviet Union and Algeria (Oil & Gas UK, 2009).

Britain imports the bulk of its coal. 76% of the coal used in Britain in 2008 was imported (DECC, 2009).

Imported fuel is not necesarily insecure; but becoming a net energy importer is a significant change for the UK. North Sea oil and gas have made a significant contribution to the UK's balance of payments (see Figure 2.3).

Based on a rough estimate of 100 billion cubic metres of gas at 2p/kWh, 680 million barrels of oil at $78 per barrel and an exchange rate of $1.64 to the pound, replacing North Sea extraction with imports would add £53 billion to the trade deficit. The Exchequer raised nearly

> *"Our forecasts of the current balance from 2007–08 to 2011–12 are affected by one major change in the last year - the sharply lower levels of production and yet higher costs in the North Sea".*

Gordon Brown responding on the decline in tax revenue from UK oil and gas production in his 2007 Chancellor of the Exchequer's Budget Statement. The revenue was 38% below prediction at £8 billion rather than £13 billion (Brown, 2007).

£13 billion in tax from the offshore oil and gas industry in 2008 (DECC, n/d).

THE RETIREMENT OF UK ELECTRICITY GENERATION INFRASTRUCTURE

Another major current issue currently affecting the UK's energy system concerns its electricity generation infrastructure.

A significant amount of our current generation capacity is due for retirement within the next ten years. In 2006, the Carbon Trust and LEK Consulting estimated that 8 of the 29GW of coal generation operating in 2005 will be retired by 2020, due to the need to comply with the EU Large Combustion Plant Directive and flue gas desulphurisation requirements. Over the same period, 8 of the UK's 12GW of nuclear capacity is also scheduled to be retired. The 2007 Energy White Paper estimates that the UK will need around 30–35GW of new electricity generation capacity (equal to more than a third of current capacity) over the next two decades, and around two-thirds of this by 2020.

The infrastructure which is built now to replace the retiring plant will go on generating many years into the future. In other words, the UK is now at a critical crossroads in terms of electricity generation.

Any investment in new generation plant infrastructure must take into account the security of its fuel supply and the potential fuel price fluctuations which may occur over the duration of its design life. Fossil fuel-powered stations require ongoing fuel, while renewables such as wind and solar power do not. The security of the electricity supplied by different generation technologies is therefore one of the many things affected by future international fuel prices, to which we now turn.

Global energy security

PEAK OIL

Non-renewable fossil fuels are clearly finite and so cannot last forever. In particular, serious concerns have been raised over the security of the world's future supply of oil and the potential volatility of the oil market. This section will summarise some of these concerns, and how they may affect the wider energy issues that face us.

Over 95% of the oil currently in production is "conventional" (Méjean & Hope, 2008) – that is, light oil that can be extracted cheaply and easily, generally using a well-bore method. In contrast, unconventional oils occur primarily in solid form, and require substantial processing before they can be used as liquid fuel. The distinction is not clear-cut and some oils may be placed in either category (Greene *et al.*, 2006).

The speed at which conventional oil can be pumped is influenced by many factors. Some are economic and political, but others are non-negotiable physical constraints that cause production to follow particular patterns, both within fields and over whole regions. Production,

either from a single well or the aggregated output over a region, inevitably rises to a peak and then declines. Most regions reach their peak production rate significantly before half of their recoverable resources have been produced (Sorrell *et al.*, 2009). A recent review from the UK Energy Research Centre (ibid.) concludes that:

"Oil supply is determined by a complex and interdependent mix of 'above-ground' and 'below-ground' factors and little is to be gained by emphasising one set of variables over the other. Nevertheless, fundamental features of the conventional oil resource make it inevitable that production in a region will rise to a peak or plateau and ultimately decline. These features include the production profile of individual fields, the concentration of resources in a small number of large fields and the tendency to discover and produce these fields relatively early. This process can be modelled and the peaking of conventional oil production can be observed in an increasing number of regions around the world".

The point at which global production of conventional oil reaches its maximum is generally called "peak oil". As it depends on many factors, it is extremely hard to determine precisely when it will occur, or how steep the ensuing descent will be.

One point to note is that world discoveries of oil peaked in the mid-1960s and have declined ever since, falling below production in the mid-1980s (City of Portland Peak Oil Task Force, 2007). Production clearly cannot exceed discovery, and it can furthermore be noted that in many oil-producing nations, declines in production have lagged declines in discovery by 25 to 40 years. For example, discoveries in the US peaked in the early 1930s, while production peaked in 1971. The world currently finds one barrel for every four or more that it uses (ibid.).

Estimates of the timing of a global peak are made harder by the lack of reliably-audited data on oil reserves (Sorrell *et al.*, 2009). There are various reasons to be sceptical of publicly-available estimates. For one thing, OPEC (Organisation of the Petroleum Exporting Countries) production quotas are set partly on the basis of proven reserves. When this quota system was introduced in the late 1980s, the reserve estimates of OPEC member nations jumped by 60%, leading to suspicion about their accuracy (City of Portland Peak Oil Task Force, 2007). In the case of private oil companies, there is a link between reserve estimates and share prices, which also provides some incentive for exaggeration. In the past two years, both Shell Oil and the Kuwait Oil Company have admitted overestimating their reserves, and they have reduced them by 20% and 50% respectively (ibid.; Sorrell *et al.* 2009).

Despite the wide variety of estimates concerning the timing of peak oil, a growing number of calculations suggest that it is likely to occur somewhere between the present day and 2031 (Greene *et al.*, 2006; International Energy Agency [IEA], 2008; Sorrell *et al.*, 2009). Some believe that it has already occurred (Campbell 2008; Vernon, 2009). Sorrell *et al.* (2009) found that:

"For a wide range of assumptions about the global URR [Ultimately Recoverable Resource] of conventional oil and the shape of the future production cycle, the date of peak production can be estimated to lie between 2009 and 2031".

The review further concludes that:

"On the basis of current evidence we suggest that a peak of conventional oil production before 2030 appears likely and there is a significant risk of a peak before 2020".

THE VOLATILITY OF GLOBAL ENERGY MARKETS

If a shortage of oil occurs, the price will rise until some customers are priced out of the market. However, because oil is crucial for so many activities, it is very price-inelastic, in other words, a big price rise is required to produce a small decrease in demand. Oil shortages therefore lead to large price rises. As prices rise, more expensive extraction technology such as enhanced oil recovery become economic. This can be expected to slow the decline in production but at the expense of higher production costs. The overall effect is rising prices, but the shape of the rise is difficult to predict. Indeed these economic effects mean that there may not even be a single abrupt peak in oil production. Instead, the push and pull of supply and demand may create more of a "bumpy plateau" (Sorrell et al., 2009).

Rising oil prices have serious effects on wider society. The prices of all fuels tend to be linked, to a degree (Nuclear Energy Agency & International Energy Agency, 1998). The coal price is affected by the oil price because oil is used in coal extraction. In Europe, policy mechanisms currently tie the gas price to the oil price.

Oil prices also appear capable of having serious effects upon food prices. Global food price spikes occurred during both the 1973 and 2008 oil shocks. Different analyses have reached different conclusions as to the importance of various causal factors but there is a consensus that oil prices were at least partially responsible (ActionAid, 2008; Heady & Fan, 2008; Mitchell, 2008). It is apparent that both food price crises occurred during sudden rises in oil prices; they were the only two such food price spikes to have occurred over many decades, and they occurred against a backdrop of a very long-term trend of falling international food prices (Heady & Fan, 2008).

If production of conventional oil peaks in the near future, unconventional oil will become increasingly important. Although unconventional oil is spread throughout the world, the bulk of it is believed to be in the form of heavy oil in Venezuela and the Canadian tar sands. Some production currently takes place from both of these sources, but it is both difficult and expensive.

Unconventional oil tends to be uneconomic to produce at an oil price of less than $70 a barrel. Because of this there has generally been a lack of commercial interest in it and the extent of global reserves is very uncertain (Greene et al., 2006). The total reserve is generally thought to be very large, but this does not in itself imply that large quantities are recoverable at a reasonable cost, or indicate the rate at which it can be extracted, processed and brought to market.

Pessimistic analysts have concluded that unconventional oil will be incapable of meeting the shortfall caused by conventional oil decline. One such analysis was produced by Söderbergh et al. (2007), who estimated that a crash programme to develop the Canadian tar sands could deliver only 5 million barrels per day by 2030. This is less than 6% of projected global production. Even if this is an underestimate, unconventional oil is considerably more expensive to extract. Therefore, as was discussed earlier, whether it is due to constraints on availability or increased production costs, it appears that the peaking of conventional oil will substantially raise the price.

A higher cost will also be paid in terms of energy. The quantity of energy used in the extraction and processing of fuels such as oil is quantified as an EROEI ratio: the Energy Return On Energy Invested. The EROEI ratio for oil has declined as production has shifted to more difficult fields in more challenging locations. With a shift to non-conventional oils, the EROEI ratio will continue to fall – the EROEI for unconventional oils are much lower than ratios for conventional forms (Sorrell et al., 2009). The EROEI for petroleum extraction in the US fell from around 100:1 in 1930 to around 20:1 in the mid-1990s. The EROEI for global oil and gas production has not suffered such a dramatic fall, but is now also in decline, falling from 26:1 in 1992 to 18:1 in 2006 (ibid.).

Some optimists have suggested that as peak oil occurs, the ensuing price rises will stimulate the development of alternatives in a timely way, leading smoothly into a post-oil world without the requirement for conscious intervention. There are many reasons to be sceptical of this.

A painless transition in a market such as energy, with a large physical infrastructure, is considerably more likely if the price rise is gradual rather than sudden. However there are some reasons to believe that the decline in oil production will be steep, particularly as current production is heavily reliant on a few large fields which have the potential to go into a rapid decline (Sorrell et al., 2009).

In terms of extraction costs, the US provides a rather disquieting historical example. Extraction costs remained steady or declined between 1936 and 1970, but then increased more than fourfold within a decade after production peaked in 1970. If a similar pattern occurs at the global level, the price rise will be too abrupt for a smooth or painless transition (ibid.).

Another reason why the transition may not be painless unless proactive steps are taken is that as the price of oil increases, the prices of other commodities such as steel also rise. This in turn raises the cost of manufacture and installation of alternative infrastructure (East, 2008).

It took many decades to create the oil-based infrastructure currently in place. It will take decades, along with substantial investment, to make a full transition to a new infrastructure. The highly regarded report completed by Robert Hirsch et al. (2006) for the US government concluded that a large-scale programme of investment in substitutes and efficiency would need to be initiated at least 20 years before the peak to avoid serious disruption. Hirsch estimated that these measures will cost in the range of $1 trillion, but the costs of acting too late will exceed the costs of acting too early.

It is therefore vital that society acts promptly, in order to minimise both the financial and the energy costs of this transition.

THE INTERACTION BETWEEN CLIMATE AND ENERGY SECURITY

It has been suggested that the limits on fossil fuel availability may themselves tackle climate change without the need for any proactive intervention. However, if we wish to avoid a 2°C rise in temperature, this view does not appear to be supported by the current climate science. In order to keep global temperatures within 2°C of pre-industrial levels, cumulative CO_2 emissions must be kept well below the amount that would be produced from burning the remaining proven economically-recoverable fossil fuel reserves (Schmidt & Archer, 2009). Meinshausen *et al.* (2009) conclude:

"Limiting cumulative CO_2 emissions over 2000–2050 to 1,000 Gt [gigatonnes] CO_2 yields a 25% probability of warming exceeding 2°C – and a limit of 1,440 Gt CO_2 yields a 50% probability [...]. Less than half the proven economically recoverable oil, gas and coal reserves can still be emitted up to 2050 to achieve such a goal".

The peaking of conventional oil could worsen climate change, due to the heavy greenhouse gas burden associated with unconventional oils. Tar sands and heavy oils release substantially more greenhouse gases over their lifecycle than

---

Fig. 2.4 Solutions to fossil fuel depletion and climate change

Fossil fuel depletion solutions

Climate change solutions

Carbon capture & storage used to enhance oil recovery

Development of unconventional oil

Excessive use of biomass

Some agricultural interventions, such as reduction in fertilizer use even at the expense of forests

Energy reduction and energy efficiency

Development of renewables such as wind and solar

Development of non-fossil fuel energy carriers such as electricity and hydrogen

Carbon capture & storage not used to enhance oil recovery

Restoration of ecosystems and tackling deforestation

Some agricultural interventions, such as reduction in ruminant livestock

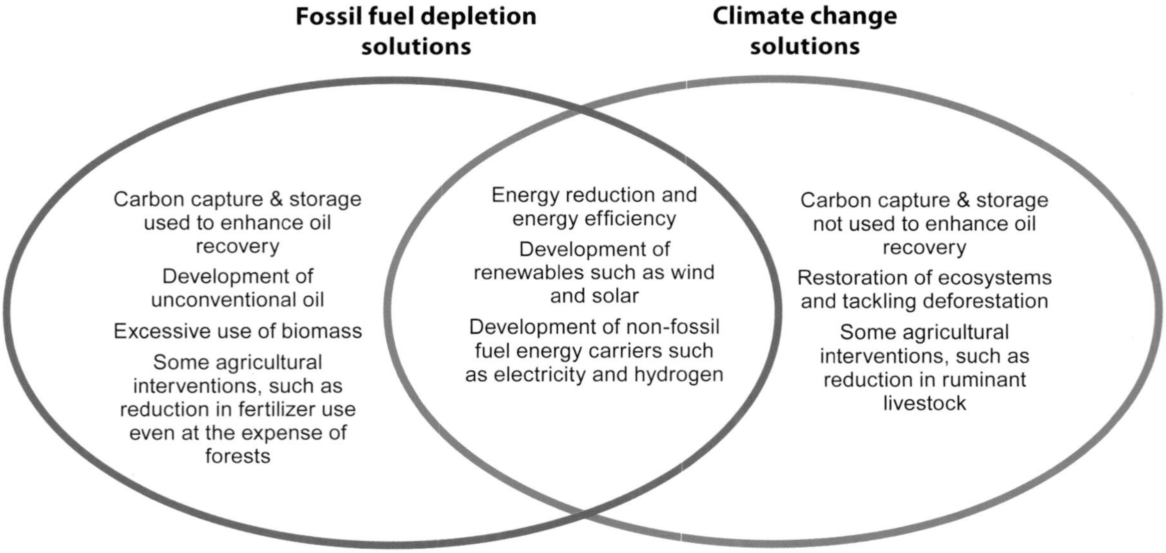

Comparison of several complementary and non-complementary solutions to fossil fuel depletion and climate change.

their conventional counterparts (NCEP, 2004).

Liquid transport fuels can also be made from coal using a process called Fischer-Tropsch synthesis, although the process is both expensive and highly-polluting. It has primarily been conducted on a large scale by countries unable to obtain conventional supplies – primarily Nazi Germany, and South Africa. However, the 2008 rise in oil prices stimulated a wave of investment in coal-to-liquids technology (Market Avenue, 2009). Such transport fuels produce approximately double the CO_2 of conventional oil per litre, rendering coal-to-liquids one of the most climate-damaging of all energy technologies (Natural Resources Defense Council [NRDC], 2007).

However, while fossil fuel depletion is unlikely to solve the climate problem on our behalf, it certainly increases the incentive to invest in a new infrastructure. The solutions do not coincide completely and there are some areas where they may be in conflict. However, there is a great deal of overlap. An illustrative diagram can be seen in figure 2.4.

Conclusion

In this chapter two major changes currently occurring in the British energy system were discussed. Firstly, for the first time in over a quarter of a century, the UK has recently become a net energy importer. Secondly, the UK faces a widening gap between electricity supply and demand, due to the retirement of plant and generation capacity. We need to replace this capacity with an energy-secure form of electricity generation.

As has been detailed, there are reasons to expect significant volatility in international fuel prices in the future. This suggests that renewable generation infrastructure, which has no ongoing fuel cost, is likely to give us a more stable and secure electricity system.

The insecurity of the future fossil fuel market, particularly oil, also affects our choices in other sectors such as transport. There are good reasons to believe that oil may be reaching a peak in its production, requiring a rapid reduction in the extent of our dependence on it.

There are some short-term solutions to the problems caused by the depletion of fossil fuels which would worsen climate change, but many solutions which align with tackling climate change. Because of the need for rapid decarbonisation to prevent a 2°C rise in temperature, reductions in fossil fuel use and investments in alternatives must occur faster than if depletion were the sole concern.

The following chapters will describe how we can reduce our dependence on energy, move away from fossil fuels and create a new sustainable energy infrastructure. This will meet the challenges of both climate change and energy security.

References

ActionAid (2008) "Cereal Offenders: how the G8 has contributed to the global food crisis, and what they can do to stop it", ActionAid policy briefing, July 2008. Available at: http://www.actionaid.org.uk/doc_lib/g8report2_final.pdf [Live: March 2010].

Brown, G. (2007) "Chancellor of the Exchequer's Budget Statement", 21 March 2007, HM Treasury [online]. Available at: http://www.hm-treasury.gov.uk/bud_budget07_speech.htm [Live: March 2010].

Campbell, C. (2009) "Reflections from Colin Campbell on Peak

Oil and ASPO", Energy Bulletin [online]. Available at: http://www.energybulletin.net/node/50427 [Live: March 2010].

Carbon Trust & LEK Consulting (2006) *Policy frameworks for renewables: Analysis on policy frameworks to drive future investment in near and long-term renewable power in the UK*, a study funded by the Carbon Trust and carried out by L.E.K. Consulting in conjunction with the Carbon Trust, London: The Carbon Trust.

City of Portland Peak Oil Task Force (2007) "Descending the Oil Peak: Navigating the Transition from Oil and Natural Gas", March 2007, report of the City of Portland Peak Oil Task Force, Portland: City of Portland Peak Oil Task Force. Available at: http://www.portlandonline.com/shared/cfm/image.cfm?id=145732 [Live: March 2010].

Department of Energy and Climate Change (DECC) (2009) *Digest of United Kingdom Energy Statistics 2009*, London: The Stationery Office.

DECC (n/d) "Government revenues from UK oil and gas production", DECC [online]. Available at: https://www.og.decc.gov.uk/information/bb_updates/appendices/UKCS_Tax_Table.pdf [Live: March 2010].

East, R. (2008) "What does cheap oil mean for renewables? Inside views from the green energy sector on oil price volatility", *Green Futures: The sustainable solutions magazine*, 18 December 2008.

Greene, D.L., J.L. Hopson & J. Li (2006) "Have we run out of oil yet? Oil peaking analysis from an optimist's perspective", *Energy Policy*, 34(5), pp. 515–531.

Headey, D. & S. Fan (2008) "Anatomy of a crisis: the causes and consequences of surging food prices", *Agricultural Economics*, 39(s1), pp. 375–391.

Hirsch, R.L., R. Bezdek & R. Wendling (2006) *Peaking of World Oil Production: Impacts, Mitigation, And Risk Management*, New York: Nova Science Publishers.

International Energy Agency (IEA) (2008) *World Energy Outlook 2008*, Paris: Organisation for Economic Development/IEA.

Market Avenue (2009) 2009 Report on China's Coal-to-Liquid Market, Market Avenue [online]. Available at: http://www.marketavenue.cn/upload/ChinaMarketReports/REPORTS_1211.htm [Live: March 2010].

Meinshausen, M. *et al*. (2009) "Greenhouse-gas emission targets for limiting global warming to 2 °C", *Nature*, 458(7242), pp. 1158–1162.

Méjean, A. & C. Hope (2008) *Modelling the costs of non-conventional oil: A case study of Canadian bitumen*, Cambridge Working Papers in Economics 0810, Faculty of Economics, University of Cambridge.

Mitchell, D. (2008) "A Note on Rising Food Prices", The World Bank Development Prospects Group, Policy Research Working Paper 4682, July 2008. Available at: http://www-wds.worldbank.org/external/default/WDSContentServer/IW3P/IB/2008/07/28/000020439_20080728103002/Rendered/PDF/WP4682.pdf [Live: March 2010].

Natural Resources Defense Council (2007) "Why Liquid Coal Is Not a Viable Option to Move America Beyond Oil", Climate Facts, Natural Resources Defense Council. Available at: http://www.nrdc.org/globalWarming/coal/liquids.pdf [Live: March 2010].

National Commission on Energy Policy (NCEP) (2004) "Unconventional Oil", staff background paper. Available at: http://www.energycommission.org/files/finalReport/I.3.a%20-%20Unconventional%20Oil.pdf [Live: December 2009].

Nuclear Energy Agency & IEA (2005) *Projected costs of generating electricity: 2005 update*, Paris: OECD.

Oil and Gas UK (2004) "Gas – The UK's Fuel of Choice", Oil and Gas UK [online]. Available at: http://www.oilandgas.org.uk/issues/gas/ [Live: January 2010].

Schmidt, G. & D. Archer (2009) "Climate change: Too much of a bad thing" *Nature*, 458(7242), pp.1117–1118.

Söderbergh, B., F. Robelius & K. Aleklett (2007) "A crash programme scenario for the Canadian oil sands industry". *Energy Policy*, 35(3), pp. 1931–1947.

Sorrell, S. *et al.* (2009) *Global Oil Depletion: An assessment of the evidence for a near-term peak in global oil production*, London: UK Energy Research Centre.

Vernon, C. (2009) "Peak Oil", presentation given to the **zero**carbon**britain**2030 Carbon Crunch seminar, 31 March 2009 [unpublished].

Figure sources

Copyright (2010) **zero**carbon**britain**2030. Based on data from Department of Energy and Climate Change (DECC) (2009) *Digest of United Kingdom Energy Statistics: 2009*, London: The Stationery Office (Fig. 1.12, pp. 154–155).

Sorrell, S, J. Speirs, R. Bentley, A. Brandt, and R. Miller (2009) *Global Oil Depletion: An assessment of the evidence for a near-term peak in global oil production*, report produced by the Technology & Policy Assessment Function of the UK Energy Research Centre, London: UKERC (Fig. 1.6, p. 8).

Copyright (2010) **zero**carbon**britain**2030. Based on data from DECC (2009) *Digest of United Kingdom Energy Statistics: 2009*, London: The Stationery Office (Fig. G.1, p. 108).

Copyright (2010) **zero**carbon**britain**2030.

Chapter 3
Equity

Introduction

zerocarbon**britain**2030 presents a vision not only of a decarbonised economy, but also of a society that is fairer, both nationally and internationally. The transition towards a decarbonised society must be equitable as well as technically feasible and sustainable.

Many of the proposed measures and interventions will either raise the cost of fossil fuels or require significant levels of investment. It is crucial that the poor are not left disadvantaged. Reducing carbon emissions is not enough. Fuel poverty must also be addressed, to ensure that today's inequities in access to energy and energy efficiency measures are not reproduced within a zero carbon society. The changes to the wider economic system that will be entailed by a transition to zero carbon must also place equity at their core.

Equity in Britain

While great improvements have been made in the last half century in reducing discrimination on the grounds of gender, ethnicity, disability and sexual orientation, economic inequality within Britain has increased enormously. Since the late 1980s income inequality has remained much higher than in the 1960s and 1970s; on some measures it is the highest in the last 50 years:

- By 2007–8, Britain had reached the highest level of income inequality since shortly after the Second World War (Hills *et al.*, 2010).
- The household total wealth of the richest 10% is over 100 times that of the poorest 10% (ibid.).
- The average ratio of chief executive officer (CEO) to worker pay rose from 47:1 in 1998 to 128:1 in 2008 (Peston, 2009).
- Within FTSE 100 companies in 2008, the largest ratio of CEO to worker pay was 1374:1 (Bowers *et al.*, 2009).

As will be demonstrated below, these high levels of inequality are neither inevitable nor functional. The UK is the most financially unequal country in Western Europe on almost all measures (Hills *et al.*, 2010). This inequality is manifested in poorer levels of individual and societal well-being, as well as in less stable economic growth. It is telling that the UK has been the last country in the G7 to pull out of the 2009 recession.

The benefits of equity

SOCIAL WELL-BEING

Equality is associated strongly with numerous positive measures of well-being, both at an individual and a societal level. Inequality on the other hand correlates with a host of negative personal and social externalities, from poor health to higher levels of violence, drug abuse, crime, teenage pregnancy, imprisonment, obesity and lack of trust (Wilkinson & Pickett, 2009).

Equality promotes populations that are both mentally and physically healthier. In highly unequal societies, people in "less equal" positions are far more likely to suffer from health problems. People working extremely long hours or for low pay are more likely to neglect or be unable to care for their personal and physical well-being.

Additionally, studies suggest that there is a particularly high level of stress associated with perceiving oneself to be "at the bottom of the heap". This applies to those in positions of financial inequality, as well as those subject to racial or sexual discrimination. This stress results not only in much higher levels of depression amongst those in "unequal" positions in society, but also in higher levels of heart problems caused by stress (Wilkinson, 2006; Wilkinson & Pickett, 2009). Differences in wealth are highly correlated with mortality rates after the age of 50 (Hills *et al.*, 2010).

Wide inequalities erode bonds of common citizenship and recognition of human dignity across economic divides (Hills *et al.*, 2010). Societal violence is significantly higher in less equal countries (ibid.). Some crime stems from the low self-esteem that is caused by poverty and discrimination. Young men and women who feel worthless, and have little opportunity for advancement, often do not ascribe any more value to the lives of others than they do to their own.

ECONOMIC GROWTH

The relationship between equality and economic growth is complex (see Ferreira, 1999). Inequality within nations has, in certain contexts, been associated with high short-term growth rates. However, inequality breeds inequality. This is typically bad for long-term investment, innovation and growth.

The costs associated with responding to higher levels of societal violence, lack of trust and poor health can dampen growth. In addition, inequality usually hampers social mobility. (Organisation for Economic Co-operation and Development [OECD], 2008). The poor or discriminated against have less access to capital and other opportunities which contribute to economic growth. Similarly, in a less equal society, access to good quality education, and just as importantly, access to the necessary care and support which must accompany education, is limited for many.

Inequalities accumulate down the generations, so that people's occupational and economic destinations in early adulthood depend to an important degree on their origins (Hills *et al.*, 2010). This limits the "talent pool", limiting long-term growth opportunities. Additionally, unequal power leads to the formation of institutions that perpetuate these inequalities in power, status and wealth.

As has been discussed, perceiving oneself to be "at the bottom" is associated with poor self-esteem and health. This has an implication for the businesses and organisations in which people work.

High pay inequalities are touted as incentives for performance, but these are effective only in specific circumstances (Marsden, 1999). High levels of pay inequality also tend to reduce morale and lower levels of teamwork.[1]

High wages are not linked to the social value of the work conducted (Lawlor *et al.*, 2009). Nor does it appear to correlate with macroeconomic performance. Whilst between 1998 and 2008 the ratio of CEO to employee pay rose from 47:1 to 128:1, the job roles remained largely the same. Despite huge pay increases for CEOs, on 31 December 1998 the FTSE 100 index stood at 5,896; ten years later it had fallen to 4,562 (Peston, 2009). The basic salaries of executives within FTSE 100 companies rose 10% in 2008 alone, despite the onset of the global recession, and despite wide-scale pay freezes and redundancies for workers (Finch & Bowers, 2009).

At the international level, despite much higher levels of income inequality (OECD, 2008), UK economic productivity, in terms of Gross Domestic Product (GDP) per worker, ranked second lowest amongst G7 countries in 2008. In terms of GDP per hour worked, Germany was 17% more productive and France 16% more productive (Office of National Statistics [ONS], 2010).

Progressive decarbonisation

The aim of reducing inequality has numerous policy implications. In particular, the Government response to the challenge of re-balancing the public finances following the recent financial crisis will have enormous implications for inequality (Hills *et al.*, 2010). Moreover, the government has a fundamental role in developing the wider social and institutional context for society.

Most such policy implications are outside the scope of this report. Instead, it will confine itself to specific ways in which decarbonisation strategies can prevent further increases in inequality and can even support its reduction.

GREENER, FAIRER CARBON PRICING SYSTEMS

Both the progressivity of the tax system and the level of benefits and credits have an important influence on equity levels (Hills *et al.*, 2010). Within the Policy and economics chapter, various policy proposals are discussed for placing a

---

[1] Institutions which highly value teamwork and employee morale have relatively low pay disparities. The Armed Forces for example has a de-facto pay disparity of 8:1 between the highest paid officer (top-level Brigadiers, Commodores and Air Commodores) and the lowest paid entry-level cadet (Armed Forces, 2010a, 2010b, 2010c).

higher price on carbon, whose current low cost subsidises the high levels of consumption by the wealthy.

Instead, distributing emissions credits or permits on an equal per-capita basis ensures an equitable share of emissions rights. With their generally lower levels of consumption, the poor acquire a tradable asset in the form of their unused emissions credits. More generally, decarbonisation should also help those on lower incomes by limiting the volatility of energy prices as fossil fuels become ever scarcer.

ENDING FUEL POVERTY

In itself, raising the price of carbon would have an immediate negative impact on the poor, especially the fuel poor, unless accompanied by targeted interventions. A household is said to be in fuel poverty if it needs to spend more than 10% of its income on fuel to maintain an adequate level of warmth (usually defined as 21°C for the main living area, and 18°C for other occupied rooms) (Department of Energy and Climate Change [DECC], 2009).[2]

People in fuel poverty are disadvantaged by three factors: poor quality housing, high energy prices (possibly accompanied by unfair payment methods), and low income. Consequently, fuel expenditure represents a much higher proportion of income. Fuel poverty has grown considerably since 2004, largely due to the dramatic rise in energy prices. In 2007, the number of fuel-poor households in the UK was

4 million – around 16% of all households (DECC, 2009). Over 5.1 million UK households were believed to be in fuel poverty by July 2009 (Bird *et al.*, 2010).

The UK Government has set targets to end fuel poverty in vulnerable households by 2010 and in all households by 2016. The Scottish Government intends to end fuel poverty by 2016, while the Welsh Assembly's aim is 2010 for vulnerable households and 2018 for all others. However these targets appear unlikely to be reached through current policies.

Although financial assistance with paying fuel bills can help in the short-term, a more sustainable and cost effective approach is to improve the energy efficiency of people's homes (Bird *et al.*, 2010). There is considerable scope for more joint action on climate change and fuel poverty by different government departments.

During the period over which decarbonisation takes place, increased carbon costs are likely to raise the cost both of energy and of energy-intensive consumer goods. In both rich and poor countries, spikes in fuel prices have been linked to spikes in food prices. Steps must be taken to ensure that the poor are not priced out of buying essential goods. It is essential that the fuel poor are assisted with implementing energy efficiency measures, so that they are less vulnerable to further energy price increases.

A Government-driven energy efficiency retrofit of homes is discussed in the chapter on the Built environment, and modes of financing such schemes are discussed in the Policy and

[2] The Built environment chapter highlights the importance of emphasising thermal comfort rather than air temperature in discussions of "warmth".

economics chapter. There is also a need for revised energy pricing schemes to replace the economically unfair and environmentally unsustainable practice of rewarding greater consumption with reduced per-unit costs.

NEW JOBS IN DEPRIVED REGIONS

Decarbonisation will create many new job opportunities, as discussed further in the Employment chapter. Some will arise through the efficiency drive over the next 20 years, while others will be created by the development of renewable energy infrastructure. The Government can promote a reduction in inequality by supporting re-skilling programmes in deprived areas.

Over the longer term, the move to a decarbonised economy will entail significant permanent changes to the economy. It may lead to more manufacturing jobs for example, for steel production and the manufacture of energy infrastructure. This offers particular potential for regeneration in post-industrial areas, where there are currently especially poor social and economic conditions.

Finally, jobs are also likely to be created within the agricultural sector, through the twin drives towards re-localisation of production and decarbonisation. The economy as a whole will consequently become less dominated by the financial and service sectors. A more balanced economy should result in reduced economy-wide pay disparities, although this should also be reinforced by focused policy interventions.

International inequality

Climate change is a notoriously unfair international problem. The contributions from poor nations to global greenhouse gas emissions, both currently and historically, is dwarfed by the contributions from rich nations, yet ironically, the impacts of climate change are predicted to hit the developing world hardest. This has been discussed in greater detail within the Climate science chapter.

Because the poorest and least influential countries are at greatest risk from climate change, it has proven easier for wealthier nations to ignore demands for emissions cuts. It is essential that future international agreements on climate change support the eradication of absolute poverty and promote wider efforts to reduce inequalities between nations across the world. Significant funds must be provided to poor countries, both for mitigation and adaptation efforts to compensate for the impacts of climate change, and to support wider development goals.

The merits of different proposals for international policy frameworks are discussed in the Policy and economics chapter. The principal recommendation is for the establishment of a global cap on emissions, with either national carbon budgets or individual permits and dividends distributed on a per-capita basis. This does not overcome the unfairness of higher historic emissions in developed nations, but does establish a good basis for a more equitable future.

Conclusion

Climate change, biodiversity decline, and maintained or growing levels of poverty and inequality are amongst the global problems which have long suggested that our current path is unsustainable, environmentally and socially. The recent financial crisis demonstrated that it is unsustainable economically as well. There is now substantial public support within the UK for government to take action. We now have a tremendous opportunity to re-evaluate the link between economic growth, social progress, human happiness, and the state of the environment (see Box 1 within the Policy and economics chapter).

Any decarbonisation strategy must be sensitively designed so as to limit growth in inequalities. But, a comprehensive national and international decarbonisation strategy also offers the opportunity to actively address many social as well as environmental ills. In combination with wider efforts to restructure our economic and financial system and re-evaluate the core values held by society, we can create a decarbonised, fairer world for ourselves, the environment and future generations.

References

Armed Forces (2010a) "Army Pay Scales (April 1 2009 – March 31 2010)", Armed Forces: The online global defence marketplace [online]. Available at: www.armedforces.co.uk/armypayscales.htm [Live: March 2010].

Armed Forces (2010b) "Royal Navy Pay Scales (April 1 2009 – March 31 2010)", Armed Forces: The online global defence marketplace [online]. Available at: http://www.armedforces.co.uk/royalnavypayscales.htm [Live: March 2010].

Armed Forces (2010c) "Royal Air Force Pay Scales (April 1 2009 – March 31 2010)", Armed Forces: The online global defence marketplace [online]. Available at: www.armedforces.co.uk/rafpayscales.htm [Live: March 2010].

Bird, J., R. Campbell & K. Lawton (2010) *The Long Cold Winter: Beating fuel poverty*, London: Institute for Public Policy Research (ippr).

Bowers et al. (2009) Executive pay survey, 2009, guardian.co.uk, 14 September 2009 [online interactive survey]. Available at: http://www.guardian.co.uk/business/interactive/2009/sep/14/executive-pay-survey-2009 [Live: March 2010].

Department for Energy and Climate Change [DECC] (2009) *Annual Report on Fuel Poverty Statistics 2007*, London: DECC.

Ferreira, F.H.G. (1999) "Inequality and Economic Performance: A Brief Overview to Theories of Growth and Distribution", Text for World Bank's Web Site on Inequality, Poverty, and Socio-economic Performance, June 1999. Available at: http://faculty.chass.ncsu.edu/stephen/inequal1.pdf [Live: March 2010].

Finch, J. & S. Bowers (2009) "Executive pay keeps rising", *The Guardian*, 14 September 2009.

Hills et al. (2010) *An anatomy of economic inequality in the UK: Report of the National Equality Panel*, Centre for Analysis of Social Exclusion (CASE) report 60, London: Government Equalities Office (GEO)/The London School of Economics and Political Science (LSE).

Lawlor, E., H. Kersley & S. Steed (2009) *A Bit Rich*, London: New Economics Foundation (nef).

Marsden, D. (1999) Pay Inequalities and Economic Performance Project Report, Project funded under the European Fifth Framework Programme, Centre for Economic Performance, London School of Economics. Available at: http://cep.lse.ac.uk/piep/papers/Final_Report_V5.pdf [Live: March 2010].

Office of National Statistics (ONS) (2010) "Statistical Bulletin: International comparisons of Productivity", revised estimates for 2008, 18 February 2010. Available at: http://www.statistics.gov.uk/pdfdir/icp1009.pdf [Live: March 2010].

context

Organisation for Economic Co-operation and Development (OECD) (2008)*Growing Unequal? Income distribution and poverty in OECD countries*, Paris: OECD.

Peston, R. (2009) "Bosses' pay and WPP", Peston's picks, 2 June 2009 [online]. Available at: http://www.bbc.co.uk/blogs/thereporters/robertpeston/2009/06/bosses_pay_and_wpp.html [Live: March 2010].

Wilkinson, R. G. (2006) *Unhealthy societies: the afflictions of inequality*, Abingdon: Routledge.

Wilkinson, R. & K. Pickett (2009) *The Spirit Level: Why More Equal Societies Almost Always Do Better*, London: Allen Lane.

> " Moderation is the centre wherein
> all philosophies, both human
> and divine, meet "
>
> Benjamin Disraeli

power**down**

Chapter 4
Climate and the built environment

Introduction

The built environment is one of the most important areas of focus for any effective policy to guide the UK towards a sustainable future. The design, construction, maintenance, refurbishment, management and operation of the country's building stock are all crucial to reducing carbon emissions. As so much time is spent in buildings, improving them can also improve occupant's day-to-day lives.

Over the past thirty years there have been substantial developments in the design and insulation of housing, to create buildings so efficient that they require little or no artificial heating and reduced electrical needs. While there are many innovative companies applying these new techniques in practice there are also high levels of inertia in the general construction industry.

Existing changes planned for the Building Regulations include incremental improvements leading up to 2016, when all new dwellings will be required to be "zero carbon". These regulations will encourage the construction industry to be more innovative. However, these regulations need significant strengthening to be in line with best practice, in terms of low heat requirements, electrical demand and the minimisation of embodied energy from the construction and use of buildings.

Currently "zero carbon" as considered in the Code for Sustainable Homes (CHS) refers to zero net carbon emissions from living in homes: heating, gas and electricity. It does not include the wider carbon emissions from occupants, from the energy used in construction, or the embedded carbon in building and repairing homes.

Existing residential, industrial and commercial buildings must decrease their energy (heat and electric) demand by over 50% with domestic heating being 70%. This should also include supporting infrastructure such as roads and bridges, energy generation and transmission, water supply and treatment plus waste infrastructure. The domestic sector has clear targets for new-build but the non-domestic sector requires more attention.

This chapter examines what actions need to be taken, technical and financial, to decarbonise Britain's buildings and the wider built environment. It offers a range of policy recommendations for the built environment that would contribute to the creation of a sustainable future.

Not only is the built environment very diverse in the variety of its characteristics and energy requirements, but there is also great diversity in the way in which the buildings themselves and the wider infrastructure are used. For example, a shift from office to home-working increases the demand for electricity and heat from the domestic sector. However, it can be beneficial in energy terms (heat and electricity) as it requires less space heating overall. In turn there could potentially be less need for commercial buildings. While this chapter touches upon some of these latter factors, its main focus is on the building envelope itself. This offers the greatest potential for decreasing the carbon impact of the built environment.

The built environment in its wider context

To begin, the current trend of energy use in buildings is considered, to give an estimate of the likely future position under a business-as-usual approach without intervention. The first zerocarbonbritain report examined the scale and distribution of energy use in buildings. It projected the likely position, with regard to energy use, of buildings in twenty years' time, under a business-as-usual scenario (see Table 4.1). It then considered and assessed the

available strategies for reducing energy and carbon demand (Helweg-Larson & Bull, 2007).

44% of UK emissions are from the use of buildings (17% from non-domestic buildings and 27% from domestic buildings), not including their construction or maintenance (Healey, 2009). In consequence there is potential to substantially decrease national emissions, through improvements to the building stock.

The domestic sector accounts for 28% of total British energy demand (Department of Energy and Climate Change [DECC], 2009a). It makes a considerable contribution to greenhouse gas emissions (Bordass et al., 2004) and is responsible for approximately 30% of Britain's total CO_2 emissions (Department for the Environment, Farming and Rural Affairs [Defra], 2001). In relation to this, in 2006 the British government announced plans to achieve zero carbon emissions in all new homes by 2016 (Banfill & Peacock, 2007). However, this is still in consultation. Future proposals may include 30% from off-site measures, such as renewable electricity. These figures do not include emissions at the power station for producing electricity consumed by domestic buildings or any other

Table 4.1 Energy use projections under a "business-as-usual" scenario

Sector	TWh Now	TWh 2027	Expected increase
Domestic	545	664	21%
Non-Domestic	199	251	26%

Energy use projections for domestic and non-domestic buildings under a "business-as-usual" scenario (TWh).
1TWh (terrawatt hour) is equivalent to 10^{12} watt hours.
Source: ZeroCarbonBritain (Helweg-Larson & Bull,2007).

supporting infrastructure, or the carbon used for ongoing building maintenance or to construct buildings in the first place.

The strategy for sustainable construction includes non-domestic buildings. Schools will need to meet "zero carbon" standards by 2016 with public buildings being by 2018 and other non-domestic by 2019.

The total embodied carbon of construction materials for domestic and non-domestic buildings added up to approximately 70 million tonnes of CO_2 in 2003: 13% of the total UK reported carbon emissions (Lazarus, 2005). This includes transport of materials which are covered in the Transport chapter.

The opportunities for reducing CO_2 emissions from buildings once they are constructed are varied. These include improvements in the building fabric and services, greater energy efficiency, and more sustainable power generation. Buildings with sustainable energy efficient technologies, coupled with environmentally-friendly appliances are further

areas for reductions in CO_2 emissions. Combining the emissions statistics from the use of buildings with their estimates for construction and maintenance, shows that around 64% of carbon emissions in the UK come from the building sector alone.

Residential construction trends

The UK currently has a low replacement rate of its building stock (Power, 2008). Of the country's approximately 24 million homes, it is projected that at least 87% will still be standing by 2050. Prior to the economic downturn, 20,000 dwellings were being demolished and replaced per annum, with a further 180,000 being newly built per annum.

The average carbon emissions for building a new home is 35 tonnes (Environmental Audit Committee [EAC], 2005).[1] Around five tonnes of this could be from bricks alone.[2] Maintenance also accounts for a significant portion of these emissions with major DIY tasks most common when a house is bought and sold (typically every

Table 4.2 Wall insulation in the UK						
Construction	**1970**	**1980**	**1990**	**1996–2002**	**2003–2006**	**From 2007**
Solid wall (SW)	1.7	1	0.6	0.45	0.35	0.3
SW thickness	240	250	270	300	300	300
Cavity wall (CW)	1.6	1	0.6	0.45	0.35	0.3
CW thickness	250	260	270	270	300	300
Timber frame (TF)	0.8	0.45	0.4	0.4	0.35	0.3
TF thickness	270	270	270	300	300	300

Changes in required U-values (W/m²K) and thickness (mm) of different wall constructions since1970 for new-build properties.
Source: Various building regulations and construction guidelines.

[1] The EAC use a figure of 9.54 tonnes of carbon, which has been converted in to carbon dioxide emissions (x 44/12).

[2] Based on 10,000 flettons, weighing around 23 tonnes in total, with carbon emissions as noted by the Inventory for Carbon and Energy (Hammond & Jones, 2008).

11 years). Impacts include replacing carpet (typically 10kg embodied CO_2/m^2) and painting (around 1kg embodied CO_2/m^2 (Hammond & Jones, 2008).

In relation to the UK's dominance of older buildings, the insulation level of the building envelope has gradually improved over time. Table 4.2 illustrates the change in U-values from 1970.[3] This table illustrate the need to upgrade the existing building stock to meet current standards.

Buildings will also have to be adapted to meet weather challenges associated with climate change. Predictions indicate that buildings will increasingly be adversely affected by overheating, flooding and water stress (Roberts, 2008). Since 1961, the duration of summer heatwaves has increased by between 4 and 16 days in all regions of the UK (ibid.). Rainfall has been decreasing in summer and increasing in winter, with heavier precipitation events occurring in winter. Building design should give real regard to occupant behaviour, energy use and the interaction of the two.

Energy consumption in buildings

The British government has set a target date of 2050 by which CO_2 emissions are to be reduced by 80% on 2000 levels. Buildings are a key element in the process of decarbonisation. They will in fact have to exceed this level of reduction, due to other sectors such as aviation, for which emissions reductions from buildings will have to compensate.

SPACE HEATING

Energy demand from buildings can be distinguished according to what that energy is used for. In particular, it is useful to differentiate the use of energy for space heating from other uses, including the use of appliances. In 2007, space heating accounted for 56% of domestic energy consumption and 46% of service sector energy consumption (DECC, 2009b). It is therefore critical, if we are to achieve energy use reductions, to improve its efficiency.

There are a whole range of measures available to decrease the heating demand from the built environment. These include improvements to the building envelope (the walls, windows, floors and roof), the heating system and thermal comfort.

Building fabric

Simple improvements to the fabric of buildings are well known. These include cavity wall and loft insulation, double glazing and draught proofing. There are also several more radical ways to decrease the energy performance of buildings, e.g. by whole house refurbishment and the addition of internal or external insulation. Improving the building fabric keeps more heat within the usable space. This in turn decreases the energy demand and eliminates cooling requirements.

Thermal comfort

In discussing heating, it is "thermal comfort" that is the real target: rather than looking at a set air temperature as a target level. By defining the goal more accurately it makes the opportunities of achieving it a lot easier to understand.

Thermal comfort is defined as a mental condition that is based upon the lack of perception of noticeable changes in temperature that results in a personal expression of satisfaction with the environment (American Society of Heating, Refrigerating and Air-Conditioning Engineers [ASHRAE], Standard 55, 2004). It is a complex area within environmental building design.

For example, to avoid being cold the level of clothing could be increased rather than increasing the air temperature. One of the advantages of this approach is that it can vary per person and therefore people can adapt to their own individual levels of warmth as required.

In addition to revising and improving the building fabric, there are a range of elements relating to building design which affect the thermal comfort of occupants. Interestingly occupants are willing to tolerate higher levels of temperature variance if they feel they are able to control their conditions (Baker & Standeven, 1996). This is most relevant to office buildings where different energy usage is found, by putting the heating control near the window (generally the coldest part of the office) or in the centre of the office (one of the warmer spots).

Our metabolic rate varies dependant on activity, for example when walking through an area such as a corridor it does not need to be as warm as for example a living room. It needs to be comfortable. These areas do not require the same level of heating. Intelligent building design can automatically adjust the heating in such transition spaces.

With an objective of thermal comfort, why heat a space which is not being used? By only heating the spaces in use, the energy demand in a building is decreased. In a domestic setting this could decrease heat demand by over 40% (Mackay, 2008). Mackay (ibid.) uses the formula below to calculate the power used in heating a building.

$$\text{power used} = \frac{\text{average temperature difference x leakiness of building}}{\text{efficiency of heating system}}$$

This is useful as it highlights the impact of the temperature difference between inside and outside. Mackay (ibid.) refers to the formula in relation to decreasing the thermostat; however, it can also be used for thermal comfort. For example, in winter occupants are more likely to accept a cooler building which decreases the temperature difference between inside and outside and therefore the energy demand. By inhabiting or heating smaller living spaces or selectively heating smaller areas there would be decreased energy demands.

Mackay (2008) highlights the importance of the amount of space heated per person which we can add to his formula as below. This adds 'multiplied by space heated' after average temperature difference.

$$\text{power used} = \frac{\text{average temperature difference x space heated x leakiness of building}}{\text{efficiency of heating system.}}$$

The four key ways to decrease space heating demand are to:

1) Improve the insulation or "fabric" of buildings;

2) Decrease draughts;

3) Decrease the heat demand through:

a. Good "passive" design to increase natural heat gains;

b. Decrease area requiring heat;

c. Decrease the thermostat/air temperature. Thermal comfort can be maintained through good design resulting in warmer surfaces and less drafts;

4) Improve the efficiency of heating technology.

The term adaptive thermal comfort has two key parts. One part considers the level of connection there is between an occupant's immediate indoor space and the outside world. The other part is the level of control (or even perceived control) an occupant has over heating, cooling and ventilation of "their space". These complex design elements have the potential to decrease energy demand and improve occupant efficiency. They are increasingly being accepted by industry.

The next step is to set a target figure for decreasing space heating demand. As a comparison, WWF (2009) suggest a decrease in energy demand of 86% by 2050. The Department for Communities and Local Government (DCLG, 2009) suggested 40% by 2020. Passive House

Planning Package (PHPP)based refurbishment companies claim 80–95% decreases in energy demand (Thorpe, 2010). Mackay (2008) suggests 75% and his research demonstrated 67% on a dwelling without adding any external or internal cladding.

The target figure for policy should be a 70% reduction in space heating energy demand for the domestic sector as a whole with variation depending on building type. Significant reductions in space heating energy demand within the non-domestic sector can also be made. Low embodied energy materials which sequester carbon are favoured for building and retrofitting properties. These tend to be cheaper and slightly more bulky. Therefore the opportunities for their application vary between building type. To summarise, by making it clear that the goal is thermal comfort rather than heating, there are a wide array of options for decreasing the energy demand from buildings. While the air in a building may be cooler the building can still be more comfortable through good design and planning.

Legislation

There is a range of legislation governing the construction industry, including issues such as sustainability, energy efficiency and carbon emissions.

CURRENT LEGISLATION

The key statutory and voluntary legislation are as follows:

The Code for Sustainable Homes (CSH)

The Code for Sustainable Homes was developed to promote sustainable building practices for new homes. It provides standards for the key elements of design and construction that affect the sustainability of a new home. The code incorporates nine sustainability issues, ranging from water usage to the health and well-being of the occupants.

Energy efficiency and CO_2 emissions are central to the code, although CSH compliance is not a legislative requirement (Osami & O'Reilly, 2009). However, builders are encouraged to follow CSH principles, as assessment under parts of the code's standards will be made mandatory for all in future (DCLG, 2008).

Some local authorities are including CSH recommendations at the planning stage now. The CSH is mandatory for social housing and grant funding is available from the Homes and Communities Agency. Under the grant scheme all social housing must achieve level CSH Level 3.

Building Regulations Part L

The Building Regulations 2000 set out broad standards and requirements which individual aspects of building design and construction must achieve. Part L deals with the energy efficiency of the building fabric and boiler, conservation of fuel and power, and some dedicated low-energy light fittings. The emphasis is on the building fabric. It is a design standard and does not influence operation or occupancy. Part L is incorporating the CSH energy aspects through amendments in 2010 and 2013. It will achieve "zero carbon" by 2016.

Standard Assessment Procedure (SAP)

The Standard Assessment Procedure is the UK Government's recommended system for measuring the energy rating of domestic dwellings. The first version was published in 1995, and was replaced by newer versions in 1998, 2001 and 2005. It calculates the typical annual energy costs for space and water heating, and from 2005, lighting. CO_2 emissions are also calculated. SAP as a regulatory tool is included in Part L of the Building Regulations and CSH.

SAP is the auditing method behind calculations in the Building Regulations and the Energy Performance Certificates (see below). It includes boilers, pumps, fans and fixed lighting. It does not cover occupant-installed appliances, electrical equipment and non-fixed lighting. Because the energy used by appliances and most lighting is not included within the auditing method, more energy efficient equipment cannot contribute to better ratings. The Government has recognised the shortcomings of SAP. It stated that "SAP in its existing form does not adequately take account of nor does it provide for proper accounting for the range of technologies that will reduce them" (DCLG, 2007a). SAP 2009 has scince been updated. It came into force as the tool for measuring Part L from April 2010.

Merton Rule

The Merton Rule was first introduced by the London Borough of Merton in 2003. It is a planning policy that requires new non-residential developments above 1,000m² to provide 10% of their total energy demand from on-site renewable sources (Merton Council, 2009). The London Plan (Policy 4A.2i) (Mayor of London, 2008) now requires all London Boroughs to provide 20% on-site renewable sources on all developments.

Energy Performance Certificates (EPCs)

Energy Performance Certificates record how energy efficient a property is as a building, and provides ratings on an A–G scale. These are similar to the labels now provided with domestic white goods such as refrigerators and washing machines. EPCs give information on the current performance of a house, along with its potential for cost-effective improvement. They have been a legal requirement on the construction, sale or rental of properties since 2008. An EPC does not give information on current energy usage, it calculates energy performance.

An EPC is accompanied by a recommendation report that lists measures (such as low and zero carbon generating systems) to improve the energy rating. A rating is also given showing what could be achieved if all the recommendations were implemented. One key feature of EPCs is that they look at performance rather than efficiency. That is, they consider how well the building meets its requirements rather than the more common criterion of the efficiency of individual components such as heating and insulation. This ensures that the design and integration of the building's components are all considered in conjunction, to help decarbonise the nation's building stock.

RECOMMENDATIONS FOR IMPROVING BUILDINGS LEGISLATION

The above examples highlight the UK Government's commitment to meeting EU directives. These directives require a reduction to direct in-use emissions from homes. They measure emissions from building stock but exclude emissions due to building construction and maintenance, or wider infrastructure emissions. The Strategy for Sustainable Construction includes a target for reducing emissions by 60% based on 1990 levels by 2050.

Domestic buildings and schools, public sector non-domestic buildings and other non-domestic buildings will be zero carbon from 2016, 2018 and 2019 respectively. Therefore how zero carbon is defined is crucial. In what follows, further mechanisms are proposed that would build upon the effects of the above policies.

An analysis of the above standards and their implementation can help identify the best route towards decarbonisation. One key advance would be to have greater consistency between standards. Currently, SAP is used to assess the carbon impact of new buildings and rd (reduced data) SAP is used for EPCs. An EPC quantifies the carbon emissions whereas CSH examines the energy consumption and carbon emissions of the whole building, including catering, computing and all small power plug loads. Part L 2010 may be mandatory and include specifying 75% of internal lighting. This is necessary to identify homes that are "zero carbon" and to establish the level a home achieves under the Code for Sustainable Homes.

Furthermore, the revised and updated CSH "zero carbon" standard should become a compulsory legal standard. This has already been proposed for the zero carbon part of Part L for 2016.

Another key issue is the need for building energy labelling. These certificates give an indication of the actual energy use of individual homes. Smart meters may be required in all buildings by 2020. There may also be a credit for them in the next version of CSH; this proposal is out to consultation. DECs (Display Energy Certificates) use actual meter readings for the home energy labels. These give a clear indication of how much energy is actually being used, and informs on how the occupants actually use energy.

Clear standards are required. Sharing best practice at a European level while taking into account the variance of climate could help evolve our building standards. This would ensure regulation of the "green industry". The standard should be written in light of the German Passivhaus standard. Passivhaus is a design methodology which maximises the comfort of buildings while massively reducing their energy consumption.

Passive houses have a combination of high insulation, lack of draughts and air leakage, advanced glazing as well as a mechanical ventilation and heat recovery system. This provides up to 80% of heating needs through warmed fresh air, resulting in properties that stay comfortable without the need for large and costly heating systems. Furthermore, a code for sustainable building design should encourage timber frame construction to promote carbon sequestration, low embodied energy and the use of natural materials. Like all legislation it should be matched with training and enforcement to ensure compliance.

Domestic properties

27% of UK emissions arise from energy use in the home. Between 1990 and 2008, total energy consumption in the UK rose by just over 5% but domestic energy consumption rose by 12% (DECC, 2009b).[4] Over the same time period, emissions from the residential sector have declined, but at a much slower rate than for several other sectors (DECC, 2010). Figure 4.1 shows energy use within domestic properties in 2007. 55% of energy was used for space heating, and a further 26% for heating water. Trends suggest an increase in consumption for lighting and appliances and a fall in consumption for cooking and hot water (DCLG, 2007a). Table

Fig. 4.1 Energy consumption in domestic dwellings

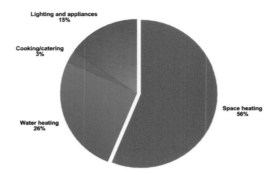

Energy consumption in domestic dwellings by use as a percentage of total final energy consumption, 2007.
Source: DECC (2009).

4.3 shows the CO_2 emissions associated with these uses. Retrofitting domestic buildings offers an effective way not only of decreasing carbon emissions but also of reducing overall energy demand. With appropriate measures, the average home's heating and lighting usage could be reduced by 80%, with the remaining heat and electrical demand being met using renewables. The nation's building stock could be transformed from among the worst in Europe to a position of leading the low carbon economy.

To meet ambitious targets at minimum cost requires optimising each opportunity to decarbonise. Rather than aiming to reduce overall energy use from buildings by a set percentage, the aim should be to achieve a set standard across the sector. The added advantage of this approach is that the actions are linked to a clearly defined outcome. The disadvantage is that it does not account

for the increases in the size and number of homes. While any standard involves a degree of compromise, one of the best examples is the Swiss Minergie label, which stipulates a consumption of 50kWh/m²/annum for heating, hot water, cooling and mechanical ventilation. Mackay's (2008) house in 2006 used approximately 160kWh/m²/annum and the same dwelling in 2007 after building fabric improvements used 54kWh/m²/annum. This was without internal insulation or external cladding which offers the potential for substantial further improvements.

A key factor is quantification based on floor area. In the case of retrofitting, the best approach may be to have target figures for each building type; however, every situation demands a slightly different solution depending on building and occupancy, so that with experience, the standards can be amended as

⁴ Domestic energy use appears to have peaked in 2004 and total energy use in 2005 (DECC, 2009b).

Table 4.3 CO_2 emissions from domestic buildings

End use	% of total
Appliances including cookers	21
Lighting	6
Water heating	20
Space heating	53
Total	100

CO_2 emissions from British domestic dwellings by use per household, 2005, as a percentage of total domestic emissions, 2005.
Source: 2005 data from DCLG (2007a).

practical knowledge develops.

In the ***zero**carbon**britain**2030* scenario, all electricity is renewable, leaving the focus on provision of heating. While the German Passive House Planning Package (PHPP) standard energy consumption is 15kWh/m^2 for new build, the standard for retrofitted buildings is 30kWh/m^2.

In the domestic sector, there are many opportunities for basic cost-effective improvements in thermal performance. In 2005, there were over 9 million uninsulated cavity walls and 6.3 million lofts in Britain with little or no insulation (DCLG, 2007b). A national refurbishment scheme would make sure that everybody could benefit from cost and carbon saving opportunities. Retrofitting existing homes could save 15 times more CO_2 by 2050 than their demolition and replacement (Jowsey & Grant, 2009). Refurbishment minimises the time and cost involved in improving the energy efficiency of a dwelling. It reduces sprawl by reducing the need for new build and it reuses

existing infrastructures and protects existing communities. In addition it can reduce energy use in buildings in both the short- and long-term. While there are increasingly impressive refurbishments at an individual house level, the first local authority to complete a large scale refurbishment (1000 or more dwellings) will be providing a great example nationally if not worldwide.

At first sight, a rundown area can often appear much easier to demolish and rebuild than to renovate. However, such areas often have considerable potential value if they are upgraded (Power & Mumford, 2003). Older, pre-First World War properties are the least energy efficient, but often the easiest to renovate and improve (Power, 2008). It must, however, be recognised that refurbishment to the required standard can be extremely disruptive.

On the one hand, there are strong social and structural reasons not to demolish and rebuild, while on the other hand, developers, planners

Box 4.1 Pay As You Save (PAYS)

PAYS is an alternative subsidising method. It offers people the opportunity of upgrading a dwelling's energy perfomance without upfront financing (Colley, 2009). A low energy refurbishment provider uses finance, from a third party, to cover the upfront costs of the low energy work. A repayment tariff is linked through a meter to the property over an extended period of time. Customers who sign up to a PAYS tariff benefit financially because the repayment tariff is set up to cost less than the amount of energy saved.

Another key feature of PAYS is that the payment obligation is attached to the property rather than a specific owner or occupant. At change of tenure the benefits of the measures and the obligation to pay is transferred with the property to the new homeowner or occupant.

The refurbishment work is undertaken by an accredited company. Rigorous enforcement of codes and standards is required. This could take the form of Sustainability Inspectors similar to those employed to enforce Health and Safety Standards on construction sites. In other words inspection is done without prior warning and the legal responsibility is at the director level of the organisation.

There are three finance options for PAYS – green bonds, finance from utilities providers and third party capital (ibid.).

and clients tend towards new buildings rather than refurbishments, because of greater certainty in the result (Helweg-Larson & Bull, 2007).

The cost of refurbishment depends on several factors, including the carbon reduction targets, the building type, the region, the extent of the necessary works, the construction of the building, the historic value and the existing environmental and thermal performance (Jowsey & Grant, 2009). One proposal is street-by-street upgrades which reduces cost and disruption.

Refurbishment at scale and in one location dramatically reduces the cost. For example, all the skills and materials can be in one place. Gaining buy-in from the housing occupants is key to getting these cost savings and achieving the larger picture of facilitating the decarbonisation. Going street-by-street, asking for an opt-out rather than an opt-in, and offering information on the need for the refurbishment and the benefits to the occupants will all play a part. Methods to improve the willingness of the public to reduce energy consumption is discussed in the Motivation and behavioural change chapter.

A whole house approach is necessary. This means designing a strategy for the house rather than seeking reactive incremental improvement. This approach outlines what measures are needed, what the priorities are of each measure, and therefore provides a sequence of events for the house to reach the desired carbon target. This will also highlight the costs of the refurbishment. In addition to

Table 4.4 The benefits of refurbishment
• Renovation preserves the basic structure of the buildings. It retains the existing infrastructure (such as roads, rail, water mains and gas pipes) in the existing built environment. Currently, this infrastructure accounts for about 15% of the UK's CO_2 emissions (Essex, 2010).
• The renewal of a single dwelling has an effect on neighbouring properties, encouraging further refurbishment.
• By adapting the existing structure and layout of a building, refurbishment is quicker than demolition and replacement.
• It involves a shorter and more continuous building process, since most of the work can be carried out under cover in weatherproof conditions. New build involves many months of exposure to the elements while the foundations and main structure are built.
• It has a positive impact on the wider neighbourhood. Renewal and reinvestment enhance long-term value, promoting a broader upgrading of the entire area.
• Renovation has a positive effect on street conditions, service quality and transport.

Source: Power, (2008).

PAYS (see Box 4.1) and ESCOs (energy service companies, see Box 4.2) there are other ways of financing the transition to an energy efficient Britain more broadly. These are discussed in the Policy and economics chapter.

HOW DO WE MINIMISE THE EMBODIED ENERGY IN REFURBISHMENT?

Whilst retrofitting will make buildings far more energy efficient over the long-term, the carbon cost associated with the retrofit of 25 million homes may be highly significant in the short-term. One of the key ways of reducing the carbon cost of the retrofit will be by selecting building materials that have low embodied energy and embodied carbon.

The embodied energy of a material or product refers to the total primary energy consumed during the resource extraction, transportation, manufacturing and fabrication of that item (Hammond & Jones, 2008). Embodied energy is measured as a quantity of non-renewable energy per unit of material, component or system. It is expressed as megajoules (MJ) or gigajoules (GJ) per unit of weight (kg or tonne) or area (square metre) of material.

There are two forms: the initial embodied energy and the recurring embodied energy. So, for a building, the initial embodied energy consists of the energy used to extract, process and manufacture its raw materials, the transportation of building materials to the building site, and the energy cost of the construction work. The recurring embodied energy in buildings is the energy consumed to maintain, repair, restore, refurbish or replace materials, components or systems during the lifecycle of the building.

The embodied energy of materials is usually calculated on a "Cradle-to-Gate" basis: this includes all the energy used within the product's creation, usually including any indirect energy costs related to this, such as the energy used for manufacturing capital equipment which are used to create the product, and the energy used for heating and lighting the factory where it is produced. However, it does not include any energy used after the product leaves the factory gate.

The Inventory of Carbon and Energy (ICE), produced by Geoff Hammond and Craig Jones at the University of Bath, details the embodied energy and carbon of a large number of building materials. The latest version (1.6) of ICE uses a "Cradle-to-Gate" methodology. It also encourages users to quantify the "Gate-to-Site".

A more complete calculation can be based on a boundary condition of "Cradle-to-Site": this includes all of the energy consumed until the product has reached its point of use, in other words, the building site. It therefore also includes the costs of transportation and retail. The optimum boundary condition is "Cradle-to-Grave", which involves not only the calculation of energy used from extraction to production, and on to transportation to site, but also the energy cost of product maintenance, and disposal at the end of the product's lifetime.

The embodied energy of a product tends to be lower when materials are locally and sustainably sourced. It is therefore very important that the retrofitting programme use such materials wherever possible.

CARBON SEQUESTRATION IN REFURBISHED BUILDINGS

Natural materials such as wood and straw contain carbon absorbed from the atmosphere. Different types of biomass and biofuels burn these natural materials which releases the stored carbon. Biomass generally refers to solid plant matter grown for fuel e.g. to generate electricity or produce heat. Biofuel refers to liquid fuel derived from plant materials. For further details please see the biofuels section in the Transport chapter. Instead of releasing this stored carbon, it could be locked away in building materials. This would result in a carbon saving i.e. a net negative emissions. Therefore the mass sustainable refurbishment of current buildings can also act as a carbon store.

The materials used for this carbon sequestration are varied. They include grown and recycled materials. The materials suggested include wood, straw, hemp, recycled cardboard, miscanthus and willow. Each has many uses, for example: timber for structural and partitioning purposes; miscanthus as particle board and straw and hemp as walling materials.

Researchers at the Graduate School of the Environment at CAT are investigating the potential use of many natural building materials.

This one process has three benefits: it saves carbon, it reduces the cost of refurbishment and locks carbon in the building. The use of this straw in new buildings and refurbishment would sequester carbon.

The land use change suggested in **zero**carbon**britain**2030 will provide further construction materials which offer sequestration potential. These include hemp, wood and miscanthus. These materials can be used for both new buildings and for refurbishments. The quantities provided will allow Britain to move from importing building materials to exporting them whilst increasing resilience and sustainable jobs.

WHY NOT DEMOLISH AND REPLACE BUILDINGS?

While demolition and replacement can reduce the energy use of inefficient buildings, the process has an energy cost. This results from the embodied energy of materials, the disposal of demolished buildings and the construction of new buildings. Often, it is used as a method to knock down a building and build a bigger one in its place. This may be justified in terms of energy efficiency but is generally motivated by developer gain.

It is generally presented by the construction industry that the embodied energy and carbon due to demolition and replacement is outweighed by the energy and carbon saved in use, where the replacement buildings are highly energy efficient. Energy in use outweighs the embodied energy of existing stock, over the average building's design lifetime – 60 years for domestic stock, 30 to 60 years for non-domestic (Bull, 2008). The trade-off between wide-ranging refurbishment (e.g. 40% of demolition and replacement) and simple retrofit is dependent on the dwelling.

The saving lies in retaining the structure of the building (e.g. timber, concrete or steel frame), the product used to give it structural integrity and thermal mass (e.g. bricks), as well as fixtures and fittings. The latter tend to be replaced when a building is replaced. The additional carbon beyond the building structure and flooring is rarely considered in comparative calculations. However, the existing infrastructure has significant embodied carbon and therefore saving it is very useful in carbon terms.

On the negative side, demolition involves the loss of a building and the financial cost of its replacement. Adjacent buildings may lose value through disrepair and decline. It is difficult to renew an area through house-by-house demolition and replacement, so that whole streets or areas may need to be demolished, destroying some perfectly viable properties. Demolition is often driven by a pressure to build more housing by infill/back-garden development, for example, by knocking down a detached house to build a small estate or by increasing the density of a council estate or town centre by increasing overall m^2 often by increasing the height of buildings. Furthermore, on average 70% of homes are occupied, making an area-based approach complex, slow and costly (National Audit Office [NAO], 2007). The highest rate of clearance, 80,000 demolitions per annum, occurred during the late 1960s, now referred to as the mass clearance era (Power & Mumford, 2003). This compares with a current rate of 20,000 per annum (Boardman et al., 2005), which even with a very high energy standard of replacement stock will only have a marginal impact on national energy demand.

In the non-domestic sector too, the rate of replacement of existing stock is also low. At prvesent, replacement is driven by economic conditions and regeneration policies rather than by building energy performance. However, the impacts of carbon trading, taxation, and increasing energy prices may promote a greater focus on energy performance, even in the absence of specific interventions in this sector.

One final factor bearing on the decision whether to demolish and rebuild concerns the timescale involved. Rebuilding is slowed by the need to renew infrastructure after demolition. It is rare for a demolition plan to deliver replacement housing in less than 10 years, even with Government backing and funding (Turcu, 2005–2007).

Whatever approach is adopted – whether demolition and replacement or refurbishment – the most central consideration is that a substantially higher energy standard be achieved in buildings with reduced carbon emissions. This not only ensures lower carbon and financial running costs of the building in use, but also that the investment and embodied energy is well spent.

As a result, Britain will avoid wasting existing carbon capital by reusing, refurbishing and deconstructing rather than demolishing existing buildings.

Non-domestic buildings

The heating, cooling and powering of non-domestic buildings accounts for 17% of UK greenhouse gas emissions (Healey, 2009).[5] Figure 4.2 breaks down energy use within the service sector. As with domestic buildings, the heating of service sector buildings is the most significant use of energy. Much of this is to heat older commercial offices, education facilities, retail spaces, hotels, and catering outlets (Department for Business, Enterprise and Regulatory Reform [BERR], 2007). Space heating also accounts for 11% of industrial energy use (DECC, 2009b).

Non-domestic buildings emit approximately 100Mt of CO_2 each year (Caleb, 2008). The Carbon Trust has identified an emissions reduction potential of 37Mt of CO_2, while the Committee on Climate Change has identified a potential of about 34Mt CO_2 for non-domestic buildings, of which 13.5Mt CO_2 could be achieved at a cost of less than £40/tonne CO_2 (ibid.).

However, adding in the work from other sectors such as having a renewably-powered electricity supply, the potential of

[5] Industry, accounted for 20.3%, and services (including agriculture) 12.5%, of total UK energy consumption in 2008 (DECC, 2009). "Industrial demand" excludes iron and steel use of fuels for transformation and energy industry own use purposes (ibid.).

behaviour change, and back-casting rather than forecasting, highlights many more opportunities.

Energy Performance Certificates have been required on the construction, sale or lease of larger non-domestic buildings since October 2008. These certificates should provide some incentives to exceed the minimum Building Regulations requirements for refurbished buildings. There is considerable evidence that EPCs underestimate the actual energy use in non-domestic buildings (Bordass *et al.*, 2004). It is an EU requirement to label public buildings with the actual energy use Display Energy Certificates. These show a higher actual energy use compared with the theoretical predictions of EPCs. This highlights the need for energy labelling based on actual energy use and highlights the potential for better energy

prediction tools.

In general, existing buildings in the non-domestic sector have poor building fabric, inefficient plant rooms, poor building controls and low levels of energy awareness among their users and occupants (Clarke *et al.*, 2006). Overheating is common. This leads to an increased cooling demand even though the climate does not warrant it. Improved controls and the appropriate use of thermal mass, glazing, shading and ventilation are important to reduce overheating. For existing, poorly-insulated office buildings, improved insulation is more important than improved solar control, whereas the reverse is true for well-insulated buildings (Arup, 2008).

The UK spends £27 billion per year on commercial and public refurbishment (Caleb, 2008). Commercial buildings account for

Fig. 4.2 Energy consumption in the service sector

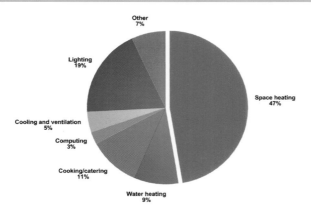

Energy consumption in the service sector by use as a percentage of total final energy consumption, 2007.
Source: DECC (2009).

about 64% of this figure. Incorporating energy efficiency into this refurbishment is much more cost effective and convenient than a mass refurbishment project. Refurbishments could be made energy efficient by ensuring they meet standards analogous to those set out in the new-build Code for Sustainable Homes, with escalating targets over time.

In any event, the Code for Sustainable Homes should be expanded into a Code for Sustainable Building, including standards for the crucial industrial and commercial sectors. There are BRE Environmental Assessment Method (BREEAM) standards that equate to the Code for Non-Domestic new build; however, the argument for a Code for Sustainable Buildings is also about applying these standards to existing stock. Energy-efficient refurbishment could become a large market, creating many jobs. This is quantified and discussed in more detail in the Employment chapter.

A strategic approach to carbon reduction in residential and non-domestic buildings

In order to achieve emissions reductions, a clear hierarchy of priorities can be identified. The starting point is demand reduction through energy efficiency, by means of passive design measures such as insulation and heat-recovery ventilation, along with high-performance specification for refurbishment and new-build.

It is far more cost-effective to design energy demand out of buildings than to invest in new energy supplies or carbon offsetting.

With high levels of passive building performance, the next priority is the provision of low or zero carbon energy supplies. Where efficient, generation should be located on-site or as close to the development as possible. This avoids distribution losses, increases local awareness of energy supply, and ensures that local renewable energy capacity is exploited.

To date, the focus of policy intervention has been on the energy performance of new buildings. The next step is to address the improvement of existing buildings through national requirements. There are examples of local good practice in this regard, which can be used to inform a wider, nationally-focused policy.

However, to improve the existing building stock will require considerable effort, in terms of providing the necessary information, advice and support, along with incentives to help reduce the high up-front costs of making such improvements (Caleb, 2008).

Another solution is the use of an alternative finance model for such work. Arup (2009) highlighted the potential to finance retrofitting by allowing the installers to capture the energy bill savings. This would enable the initial capital to come from a variety of interested parties rather than relying on capital from the building owner. This is a key issue for all buildings. The emergence of energy service companies

(ESCOs) is one example of such an approach.

However, in relation to all of this, domestic energy efficiency tends to follow the "rebound effect" in which efficiency savings are partly offset by greater consumption in other areas. This can be due to changes in the use of the building, the addition of new energy loads, or increased lighting levels (ibid.).

Sanders and Phillipson (2006) have found that currently only 50% of the theoretical savings from improving Building Regulations are actually achieved in practice. This results from occupant's choosing to heat buildings to a higher temperature.[6]

There are several ways to address this "rebound effect". Firstly this would not happen if there was a pre-agreed service level with an energy supply company. For other customers there are ways of pricing electricity so that beyond a set usage level the price increases therefore preventing rebound. In addition to reducing emissions a core benefit for this retrofit is to avoid fuel poverty. The term fuel poverty refers to a household needing to spend more than a tenth of their income on energy (Boardmann *et al.*, 2005). Better insulated homes are a major step towards both objectives but will of course be supplemented by other measures. These other measures include a cap on national emissions.

Recommendations

A Code for Sustainable Building Design (both domestic and non-domestic) would be one of the key steps needed to encourage and enforce decreased energy demand and

Box 4.2 Energy service companies (ESCOs)

The idea behind energy service companies is that, rather than paying per unit of electricity, gas or other heat source, the customer pays for the service provided. ESCOs still require metering and charge per unit of heat or electricity. For example a customer pays the ESCO to keep their dwelling at a set temperature throughout the year. Energy supply companies are normally used in the domestic sector but they also have the potential to reduce energy use in the industrial and commercial sectors.

Conventional economics suggests that whenever a saving can be made; for example, insulating a building, the rational consumer will do so. However at a domestic scale, homeowners seldom have easy access to information showing that such improvements are in their best interests. Furthermore, even when such information is provided, there may be an element of inertia. By contrast, in an ESCO model, the service provider has both the information and the incentive to insulate the building, potentially promoting large-scale implementation of improvements.

The ESCO approach is currently being investigated by both Government and the private sector. Alternatively, the inception of street-by-street improvements is an even more cost-effective approach. This however requires buy-in from homeowners, along with some form of public-private partnership to plan its implementation. Both Arup and Wates, two leading building construction companie, have highlighted the cost savings of large-scale retrofitting. There are other similar models where energy savings are captured by installers such as Pay As You Save (PAYS) (see Box 4.1), potentially making energy efficiency measures free to the homeowner.

[6] The average internal temperature of homes in the UK has increased by 7°C since 1970. The advent of central heating has led to an increase in comfort but the average energy use per dwelling has remained roughly the same.

carbon emissions from buildings. Such a code should provide clear definitions of zero carbon buildings, and include a consideration of the embodied energy involved in construction.

A total cap and reduction in emissions from construction and maintenance is key to minimising emissions from the built environment. This should include limiting the expansion of emissions of all other sectors. It should also indicate how low or zero carbon design and technologies can be incorporated. All elements of architecture and design must become integrated, rather than treating each discrete element in isolation. The code might also consider wider aspects such as indoor air quality, as in North America's Leadership in Energy and Environmental Design (LEED) standard or Britain's BREEAM.

Research is needed into what materials should be included or excluded in this type of design. A clear framework for building design should be drawn up, allowing for different routes to zero carbon. Without this research, there will be continued ambiguity regarding low and zero carbon technologies and their implementation.

The largest decrease in emissions from building stock will come from refurbishment. In consequence, a Code for Sustainable Refurbishment is also required. This could be designed in conjunction with the Code for Sustainable Building Design. It could be based on the CSH, outlining measures to be improved such as glazing, insulation, boilers and other energy efficiency measures.

All new homes have to meet the CSH Level 3 CO_2 emissions from April 2010, and code level water consumption requirements later in 2010. A further step for such codes would be to incorporate them into European legislation to create a set of European Sustainability Standards.

In addition to legislative backing, financial incentives are also required, such as those outlined in Table 4.5, complemented by national legislation on carbon to ensure they meet their potential. Research from the Energy Saving Trust showed that once built, around 43% of buildings fail to achieve the Building Regulations standard they were designed to. Therefore, it is not enough to design a zero carbon standard; enforcement is crucial (see Grigg, 2004). Legislative backing could take the form of sustainability or low carbon inspectors similar to those employed to enforce Health & Safety Standards on construction sites. Inspection would be without prior warning, with legal responsibility devolving upon the organisation's directors.

Another key factor in achieving low carbon buildings is in the attitudes of users and occupants, as well as of the designers and builders involved in their construction. Substantial education is needed to ensure that people appreciate not only the benefits of low carbon homes, but also the ways in which their own choices and actions can influence the effectiveness of the end result (Osami & O'Reilly, 2009). Action can be achieved through education, marketing and legislation. Social

Box 4.3 Sustainable communities

Sustainable communities are designed as places where people can both live and work, now and into the future. Such communities aim to meet the diverse needs of existing and future residents, as well as being sensitive to the environment. They must offer hospitals, schools, shops, public transport, and a clean, safe environment (Office of the Deputy Prime Minister [ODPM], 2003).

A programme was issued by the government to set a framework for delivering sustainable communities over the next 15–20 years. The main areas of focus are housing supply, new growth areas, decent homes and the countryside and local environment. Other similar ideas have also been proposed, such as new urbanism and mixed-use development. For the purposes of this report, all such ideas are considered under the title of sustainable communities.

The idea of mixed-use development is that, rather than zoning land for a single purpose such as residential or commercial, having a mix in one area can provide a range of benefits including fuel use, cost saving and quality of life.

Careful planning of the built environment can substantially reduce travel. Having schools, shops, businesses and homes all within walking distance requires integration at the town planning and development stages, but can significantly decrease travel requirements. Such initiatives save time, energy use and infrastructure requirements, as well as providing a better quality of life and a stronger sense of community.

marketing could be used to incentivise positive action.

This education programme requires both a grass roots and a central component, involving local councils and communities as well as action at a national level. The training of construction professionals must also be directed at producing a more flexible and adaptable workforce, with an understanding of the whole construction process. University-level architecture, engineering and construction education needs to incorporate sustainability as a central issue, to ensure the necessary skills and awareness. Professional on-tools training for builders and tradespeople is essential. There is also a need for increased financial incentives to make new technologies more affordable, as shown in Table 4.5.

Reduced energy and resource use requires the mutual involvement of all stakeholders – owners, investors, developers, designers and builders. Gann (2000) comments that there is a danger of 'overemphasising the physical characteristics of construction' by considering the building separately from its social and environmental setting. A more integrated approach to programming, planning, design, and construction is needed (Adeyeye et al., 2007), involving cross-disciplinary teams at the planning, design and construction stages.

Future research

Further research is required into the potential for new buildings to be designed for their ultimate dismantling. At the design stage, engineers, architects and designers should

Table 4.5 Zero carbon incentives
• Stamp duty rebates on the sale of existing properties, to encourage improvements in energy efficiency, such as increased insulation, double/triple glazing, and more efficient heating systems.
• Low-interest loans for substantial energy efficiency improvements that will increase a home's energy performance certificate or SAP rating.
• PAYS should form part of the Government's strategy to encourage the refurbishment of existing buildings both domestic and non-domestic.
• VAT reduced to 5% on energy-efficient products to equalise the rate on energy use. New-build is currently VAT-free. However, almost all repair and reinvestment works are subject to 17.5% VAT, falling to 5% for property that has been empty for more than three years (Power, 2008).
• Green mortgages providing lower interest rates for investment in energy efficiency. This differs from existing green mortgages which include energy audits and carbon offsets. The Energy Efficiency Partnership for Homes defined green mortgages as mortgages for dwellings with above-average levels of energy efficiency or where the owner commits to undertake an agreed list of improvements.
• Council tax rebates for energy efficiency improvements. For example, the occupier pays for cavity wall insulation but receives a rebate equivalent to the original investment. For example Rochford District council funds a one-off Council Tax rebate of £75 once insulation has been installed by British Gas in a dwelling.

Potential incentive mechanisms to encourage the decarbonisation of buildings.

consider how a building could be taken apart so that constituent parts and materials could be easily reused or reclaimed.

Domestic appliances in the UK currently contribute 30% of domestic CO_2 emissions (Association of Environmentally Conscious Builders [AECB], 2006) together with growing home entertainment systems energy use. There are energy star and similar schemes, and integration of devices may lead to a lower quantity of appliances and decreased electrical demand. There is a need for further research into how this can be achieved. This not only involves the development of low-wattage appliances themselves, but also of methods of monitoring the appliances' energy consumption in use. The integration of this with the rapid roll-out of smart meters could collate huge quantities of real data to help drive further efficiencies.

Post-occupancy evaluation of building systems offers opportunities for innovation. Innovative case study buildings not only inspire, they also provide information to help future developments in building science. Information on actual energy use and occupant behaviour in both new and refurbished buildings should be collated. Building regulations should mandate follow-ups to check that energy criteria as per the building specification are being met.

Conclusion

The built environment can play a significant role in reducing the UK's greenhouse gas emissions through measuring and reducing emissions to construct and maintain our built environment, as well as regulation to enforce the reduction of emissions from both new buildings and the existing stock.

Cutting emissions from the buildings sector forms part of the overall strategy for decarbonising. Putting a price signal on carbon will further encourage businesses and individuals to upgrade their buildings. Planning regulations should be used to monitor the expansion of the built environment. This should be evaluated in terms of carbon emissions. To combat inertia and financial constraints, creative business models such as ESCOs can play a vital role. Through good planning, the need for new-build can be reduced.

Other strategies include improved design and refurbishment standards, better urban and rural planning, and the integration of renewable energy generation into buildings.

However, the most effective method of lowering carbon emissions is improving the performance of the existing building stock (Strong, 2008). Energy legislation and Building Regulations need to be more transparent and relevant at both the national and international level, leading to a more closely-regulated construction industry.

In promoting zero carbon buildings and technologies, it is imperative to ensure that fuel poverty and build quality do not deteriorate.

However, of equal importance is the need for action at a scale that matches the magnitude of the challenge of climate change. British homes, offices, business and industry can be refurbished to decrease their impact on the environment and decrease fuel bills.

Through careful selection of building materials a national campaign can have minimal impact on the environment. In fact wise material selection can enable the building stock to lock away carbon, helping to reduce atmospheric levels of CO_2 and therefore helping to decrease the chance of hitting a tipping point in our climate system.

References

Adeyeye, K., M. Osmani & C. Brown (2007) "Energy conservation & building design: the environmental legislation push and pull factors", *Structural Survey*, 25(5), pp. 375–390.

Arup (2008) *Low Carbon Technical Project Management and Consultancy*, Building Fabric Technical Review for the Carbon Trust, London: Arup.

Association of Environmentally Conscious Builders (AECB) (2006) *Minimising CO2 Emissions from New Homes: A Review of How we Predict and Measure Energy Use in Homes*, London: AECB.

Baker, N. & M. Standeven (1996) "Thermal comfort for free-running buildings", *Energy and Buildings*, 23(3), pp. 175–182.

Banfill P.F.G. & A.D. Peacock (2007) "Energy-efficient new housing – the UK reaches for sustainability", *Building Research & Information*, 35(4), pp. 426–436.

Berge, B. (2009) *The Ecology of Building Materials*, Oxford: Architectural Press.

Boardman, B. *et al*. (2005) *40% House*, Oxford: Environmental Change Institute, University of Oxford.

Bordass, W., R. Cohen & J. Field (2004) "Energy performance of non-domestic buildings: closing the credibility gap", Building Performance Congress. Available at: http://www.usablebuildings.co.uk/Pages/Unprotected/EnPerfNDBuildings.pdf [Live: March 2010].

Bull, J. (2008) *New Tricks with Old Bricks – how reusing old buildings can cut carbon emissions*, London: Empty Homes Agency.

Caleb (2008) "Non-Domestic Buildings – the missed opportunity", Caleb Management Services Ltd. Available at: http://www.chrispearson.net/epic_downloads/non_domestic_buildings.pdf [Live: March 2010].

Clarke *et al*. (2006) "The role of built environment energy efficiency in a sustainable UK energy economy", Energy Systems Research Unit, Department of Mechanical Engineering, University of Strathclyde, Glasgow. Available at: http://www.foresight.gov.uk/Energy/The_role__of_built_environemnt_energy_efficiency_in_a_sustainable_UK_energy_economy.pdf [Live: March 2010].

Colley, J. (2009) "Pay as you save", *Construct Ireland: for a sustainable future*, 9(4). Available at: http://constructireland.ie/Vol-4-Issue-9/Articles/Policy/Construct-Ireland-proposal-to-energy-upgrade-the-majority-of-Irish-buildings.html [Live: March 2010].

Department for Business Enterprise and Regulatory Reform (BERR) (2007) *Energy Trends*, September 2007, London: BERR.

Department for Communities and Local Government (DCLG) (2007a) *Building a Greener Future: policy statement,* July 2007, Wetherby: Communities and Local Government Publications.

DCLG (2007b) *English House Condition Survey 2005, Annual Report: decent homes and decent places*, Wetherby: Communities and Local Government Publications.

DCLG (2008) *Greener homes for the future*, London: DCLG.

Department of Energy and Climate Change (DECC) (2009a) *Digest of United Kingdom Energy Statistics 2009*, London: The Stationery Office (TSO).

DECC (2009b) "Energy consumption in the UK: Overall data tables, 2009 update", URN 09D/452, July 2009. Available at: http://www.decc.gov.uk/en/content/cms/statistics/publications/ecuk/ecuk.aspx [Live: March 2010].

DECC (2010) "UK Climate Change Sustainable Development Indicator: 2009 greenhouse gas emissions, provisional figures and 2008 greenhouse gas emissions, final figures by fuel type and end-user", statistical release, 25 March 2010. Available at: http://www.decc.gov.uk/en/content/cms/statistics/climate_change/gg_emissions/uk_emissions/2009_prov/2009_prov.aspx [Live: March 2010).

Department for the Environment, Farming and Rural Affairs (Defra) (2001) *Digest of Environmental Statistics*, London: Her Majesty's Stationery Office (HMSO).

Environmental Audit Committee (EAC – House of Commons) (2005) *Housing: Building a Sustainable Future*, First Report of Session 2004–05, Volume 1: Report together with formal minutes, London: TSO.

Essex, J. (2010) Reclaimed Materials Manager, Bioregional [personal communication], 19 January 2010.

Fiennes, J. (2009) "Homes and communities offer the biggest possible savings: how do we make 40% energy savings by 2020?", Department for Communities and Local Government. Presentation given at "The Great British Refurb Workshop: 40% energy reduction in homes and communities by 2020 – Can we do it?", London, 8 December 2009. Available at: http://sticerd.lse.ac.uk/textonly/LSEHousing/Events/Great_British_Refurb/session1/john_fiennes.pdf [Live: March 2010].

Gann, D. (2000) *Building Innovation: Complex Constructs in a Changing World,* London: Thomas Telford.

Grigg, P. (2004) *Assessment of energy efficiency impact of Building Regulations compliance*, report for the Energy Savings Trust and Energy Efficiency Partnership for Homes, Client Report No 219683, 10 November 2004, Watford: Building Research Establishment.

Hammond, G. & C. Jones (2008) "Inventory of Carbon and Energy", Version 1.6a, Sustainable Research Team, Department of Mechanical Engineering, University of Bath, UK.

Healey, J. (2009) "Zero Carbon Standards (New Buildings)", written statement by the Minister for Housing and Planning, 24 November 2009. Available at: http://www.communities.gov.uk/statements/corporate/zerocarbonstandards [Live: March 2010].

Helweg-Larson, T. & J. Bull (2007) *zerocarbonbritain: an alternative energy strategy*, Machynlleth: Centre for Alternative Technology.

Jowsey, E. & J. Grant (2009) "Greening the Existing Housing Stock", faculty of Development and Society, Sheffield Hallam University. Available at: http://www.prres.net/papers/Jowsey_Greening_The_Existing_

Housing_Stock.pdf [Live: March 2010].

Lazarus, N. (2005) "Potential for reducing the environmental impact of construction materials", commissioned by Bioregional Development Group, January 2005. Available at: http://www.bioregional.com/files/publications/Z-squaredImpactMaterials_Jan05.pdf [Live: March 2010].

Mackay, D. (2008) *Sustainable Energy – Without the Hot Air*, Cambridge: UIT Cambridge.

Mayor of London (2008) *The London Plan: Spatial Development Strategy for Greater London (Consolidated with Alterations since 2004)*, February 2008, London: Greater London Authority.

Merton Council (2009) "Merton Rule – the exact policy text", Merton Council, 27 November 2009 [online]. Available at: http://www.merton.gov.uk/living/planning/planningpolicy/mertonrule/merton_rule_the_exact_policy_.htm [Live: March 2010].

National Audit Office (NAO) (2007) *Housing Market Renewal*, report by the Controller and Auditor General, November 2007, London: TSO.

Office of the Deputy Prime Minister (ODPM) (2003) *Sustainable Communities: Building for the Future*, Wetherby: ODPM.

Osami, M. & A. O'Reilly (2009) "Feasibility of zero carbon homes in England by 2016: A house builder's perspective", *Building & Environment*, 44(9), pp. 1917–1924.

Power, A. & K. Mumford (2003) *Boom or Abandonment: Resolving Housing Conflicts in Cities,* Coventry: Chartered Institute of Housing.

Power, A. (2008) "Does demolition or refurbishment of old and inefficient homes help to increase our environmental, social and economic viability?", *Energy Policy*, 36(12), pp. 4487–4501.

Roberts, S. (2008) "Altering existing buildings in the UK", *Energy Policy*, 36, pp. 4482–4486.

Sanders, C. & M. Phillipson (2006) "Review of Differences between Measured and Theoretical Energy Savings for Insulation Measures", Centre for Research on Indoor Climate and Health, Glasgow Caledonian University. Available at: http://www.decc.gov.uk/en/content/cms/what_we_do/consumers/saving_energy/analysis/analysis.aspx [Live: March 2010].

Strong, D. (2008) "The UK Approach to Sustainable Refurbishment", Opinion piece written for *Daylight & Architecture* magazine, October 2008. Available at: http://www.inbuilt.co.uk/media/232443/uk_approach_sustainable_refurbishment_oct08.pdf [Live: March 2010].

Thorpe, D. (2010) *Sustainable Home Refurbishment: The Earthscan expert guide to retrofitting homes for efficiency*, London: EarthScan

Turcu, C. (2005–2007) "Comparing the sustainability of demolition and refurbishment at LSE", PhD research on HMR Pathfinder, Centre for Analysis of Social Exclusion (CASE), London School of Economics and Political Science.

Twinn, C. (2009) "Energy usage in new and existing buildings", presentation given at the **zero**carbon**britain**2030 Buildings and the Built Environment seminar, 5 May 2009 [unpublished].

WWF Germany (2009) *Blueprint Germany: a strategy for a climate safe 2050*, Berlin: WWF Germany.

Figure sources

Copyright (2010) **zero**carbon**britain**2030. Based on data in Department of Energy and Climate Change (DECC) (2009) "Energy consumption in the UK: Overall data tables, 2009 update", URN 09D/452, July 2009 (Table 1.2: Non-transport energy consumption by end use1 1990, 2000 and 2005 to 2007). Available at: http://www.decc.gov.uk/en/content/cms/statistics/publications/ecuk/ecuk.aspx

Copyright (2010) **zero**carbon**britain**2030. Based on data in DECC (2009) "Energy consumption in the UK: Overall data tables, 2009 update", URN 09D/452, July 2009 (Table 1.2: Non-transport energy consumption by end use1 1990, 2000 and 2005 to 2007). Available at: http://www.decc.gov.uk/en/content/cms/statistics/publications/ecuk/ecuk.aspx

Chapter 5
Transport

Introduction

In **zero**carbon**britain**2030 electricity will be the new fuel of choice. The roads and rails will buzz with the sound of power lines, batteries and fuel cells. We will be fitter and more active; our towns and cities will be alive with the sound of people talking on the walk or cycle to work. We will have better and faster train services and we will waste less time travelling by working more efficiently. We will holiday closer to home and use teleconferencing for business meetings, all but eliminating the need for aviation. Cargo will travel around the world on ships powered by solar panels, sails and sustainable fuels. We will not only have a zero carbon transport system, but we will be healthier and happier too. Sounds good? Well, how do we get there?

This chapter outlines the transport challenge, highlights key interventions, and presents a vision of a decarbonised transport system.

The transport challenge

The transport sector is one of the most difficult to tackle in terms of reducing emissions. Measures are often more expensive than interventions in other sectors, added to which there are strong links between economic growth and growth in transport demand. While the UK is broadly on track to meet its Kyoto targets, transport is the only sector where emissions have continued to rise, cancelling out many of the savings made elsewhere.

Since 1990 CO_2 emissions from road transport have increased by 11%, while they have reduced from the energy supply industry by 12% and business emissions by 19% (Baker *et al.*, 2009). This is extremely frustrating, as tackling the transportation issue offers some of the greatest societal benefits of all decarbonisation measures, simultaneously improving the quality of our towns and cities, tackling social exclusion, bringing economic efficiency, and of course providing health and environmental benefits (see Shaw *et al.*, 2003; Batterbury, 2003).

Each UK citizen spends an average of 376 hours per year travelling, covering a distance of just under 7,000 miles. While this distance has increased dramatically over the past 50 years, the time spent travelling has remained largely constant throughout history (Department for Transport [DfT], 2008a). Worldwide, people spend approximately between 1 to 1.5 hours per day travelling, and devote around 10–15% of their income to do so (Jackson *et al.*, 2006).

The transport sector currently accounts for around 24% of UK domestic emissions, producing approximately 130 million tonnes of CO_2 per annum. Including the UK's share

Fig. 5.1 UK transport CO₂ emissions

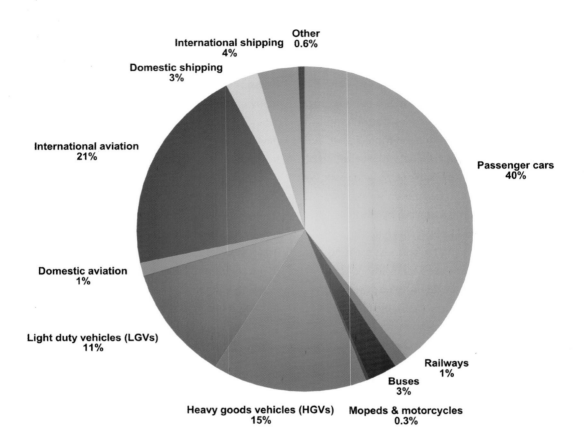

International shipping 4%

Other 0.6%

Domestic shipping 3%

International aviation 21%

Passenger cars 40%

Domestic aviation 1%

Railways 1%

Light duty vehicles (LGVs) 11%

Buses 3%

Heavy goods vehicles (HGVs) 15%

Mopeds & motorcycles 0.3%

UK CO₂ emissions from domestic and international transport by source, 2006.
"Other" includes liquefied petroleum gas (LPG) emissions (all vehicles); other road vehicle engines, and other mobile sources and machinery. Emissions from rail travel given above are from diesel trains only. The total CO₂ emissions from transport in 2006 equalled 173 million tonnes.
Source: DfT (2008).

of international aviation and shipping adds another 43 million tonnes, and increases transport's overall share of the nation's total CO_2 emissions (DfT, 2008b). A breakdown of the UK's transport emissions by mode is shown in Figure 5.1.

The figure shows that passenger cars and international aviation dominate the carbon emissions from transport, and many policies rightly target these areas. In contrast, public transport modes such as bus and rail have minor carbon impacts. However, emissions from heavy goods vehicles (HGVs) and light goods vehicles (LGVs) also contribute a significant proportion to total emissions, and more attention must be paid to tackling emissions from freight transport.

What is not shown in Figure 5.1 is the non-carbon greenhouse gas impacts. For example, the total climate change impact from aviation in the short term is estimated to be two to four times greater than that of carbon alone. This is due primarily to the release of water vapour and NO_x at high altitudes where they have a short-term warming effect which they do not have when released at ground level.[1] The exact amount of extra warming caused by these is unclear, due largely to uncertainty over their effect on the formation of cirrus clouds (Royal Commission on Environmental Pollution, 2002).

As shown in Figure 5.1, passenger cars are responsible for the largest proportion of CO_2 emissions, at 39.7%. These trips can be broken down further into trip type and trip length, as demonstrated in Figure 5.2.

As might be expected, commuting and

Fig. 5.2 CO_2 emissions from household car journeys in Great Britain

Fig. 5.2a

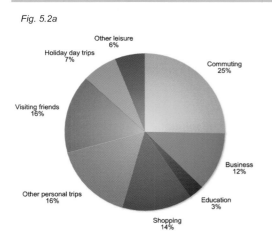

Fig. 5.2b

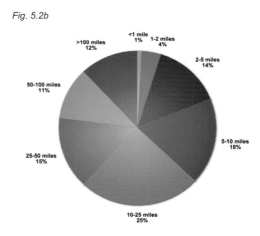

CO_2 emissions from household car journeys in Great Britain by (a) journey purpose (2006) and (b) journey length (2002/2006 average).
Source: Based on data from DfT (2008).

[1] Nitrogen oxides NO and NO_2, are indirect greenhouse gases. That is, they give rise to greenhouse gases via various spontaneous processes of atmospheric chemistry.

business trips make up a significant proportion of emissions (Figure 5.2a). However, the largest share is due to leisure trips such as holidays and visiting friends. Therefore, although commuting tends to be the least efficient form of transportation due to low occupancy rates, attention must also be paid to leisure travel if transport emissions are to be effectively reduced.

Travel linked to education makes up only 3% of emissions. This may at first seem surprising, given the large amount of attention and funds devoted nationally to developing school travel plans. However, tackling the school run is still worthwhile as it brings a range of other benefits such as improved health, reduced congestion, engaging children in climate change issues and developing active travel habits.

Finally, the breakdown of journey lengths shown in Figure 5.2b is perhaps the most surprising. Although approximately 70% of all car journeys are less than 5 miles long, these are responsible for a total of just 19% of carbon emissions from cars. Medium length car journeys contribute significantly to all CO_2 emissions from cars. As other modes of transport including HGVs, LGVs and aircrafts all make significantly longer journeys than passenger cars, the majority of carbon emissions from transport can be shown to be from medium- and long-distance trips. Therefore, the key to tackling carbon emissions from transport is either to reduce the number of medium- and long-distance trips themselves, or to eliminate the emissions that they produce through technological change.

FORECAST GROWTH IN TRANSPORT DEMAND

Transport's share of carbon emissions is forecast to grow as other sectors begin to decarbonise. In a "business-as-usual" scenario, transport demand is predicted to continue increasing in the future. The Eddington Transport Study forecast an increase of 28% in vehicle kilometres between 2003 and 2025 (Eddington, 2006).

Similarly, aviation is one of the fastest growing sectors of the world economy, and has grown globally at nearly 9% per annum. In the UK, the Department for Transport forecast that there will be roughly 200% more air passengers by 2030 based on 2007 levels (DfT, 2009a). If this comes to pass, it represents a serious threat to combating climate change because, as is described later in the chapter, aviation is an area in which the technological options for decarbonisation are limited.

Transport solutions

Many of the solutions to the transport challenge are not in themselves transport measures. These include improving the urban environment for example through better land use planning, so that less transportation is needed, and reducing society's consumption of material goods, thus reducing freight transport. Car-free cities such as Masdar, Abu Dhabi, in the United

Arab Emirates, show that with intelligent and integrated planning, transport emissions can be all but eliminated using existing technologies. Changes to the urban environment typically occur at around 1% per annum so the process of adapting our towns and cities to be car-free will take some time.

The majority of the transport carbon savings in **zero**carbon**britain**2030 come from efficiency savings and new fuels. Behavioural change also has a key role to play and there must be more focus on targeting the use of the car for medium- and long-range trips, where the majority of transport carbon emissions arise.

A key advantage to promoting and creating new markets for efficient vehicles in the UK is that this will encourage their uptake around the world and achieve far greater emissions reductions than we could achieve in the UK alone. As such, we first explore alternatives to petrol and diesel fuels, before examining various modes of transport and alternative behaviour and business models.

Fuels

Electricity

Electricity is well positioned to be the dominant transport fuel of the future. 2010 sees the roll-out of several breakthrough electric vehicles and, as discussed in subsequent sections, electricity also has a major role to play for rail, and other modes. In 2008, the Government published the findings of Professor Julia King's *King Review of Low Carbon Cars*. This provided an excellent review of the possibilities for low carbon road transport, and suggested policy measures that would encourage the uptake of such vehicles. It stated:

"Fully electric, battery-powered vehicles – if using zero or low-carbon electricity – offer the most direct opportunity to decarbonise road transport over the longer term… Recent developments in battery technology raise the expectation that, in the longer term, batteries could offer acceptable range, performance and recharging time".
(King, 2008)

The Government is to provide support for the development of battery electric cars through subsidies of £2000–5000 per vehicle, and up to £20 million to provide the recharging infrastructure for a trial group of cities (DfT, 2008c). The Mayor of London's *Electric Vehicle Delivery Plan* for London provides an excellent case study showing measures local authorities can implement to support the roll-out of electric vehicles (Mayor of London, 2009).

The Government also supports the EU's emissions target for cars of 95g CO_2/km by 2020, and hopes to see the introduction of similar targets for vans. It has set a UK goal of 130g CO_2/km by 2011 for all cars owned by the public sector (DfT, 2008c). This, however, is a weak target, as today's most efficient cars can already do considerably better, with several emitting less than 100g CO_2/km (Department of Energy and Climate Change [DECC], 2009).

Electric vehicles are currently confined to niche markets. This will remain the case until batteries with a higher energy density are commercially available. In order to ensure that hybrid and plug-in hybrids are cost-effective for consumers, battery technologies must continue to develop.

Lead-acid batteries are very heavy and have

Box 5.1 Recharging batteries

A company called Better Place has developed an innovative yet simple way to overcome the recharging hurdle for electric vehicles and increase their range. Instead of waiting for the vehicle to charge, drivers, for a small fee, are able to pull into a service station and exchange their used battery for a fully-charged one.

Better Place is currently building the first such network in Israel, with the electric vehicles to be developed by Renault-Nissan. As the upfront cost of the battery is no longer paid by the consumer, the price of these electric vehicles should be similar to conventional gasoline models.

Box 5.2 Peak lithium and peak platinum?

Lithium

Concerns over a peak in lithium supplies similar to a peak in conventional oil are unfounded. The majority of peak lithium material originates from William Tahil, who releases reports under the name of Meridian International Research. However, his research has been widely discredited, and his credibility is not helped by his continued adherence to a paper he wrote claiming the destruction of the twin towers on 9/11 was caused by nuclear bombs (Tahil, 2006). Major car companies have commissioned a range of professional consultants to investigate lithium supply trends and are continuing to invest huge amounts of money into lithium battery-based cars.

In contrast to the peak lithium claims, lithium is extremely abundant. Current reserves come from a few countries with extremely cheap extraction costs. However, a wealth of other sources exists, and new extraction methods are continually being developed. In contrast to oil, lithium exploration and extraction is in its infancy (see SQM, 2009). Greater extraction costs are likely to make little difference to battery prices, as lithium itself only accounts for around 1% of the final battery price. In addition, lithium can be recycled from old batteries. This is not currently profitable, but is often required on environmental grounds.

Platinum

Platinum on the other hand, a key ingredient in hydrogen fuel cells, is a very rare and expensive metal, with the largest deposits found in South Africa, Russia and Canada. However the hydrogen industry is currently investigating materials to replace platinum in hydrogen vehicles' fuel cells (see Reuters, 2007). The amount of platinum required to make a fuel cell is constantly reducing and platinum can also be recovered from the fuel cell at the end of its lifecycle.

a low energy density. The current generation of hybrid vehicles such as the Toyota Prius use nickel metal hydride (NiMH) batteries, which can offer a range of up to 120 miles. Lithium ion (Li-ion) batteries, currently used in laptops and mobile phones, can offer ranges of 250–300 miles per charge, but their cost is currently a major barrier (King, 2008).

Further development of battery technology is likely to provide increased range, lower cost and shorter recharge times. Possible future battery types include Li-ion polymer, Li-sulphur, air power, and ultra-capacitors, which provide exceptionally quick recharge times (ibid.).

Under the current grid mix, electric vehicles' power consumption represents just over a 50%

CO_2 saving compared to petrol/diesel vehicles. This will increase as the energy sector continues to decarbonise. Analysis by E4Tech for the DfT's (2007) Low Carbon Innovation Strategy suggests that a total conversion of the UK car and taxi fleet to electricity would equate to 16% of current electricity demand.

This additional 16% in energy demand could necessitate the construction of additional generation capacity. However, with the use of smart meters and smart charging for electric cars, electric cars may require little or no additional electricity capacity. Cars could be set to charge when demand for electricity is low – for example, during the night, preventing any increase in peak demand.

Box 5.3 Using electric vehicles to balance the electricity grid

Electric vehicle batteries can help to balance a renewable electricity grid by providing a significant variable load. Smart chargers can be programmed to draw electricity when it is cheap (such as during the night) when a heavily wind dependent electricity system will be generating excess electricity that might otherwise have been dumped. By this means, it is not only possible to run a significant number of electric vehicles without having to build any more electricity generation capacity, but electric vehicles can also make building renewables more cost effective and better able to compete financially against fossil fuels by enabling more of the energy they generate to be used.

Another suggestion is that the grid should be able to actually draw on the energy stored in the batteries of electric cars, allowing the electric vehicle fleet to act not just as a variable load but also as storage for the grid. This idea is called Vehicle to Grid (V2G). However, this is unlikely to be realised for several reasons. Due to the high cost of electric vehicle batteries and their limited cycle life it is better to preserve them for as long as possible for the high grade energy use needed for driving, and use other storage methods such as pumped storage and extra generation capacity as grid backup.

It is also unlikely to be cost effective for the consumer. There is a large gap between the cost at which electricity can be bought from the grid, and the price at which it can be sold back, as only a small proportion of the cost of purchased electricity covers the cost of its generation. Most of the price covers the cost of distribution, transmission and administration. As such, we estimate that the major contribution that electric vehicles will be able to make to balancing the grid will be through providing a variable load and V2G systems will only have niche applications.

Hydrogen

Hydrogen-fuelled vehicles fall into two categories – combustion and fuel cell:

- **Combustion:** hydrogen is used instead of fossil fuels in a modified internal combustion engine. This produces a very clean exhaust, consisting largely of water vapour. Some pollutants also remain, although in a greatly reduced form.
- **Fuel cell:** hydrogen is mixed with oxygen within a fuel cell, directly generating electricity. This is used to drive highly efficient electric drive motors.

On the surface, hydrogen appears to provide a silver bullet to the problem of transport carbon emissions. It is one of the most common elements on Earth, and its tailpipe emissions are zero carbon. However, pure hydrogen is not found on Earth, and it must be created through a process that uses energy, such as natural gas or electricity. Hence, as with electricity, it is not a fuel in itself; instead, it is only an energy carrier.

Due to the energy losses involved in the production of hydrogen, it will never exceed the efficiency of using electricity directly. As noted in the *King Review of Low Carbon Cars* (King, 2008), hydrogen faces a number of other challenges, and is unlikely to displace batteries as the favoured technology for a low carbon transport system.

Running cars on hydrogen made from natural gas produces a 50–60% CO_2 saving compared to running them on fossil fuels (King, 2008), but this method still leaves a considerable

"The use of hydrogen cars would require major new supply infrastructure. Use of hydrogen in captive bus and car fleets (where the need for diffuse refuelling is limited) is therefore the most likely intermediate step. A large supply network is only likely to be developed if hydrogen emerges as a fuel that can be widely supplied in a low CO_2 way and at a reasonable cost, and if developments in battery technologies do not provide a more cost-effective electric alternative".
(King, 2008)

amount of carbon in the transport system and must therefore be discounted in our ***zerocarbonbritain2030*** scenario.

Under the current grid mix, running vehicles on hydrogen produced by electrolysis produces slightly more CO_2 than running them on petrol or diesel (ibid.).[2] This situation will improve as the electricity sector decarbonises. In the ***zerocarbonbritain2030*** scenario in which the grid is completely decarbonised, electrically-derived hydrogen will be effectively carbon neutral.

Other methods of producing hydrogen, for example from algae, are currently being investigated, although it is too early to tell if and when these will become commercially viable.

Using a number of assumptions, King (2008) estimates that running vehicles on hydrogen

[2] Electrolysis is the process of using electricity to split water into hydrogen and oxygen

produced by electricity (electrolysis) requires twice as much electricity as running them on battery electric power. Converting the entire car and taxi fleet is estimated to require an additional 30% on top of current electricity demand, rather than the 16% required for batteries (ibid.).

The major advantage that hydrogen has over batteries it that it is able to store more energy for less weight and so it is useful for applications where a very large amount of power is needed, or when stopping to exchange or recharge batteries is difficult. It is therefore predicted that hydrogen will be limited to several significant niche markets including HGVs, buses, and possibly taxi fleets. However, the conversion of diesel buses to grid-connected trolleybuses offers a cheaper, widely-proven alternative.

Biofuels

Biofuels are plant crops used as fuel. Plants take up carbon from the air while growing and then release it back when they decompose or burn. However in reality biofuels have some climate impact, from fossil fuel energy and nitrogen fertiliser used in their production and sometimes from the clearing of land in order to grow them. Transport biofuels currently consist almost entirely of bioethanol made from sugar or starch, which replaces petrol, and biodiesel made from vegetable oil, which replaces diesel.

In general the use of bioenergy for transport is highly controversial and raises complex issues, many of which are inescapably international.

The greenhouse gas impact of many biofuels has been seriously questioned and, when all factors are taken into account, it is unclear whether most transport biofuels currently in use have better or worse greenhouse gas balances than the fossil fuels they are replacing. This is partially due to the emissions from the growing process and partly due to their association with destructive land use change such as deforestation, either directly through displacement, or indirectly through price mechanisms (Fargione et al., 2008; Searchinger et al., 2008).

Growing biofuel feedstock in large quantities also has other environmental impacts, including intensive water use and negative biodiversity effects. The former is clearly more of a problem in regions that suffer from water shortages. Many authorities also voice concerns over the impacts of biofuel production on global hunger. The economic relationships involved are complex and controversial as demonstrated in Box 5.4.

Biofuels made from lignocellulosic feedstock such as wood or grasses may be less plagued by some of these issues. Biofuels can be made from any biomass using currently available technology, but at the moment the process of breaking down cellulose is too expensive to compete with biofuels made from sugar or oil. However, the cost is expected to fall in the future, particularly if research breakthroughs materialise.

Lignocellulosic biofuels still have a land and

water impact and how sustainable they are will still depend on where and how they are grown. However, higher yields are available from these feedstocks, meaning land requirements are less. The feedstock can be grown on a wider variety of types of land, so should compete less with food for prime arable land. Waste can also be

used as feedstock. Such biofuels tend to have far better greenhouse gas balances than the "first generation" biofuels made from the oily, starchy or sugary fraction of crops. This is discussed further in the Land use and agriculture chapter. We use some lignocellulosic biofuels in the ***zero**carbon**britain**2030* scenario, mainly to

Box 5.4 Biofuels and hunger

In many parts of the world, particularly sub-Saharan Africa, agricultural yields are very low due to lack of investment in agricultural technologies (Food and Agriculture Organisation [FAO], 2008). There is therefore the potential in many parts of the Global South (less industrialised countries) to raise yields quite substantially for all agricultural products. It is therefore an oversimplification to imagine a straightforward trade-off between different land use products.

Although most of the world's undernourished people are themselves involved in food production (about half are small farmers), the majority of these are overall net food buyers (von Braun, 2007; FAO, 2008). Therefore, although some of the poor can gain from increased food prices, overall it is likely that increased food prices will increase hunger (ibid.). Increased demand for agricultural products such as biofuels can be expected to increase food prices.

It is disputed how much of the 2007/2008 food price crisis was caused by biofuels. The highest estimate is 75% but the majority of estimates suggest around the 30% mark, with the remainder being attributed to various other factors including increased transport and fertiliser costs due to high oil prices and compounding effects such as financial speculation (ActionAid, 2008; Heady & Fan, 2008). Food prices have subsequently fallen but are not back to pre-crisis levels (FAO, 2009).

There is some potential for the poor to gain if they can actually be involved in the production of biofuel feedstocks. Many feedstock crops such as sugar cane grow particularly well in tropical regions. Leturque and Wiggins (2009) calculate that with an oil price of around $65 a barrel, small farmers producing sugar cane or palm oil for biofuel could earn significantly more than they could generally earn from other crops. However, since biofuel feedstock production is subject to substantial economies of scale, it is likely to tend towards large-scale production and increasing mechanisation which provides little employment potential, as has been seen in countries such as Brazil with long running biofuel programmes.

There is some possibility that policy intervention may be able to counteract this. An example is the Social Fuel Seal introduced recently in Brazil which offers companies tax exemptions if they buy a proportion of their biodiesel feedstock from small farmers. There is, however, no guarantee that such schemes will be implemented, creating a significant risk that the poor may be harmed by biofuel use while receiving no counteracting benefit.

There is also a related danger of the poor losing their land if it suddenly becomes a much more valuable commodity, especially as many of the world's poor do not have formal titles to the land that they use (Cotula *et al.*, 2008). This is particularly concerning in light of the huge land grab by foreign investors that is currently occurring in many poor countries (GRAIN, 2008).

Fig. 5.3 CO_2 emissions from passenger transport

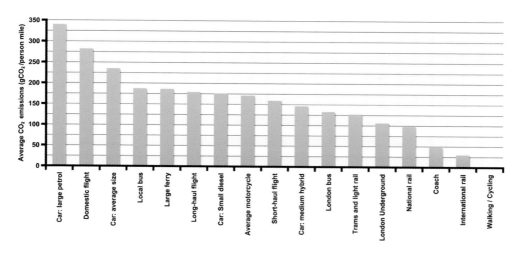

Fig. 5.3 CO_2 emissions from passenger transport

Average CO_2 emissions per passenger mile (gCO_2 / person mile) by passenger transport mode in Great Britain.
Public transport tends to be far more efficient than flights and car journeys. The average CO_2 emissions per passenger mile depends significantly on the number of passengers in each vehicle.
Source: Based on data from Defra (2008).

power the sectors for which there is currently no alternative to liquid hydrocarbon fuels. More details are given later in this chapter.

Another possibility for the future is fuel from algae, grown in large ponds. Algae are much more efficient photosynthesisers than terrestrial crops. They may be able to yield an order of magnitude more fuel energy per unit land area, than other biofuel sources as well as being able to grow in places where there is minimal competition with other land uses (Vera-Morales & Schäfer, 2009). However, for such high productivity they require more CO_2 than is present in the air and hence would need to

be fed extra CO_2 (ibid.). Flue gases from power stations have been suggested as an option, but in a decarbonised society these will be less available. Currently biofuel production from algae is too expensive to make it viable, and it has to be viewed as a speculative research project.

Passenger transport modes

As demonstrated in Figure 5.3, walking and cycling are the modes of transport which produce the least carbon emissions, with aeroplanes and cars currently producing the most. However, the carbon emissions per

Box 5.5 The use of gas for transport

Natural gas is an emerging vehicle fuel. However, it is not emissions free. Therefore, there is no natural gas used in the **zero**carbon**britain**2030 transport scenario. Biogas could also be used in small quantities in a sustainable transport system. The potential sustainable generation of biogas is discussed in the Renewables chapter.

While there is some biogas in the **zero**carbon**britain**2030 scenario, this is under huge demand. It could be used for heating, electricity, hydrogen creation or directly in vehicles. Due to the dispatchable nature of gas turbines, they are very effective at helping to manage the variability of supply of electricity with the variable demand for it. Therefore after careful consideration the primary use of biogas selected was to support grid management.

If dedicated energy crops are to be grown for transport fuel then biogas does not appear to be the best option in terms of greenhouse gases. Although much depends on the details of the case, in general growing woody biomass and turning it into liquid biofuels has a smaller greenhouse gas impact than growing wet biomass to turn into biogas. This is discussed in more detail in the Land use and agriculture chapter.

person mile of most modes depend largely on occupancy rates. This is demonstrated by the difference between London buses and local bus services elsewhere in the country, with much higher occupancy rates in London. A bus with one passenger produces far more carbon emissions per passenger mile than a car with one passenger.

In future, the absolute figures will dramatically change as alternative fuels become widespread and car efficiency standards improve. The difference between international rail and national rail is due to the Channel Tunnel being electrified and utilising French nuclear power.

To achieve a zero carbon transport system, we must find a way to eliminate emissions from all of these modes. The following discussion first considers cars and vans which can be used for a range of trip lengths, before considering modes of transport for short, intercity and international trips.

Cars and vans

Reducing the weight of the vehicle per person moved is a key way to improve efficiency and therefore reduce emissions. One way to reduce this weight is for more people to use the same vehicle, whether this be through car-sharing or high occupancy public transport such as buses, trains and coaches. Another is to reduce the weight of the vehicles themselves.

Over the past 20 years, mid-sized cars have become 20% heavier to accommodate safety features, sound-proofing and accessories (King, 2008). Reduced weight would enable the same performance to be achieved with a smaller engine. *The King Review of Low Carbon Cars* found that such "lightweighting" could offer efficiency gains of 10%, at a cost of £250–500 per vehicle, while low-rolling resistance tyres and improved aerodynamics could give potential efficiency savings of 2–4% each.

Another approach to weight saving is to make

Box 5.6 Riversimple

Riversimple, a small UK-based business, has developed a small, lightweight vehicle which demonstrates the efficiency savings that can be made through lightweight vehicle design. It provides an example of how car companies in a zero carbon future may operate. Their first vehicle was unveiled in 2009, and is designed to show what is possible with today's technology.

The Riversimple approach has five key elements:

Environmental vehicle design: A lightweight electric vehicle is constructed from carbon composites and powered by hydrogen fuel cells.

Open source design and development: Riversimple invites the community to help develop its vehicles, by making its designs available under open source license through the independent 40 Fires Foundation, thus encouraging adoption of the technology as widely as possible.

Service concept: cars are leased, not bought. This aligns the interests of the manufacturer with those of the consumer and of the environment – everyone wants cars that have a long lifespan with maximum efficiency and minimum materials usage. This rewards longevity and low running costs rather than obsolescence and high running costs.

Distributed manufacturing: The economies of scale of carbon composite frames are very different from those of steel-bodied vehicles. Riversimple vehicles are likely to be built in small factories producing 5,000 units per year. This allows for considerable local variation in the car.

Broader ownership: The corporate structure of Riversimple is designed so that ownership is shared between all stakeholders in the enterprise, including the environment, and they share in the benefits of a successful business.

Fig. 5.4 The Riversimple vehicle.
Source: Riversimple LLP.

a step-change in vehicle design. Reducing the weight of an individual component produces positive knock-on effects. If one component gets lighter, the car needs less power for the same performance, and so this enables further weight reductions in the power train.

It takes over a decade for the entire national car stock to be replaced (ibid.). Thus, in order to eliminate emissions by 2030, strong incentives to promote the uptake of low carbon vehicles must

be implemented as a matter of urgency. However, taking into account the full lifecycle cost of cars, there will nevertheless be a significant carbon cost to replacing the vehicle fleet.

There are currently over 30 million cars and light vans in the UK (DfT, 2008a). The embedded carbon used in the manufacture of each one is between 3000 and 5000kg (Pearce, 2007). The embedded carbon in replacing the car stock in the UK would therefore be between 90 and 150 million tonnes – roughly equivalent to a year's worth of carbon emissions from all transport operations in the UK. While this figure is large, the embedded energy from manufacturing and the disposal or recycling of a car is small compared to the carbon emitted in use.

If initiatives such as those of Riversimple are successful, and with an adequate vehicle lifespan to reduce the embodied energy costs, it would be beneficial to develop modular designs that allow cars to switch between fuel sources such as battery and hydrogen power. Such systems are already in development, using series hybrid technology. At present this uses a small diesel engine to charge an electric battery linked directly to the drive train. In the future, the diesel engine could be replaced with a large battery or hydrogen fuel cells (see Box 5.6).

LOCAL MODES OF TRANSPORT

In **zero**carbon**britain**2030, trips must be shorter, and it is therefore essential to develop an effective low carbon local transport system. This will not only cut carbon emissions, but allow us to become more connected to our local communities and remove the frustrations of sitting in traffic jams. There are also considerable health and local air quality advantages to promoting sustainable local travel.

Local transport also acts as the first step in long-distance public transport, such as taking the bus or cycling to the train station. Creating high-quality local transport solutions has the potential to unlock more sustainable long distance travel. Currently 19% of car passenger emissions come from trips under 5 miles long.

Walking and cycling

Walking and cycling are the most environmentally- and socially-friendly forms of travel, and should be at the forefront of local transport solutions. Walking trips in particular often form the link between other transport modes and it is vital that towns and cities develop a pleasant, high-quality walking environment as the first step towards developing a zero carbon transport system.

The bicycle is 'the only vehicle that addresses all the liabilities of the oil dependent car' (Horton, 2006): it alleviates congestion; lowers pollution; reduces obesity; increases physical fitness; and is affordable for billions of people. As such, increasing cycling levels must be seen as a key component in realising a more sustainable transport system, as well as being at the heart of "joined-up" policymaking – tackling a range of issues including public health, the environment, land use, freedom and transport (The European Network for Cycling Expertise [ENCE], 1999). The UK currently has one of the lowest levels of bike use in Europe (see Rietveld & Daniel, 2004).

One method of encouraging bicycle use may be to encourage the use of electric bicycles, which enable people to get fit at their own pace; so that they can gradually decrease the amount they use the motor. The low weight keeps the electricity required to a minimum and on average electric bicycles use only about 1.3 KWh per 100 km (Cherry *et al.*, 2007). Motors between 200W and 700W are common internationally. In the EU, wattages tend to be at the lower end because a bicycle with a motor rated above 250 watts is categorised as a moped, requiring road tax and insurance.

Guthrie (2001) found that owners of electric bicycles were travelling an average of 1200 miles per annum on their bikes, ten times more than the owners of conventional bicycles. Only 14% of journeys were for leisure, a much lower percentage than that for conventional bicycles, suggesting that the motor was encouraging the use of the bicycle as a more serious means of transport. 23% of those surveyed had replaced a car with an electric bicycle, 38% used the electric bicycle for commuting to work when they had previously used a car, and 42% used the electric bicycle for shopping trips for which they had previously used a car (ibid.).

Trams and Electric Light Rail

In cities where tram systems have been installed, trams are generally very popular. Being electrified, they are a potential form of zero carbon transport. Electric Light Rail is another option. It has a lower capacity and lower speed than heavy rail and metro systems, but a higher capacity and higher speed than street-running tram systems.

The costs of most light rail systems range from £8–50 million per mile, depending on the extent of tunnelling and elevated sections that are required. For comparison, new motorways cost approximately £29m a mile, and the M25 widening scheme is expected to cost a staggering £79m per mile (Chester & Horvarth, 2009).

The development of tram and light rail projects typically involve long time frames, and the high capital cost is often a major barrier. However, such systems should undoubtedly form part of effective local transport solutions.

Trolleybuses

Trolleybuses are a well established form of zero carbon transport, with over 360 systems currently in operation worldwide (Bell, 2006). They work by drawing electricity from overhead wires using spring-loaded trolley poles. Recent technological improvements include dual-fuelling and the installation of batteries or super-capacitors which allow the buses to run "off-wire" for considerable distances.

The UK once had 50 such systems in operation, but these were gradually removed. The last to be removed was that in Bradford in 1972. However, the Leeds tBus is set to be the first trolleybus to be reinstated in Britain, marking a welcome return for this mode of zero carbon transport. This approach is likely to have lower lifecycle costs than using batteries, and could be used in the development of Bus Rapid Transport systems.

Personalised Rapid Transit

Personalised Rapid Transit (PRT) is a public transportation concept that offers on-demand, non-stop transportation, using small, independent vehicles on a network of specially-built guideways. The concept has been considered and trialled since the 1960's with a new pilot project built at London Heathrow Airport based on the ULTra (Urban Light Transport) model, and larger-scale projects currently in planning stage for cities around the world including Masdar.

Buses

Bus use has been declining in most of the UK, with the notable exception of London, which has seen substantial investment in bus services. However, if buses are to assist the move towards a zero carbon transport system, incentives must be provided for their use, as increased service without increased uptake will simply raise carbon emissions.

Transport for London (TfL) recently unveiled a new range of single- and double-decker hybrid buses, with over 350 to be in operation by 2011. TfL (2009) state that the new hybrid buses will produce 40% less CO_2 emissions than conventional buses.

INTERCITY MODES

Trains

Rail use has been growing steadily in the UK, and trains now carry more passengers than at any time since 1946, on a network around half the size of that at its peak in the early 20th Century. Following the "Beeching Axe" of the 1960s, the network was reduced in a failed effort to cut costs. The closure of branch lines, which had acted as feeder services to the main lines, led to further reductions in revenue.

Some of the lines were uneconomic, but even if that is regarded as the only priority, it is widely recognised that Beeching went too far (DfT, 2009b), and some of the lines have since been reopened. In 2009, the Association of Train Operating Companies (ATOC) called for a total of 14 lines and 40 stations to be reopened. In some cases however, lines cannot be reopened due to housing developments and other land use changes.

From the emissions perspective, it is vital that rail services are well utilised, as the carbon emissions from an empty train are far higher than for any car. In addition, rail infrastructure has an embedded carbon footprint which may be greater than the carbon emitted in operation. Embodied energy is a major component of rail infrastructure, due to staffing, stations, ticketing and other supporting systems. For new lines, the construction of new track brings further embodied energy costs.

Rail works are a lengthy undertaking, with even modest projects such as new stations taking around 3 to 5 years to complete. In addition, as with most transport infrastructure, major rail projects are expensive. London's CrossRail link is estimated to cost £16 billion, while the upgrade of Reading station is variously quoted at between £425 million and £1 billion.

Rail electrification: Less than 35% of the

UK rail network is currently electrified, which compares poorly to most other European nations. Electrification of the rail network is a vital component in moving rail towards zero carbon. At present an electric train emits 20–35% less carbon per passenger mile than a diesel train, and this advantage will increase over time as the power generation mix becomes less carbon intensive.

Electric trains also have other advantages over diesel-powered trains. They are 35% cheaper to operate, and can provide greater capacity and reliability. They are also lighter, consequently causing less track damage, and are 20% cheaper to purchase (DfT, 2009c).

In 2009's *Low Carbon Transport: A Greener Future* (DfT, 2009d), the Government performed a U-turn and agreed that there is a good case for electrifying more of the rail network. In the *Rail Electrification* document that followed shortly afterwards (DfT, 2009c), the Government stated that electrification has a central role to play in the next phase of rail modernisation, and announced two major electrification schemes – the Great Western Main Line, and Liverpool to Manchester.

A key barrier to change is the long life of rail rolling stock, which typically lasts for 20–40 years, as well as the cost of electrifying the routes. The West Coast Mainline will cost £1.1 billion, although this will be recouped through lower running costs after 40 years (DfT, 2009c).

The Government should move ahead with electrifying another major diesel route, the Midland Main Line between London and Sheffield, and investigate other potential routes as fast as possible. Ultimately, in order to create a zero carbon Britain, the entire rail network will need to be electrified.

The increase in overall energy demand would be negligble, with current UK rail using some 50 times less energy than UK road vehicles. In 2007 the UK's railways used 0.64 million tonnes of oil to account for around 4% of passenger kilometres, compared to 29 million tonnes used by cars, vans, and taxis which accounted for 80% of passenger kilometres (DfT, 2008a).

Coaches

Coaches not only use less energy per passenger mile than do trains, but in addition the UK already has an extensive road and motorway network. Per passenger, coaches take up less than thirteen times the space of cars on motorways, greatly easing current congestion.

However, coach journeys are currently slow, requiring the rapid development of an improved system to overcome this. One possibility is to convert one lane in each direction on the UK's busiest motorways into a dedicated coach lane. Some 200 coaches could continuously circle the M25, while other services could travel up and down the M1 and M6, along with orbital coaches for Birmingham and Manchester (Storkey, 2007). Well placed Park & Ride sites could play a key role in gathering trips for the coach network, although care must be taken to minimise congestion around the coachway stops.

Public transport should be extended or improved to transform existing motorway service stations into coach stations. Waiting times could be reduced to a few minutes, making it quicker to travel by coach than car for most journeys. Coaches could also be battery electric vehicles, of perhaps 100kW each, with overhead cables installed on some sections of the dedicated coach lanes for long-distance routes.

Such a network could be developed very quickly. The infrastructure is already largely in place, and could be operational in around 5 years. It would also be a very cheap transport infrastructure measure, costing around £200 million to set up a scheme around the M25 and around £70 million for the Birmingham Orbital.

The success of such a coach network would require a substantial behavioural change. It would also be a gamble for the Government, as it requires a "big bang" approach. The entire network must be in place for it to be fully effective, and a poorly-utilised network would actually increase emissions. Storkey (2009) recommends that around 250 coach transfer stations are needed for a national coach network.

However, such networks require people to make regular changes. This has been shown to be unpopular for trains and buses, but may become acceptable if waiting times can be kept consistently below 5 minutes. The proposed coach network for the London 2012 Olympics could be a great opportunity to test the principle if the current plans are revised.

INTERNATIONAL MODES OF TRANSPORT

Long-distance travel is dominated by aircrafts, but in almost any model of a zero carbon future this must change. A significant number of trips could be reduced through the wider use of teleconferencing; high-speed rail could serve short-haul trips; and more speculatively, airships might make a welcome return. If society is truly serious about a zero carbon future, then it must also consider whether long-haul leisure and business travel is such a vital necessity.

Aviation

International aviation accounts for approximately 21% of Britain's current transport CO_2 emissions, and the percentage is forecast to grow dramatically as demand for air travel increases and other sectors decarbonise. As such, this is a crucial area to tackle in moving towards a zero carbon transport system.

Aviation is a difficult area to tackle because it is not possible to electrify planes. Hydrogen offers potential as an aviation fuel, but hydrogen-fuelled aircraft would produce around 2.6 times more water vapour than their fossil-fuelled counterparts (Committee on Climate Change [CCC], 2009; Intergovernmental Panel on Climate Change [IPCC], 2007). Because water vapour released at altitude may have a temporary warming effect due to increased cirrus cloud formation, the degree of climate benefit from flying planes on hydrogen remains unclear.

Measures that could increase the energy efficiency of aviation in the short term include optimising air traffic routes, using electric motors while taxiing, and new designs such as the Blended Wing Body, although this is still over a decade away from production (Royal Commission on Environmental Pollution, 2002). Aircraft typically have long lifespans, but with significant cost savings through efficiency improvements, changes could be made quite rapidly. 99% of an aircraft's lifecycle energy use is linked to its operation, while only 1% is due to its construction. Some of these developments may be encouraged by the inclusion of aviation in the EU emissions trading scheme.

However, aviation is already optimised for fuel efficiency; further savings may be marginal. If aviation keeps expanding, any emissions savings will all be cancelled out by the increase in the number of flights.

Biofuels for aviation: It is possible to use biofuels in jet engines. Aviation fuel can be made as a "second generation" or lignocellulosic biofuel from woody biomass using gasification followed by Fischer-Tropsch synthesis. The process is sometimes known as biomass-to-liquids. It is still a developing technology but a commercial biomass-to-liquids plant is being run in Germany by Choren Industries.

The implications associated with the production of biofuels have been discussed above. The core *zerocarbonbritain2030* scenario uses Fischer-Tropsch biofuels for aviation as there is currently no alternative to liquid fuels in this sector. This biofuel is made from short rotation coppice willow and miscanthus grown indigenously on UK land that is currently unused or used for grazing livestock.

There are also some other sectors for which it is currently very hard to find viable alternatives to liquid fuels, including heavy goods vehicles, ships and some farm machinery. Biofuels are partly used for these applications in the core *zerocarbonbritain2030* scenario. The Fischer-Tropsch process inevitably produces a mixture of hydrocarbon fuels; although it can be optimised for either diesel or kerosene (jet fuel). We use a mixture of the kerosene and diesel pathways. Some naphtha is produced as well, which can be converted to petrol. It is also possible to increase the quantity of fuel produced by adding extra hydrogen into the process (Agrawal *et al.*, 2007).

In total, 1.67 million hectares of land is devoted to producing biofuel feedstock in the *zerocarbonbritain2030* scenario. This is no cottage garden; the total area of Great Britain (including urban and mountainous areas) is about 23 million hectares. However, we assume a corresponding reduction in meat consumption to allow for this. About a third of the fuel produced from this area will be kerosene; the remainder will be diesel and petrol.

The greenhouse gas emissions from the production of miscanthus and short rotation coppice willow on grassland are very low. These are discussed in detail within the Land use and agriculture chapter. Financial costs are currently quite high but they are expected to fall in the future. Sims *et al.*, (2010) estimate that should Fischer-Tropsch fuels of this type be successfully commercialised by 2015, then by 2030 they may be cost competitive with crude oil at around US $80/bbl. Carbon pricing and other legislation have the potential to accelerate this.

The DfT predicts that a 29.7% increase in aircraft efficiency is possible by 2033 corresponding to an annual (compound) improvement of 1.05% (Aviation Environment Federation [AEF], 2010). Allowing for the 24% increase that this suggests is possible by 2030, the 34 TWh of kerosene produced is sufficient to power about a third of 2008 UK aviation (based on figures from DfT, 2008a). The total aviation fuel used must therefore be reduced. Some reduction can be achieved by reducing air freight.

Short-haul passenger flights can be replaced with trains and ships. Unfortunately however, while short-haul flights currently account for 78% of aviation passengers, they account for less than 40% of passenger kms (CCC, 2009). It is long-haul flights that are responsible for the largest portion of the fuel used and about 66% of the greenhouse gas emissions from UK aviation (ibid.). The reduction of short-haul flights must be complimented by a reduction in long-haul flights, and there is unlikely to be an alternative to an absolute reduction in transit.

However, with good management, the air travel that remains can be the air travel that is really useful and beneficial.

It should be emphasised that the limited use of transport biofuels is specific to the ***zero**carbon**britain**2030* scenario in which there is control over where and how the feedstock is grown and the expansion of biofuel use is accompanied by a large reduction in meat consumption. Transport biofuels may be a dangerous technology if pursued in isolation and their use is not advocated unless sufficient mechanisms exist to ensure that the growing of the feedstock does not have damaging consequences for the climate or vulnerable people.

High-speed trains

High-speed trains are already a lower carbon option than short-haul flights. If they were electrically powered, with electricity provided from renewable sources, they could be near zero carbon in use.

The greenhouse gas benefits of high-speed trains depend on what they are compared to and whether their embodied energy is accounted for. Lower-speed trains use less energy per passenger km, but higher-speed trains generally include efficiency gains such as aerodynamic improvements. This makes direct comparison difficult.

High-speed trains are likely to be in greater demand, but the energy savings from the switch from private transport will be slightly offset by their higher use of energy. As modern trains (high or low speed) tend to provide more passenger services such as electrical sockets this will also increase their energy demand. High speed trains should be developed to minimise the energy used per seat km.

The most serious concerns surrounding high-speed rail centre around the cost (financial, energy and CO_2) of building the infrastructure. The longer the infrastructure lasts and the more it is used, the less significant this becomes. However, in the twenty-year time horizon adopted in this report, allowing sufficient time for the deployment would leave high-speed rail only around ten years to payback its embodied emissions. In addition, the construction of high-speed rail lines would have to compete with other areas such as agriculture and adaptation for a limited cumulative emissions budget.

zerocarbonbritain2030 aims to provide the maximum benefit from renewably-derived electricity. Further analysis would be needed to determine how compatible building high-speed rail is with this objective. Carbon pricing will allow individuals to decide if they are willing to pay more for a higher speed service on the same route. Expected passenger numbers are needed to consider the importance of the embodied energy of new infrastructure. Clearly if the embodied energy of rail is considered, the same should go for roads. The energy in-use for rail is a lot lower.

Looking at Europe as a whole, 45% of flights are less than 500km, a distance at which high-speed rail is particularly attractive (AEF, 2000). Since opening, Eurostar has taken 60% of the London–Paris traffic, with a million fewer air passengers a year. The EU's Trans-European Transport Network (TEN-T) programme has a strong focus on promoting high-speed rail across Europe, but lack of funding is proving to be a major challenge.

Freight solutions

Freight accounts for around one quarter of the UK's transport emissions, warranting considerable attention. The fabric and contents of every shop, office, factory and home have been transported at some stage. In consequence, a direct way to lower the carbon impact associated with freight is to reduce consumption, increase recycling, and reduce the distances that goods must travel over their lifecycle. In addition however, there are a number of methods and technologies that can be used to minimise the carbon impact of freight transport.

FREIGHT MODE SHIFT

As with passenger transport, there is a huge potential to increase the efficiency of goods transportation by shifting freight from road to rail and sea. Both rail and sea freight transport will require greater integration between modes, such as building greater interchange facilities at ports. Figure 5.5 shows the current carbon emissions from freight transport, with large ships being the most efficient, and light goods vehicles (LGVs) being the least efficient in carbon terms.

However, as with passenger transport, in a zero carbon Britain the emissions from all of these modes must be eliminated.

A zero carbon future is likely to see a renaissance in the use of canals and inland waterways for delivering non-perishable goods. The DfT has several schemes including the Sustainable Distribution Fund, Freight Facilities Grant, and Waterborne Freight Grant which are already supporting several such projects (DfT, 2008d). At the EU level, the promotion of shipping and rail to transport goods is currently supported through the Marco Polo II programme and the "motorways of the sea" aspect of TEN-T.

International shipping is one of the most efficient forms of transport based on CO_2 per freight-tonne-kilometre. However, due to the extremely large volumes of international trade engendered by globalisation, it is still a significant source of carbon emissions, accounting for 3–4% of the global total. Working Group III of the IPCC Fourth Assessment Report is focussed on climate solutions and has examined various measures to reduce this impact, including a combination of solar panels and sails. The use of large sails and kites on supertankers is currently being tested in Germany, with promising results. Large sails can be retrofitted to existing ships. The introduction of hydrogen-propelled ships also remains a possibility.

Fig. 5.5 CO_2 emissions from freight transport

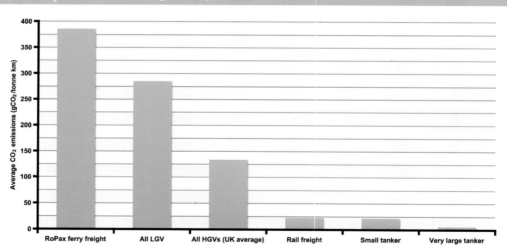

Estimated average CO_2 emissions per freight-tonne-kilometre (gCO_2/tonne km) by freight transport mode.
International shipping is one of the most efficient forms of transport based on CO_2 per freight-tonne-kilometre. Road vehicles are amongst the least efficient forms of freight transport.
Source: Based on data from Defra (2008).

More efficient HGVs

There are currently very few incentives or legislation to promote low carbon trucks or HGVs. In 2009, a review of low carbon technologies for trucks for the DfT found that over half the energy of an HGV is used to overcome rolling resistance and a third to overcome aerodynamic drag (Baker *et al.*, 2009). The technologies that were found to offer the greatest CO_2 reduction for HGVs are aerodynamic trailers (which cut carbon by 10%

on high-speed routes), low-rolling resistance tyres (5%), automatic tyre pressure adjustment (7%), and technology to allow vehicles to drive extremely close together (20%) (ibid.).

Training in eco-driving for truck drivers is proven to cut emissions by 10% (DfT, 2008c), and should become a compulsory element of the mandatory Driver Certificate of Professional Competence (Driver CPC) training that all bus and truck drivers are required to take for five days every five years.

Fig. 5.6 Potential HGV fuel efficiency improvements

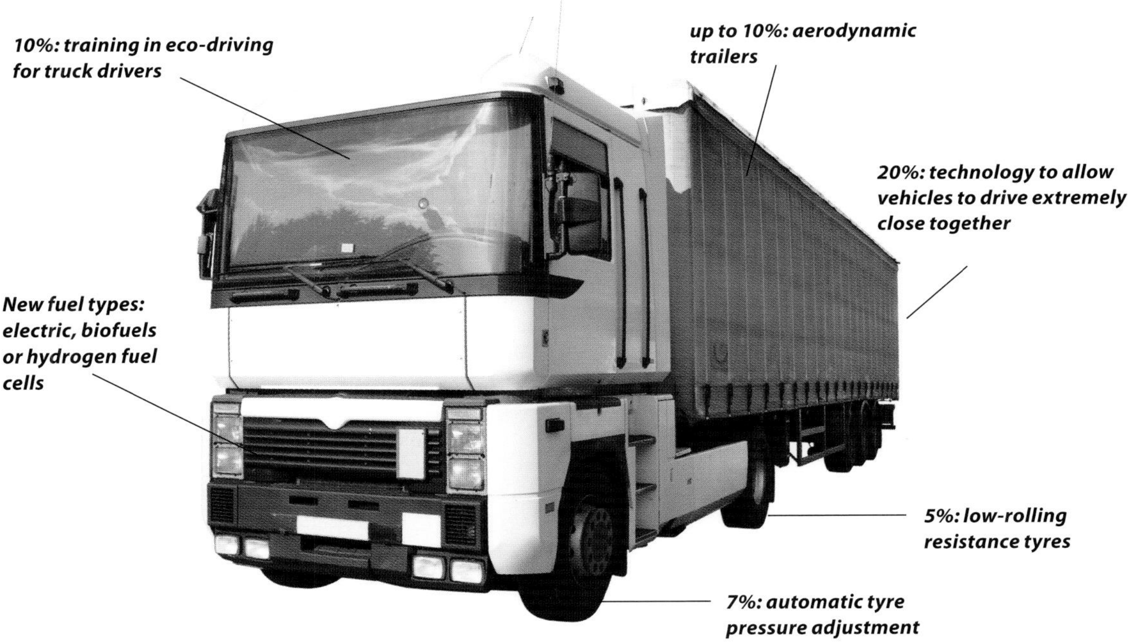

10%: training in eco-driving for truck drivers

up to 10%: aerodynamic trailers

20%: technology to allow vehicles to drive extremely close together

New fuel types: electric, biofuels or hydrogen fuel cells

5%: low-rolling resistance tyres

7%: automatic tyre pressure adjustment

Technologies and initiatives for HGVs which reduce CO_2 emissions.
Technologies which reduce rolling resistance or aerodynamic drag increase fuel efficiency and can therefore reduce CO_2 emissions.

For larger road vehicles such as goods vehicles, electrical power is a possibility, although their range is currently limited. The logistics and delivery company TNT bought 200 electric delivery trucks in 2008. Although the capital cost is greater than a conventional diesel truck, lower running costs recoup this over the vehicle's life. Their 70-mile range covers city deliveries, and the conventional fleet deals with longer distances (TNT, 2008).

For longer-range deliveries it is not possible to stop and change batteries as the high energy use of HGVs would require stops too frequently. An American company has developed the Tyrano, a plug-in electric/hydrogen fuel cell-powered HGV. It carries 33kg of hydrogen and has a range of over 550km. However, hydrogen vehicles currently cost 3–6 times the price of a diesel equivalent, and require three times as much fuel storage space due to the lower density of hydrogen (Vision Motor Corp, 2009). In the short term, sustainably-sourced biofuels are likely to provide the best solution for longer-range vehicles, until breakthroughs in battery or hydrogen technology materialise. The *zerocarbonbritain2030* scenario uses some Fischer-Tropsch diesel in a number of niche applications including some for HGVs. This is produced from woody biomass as has been discussed in the aviation section.

Due to the high fuel bills incurred by road haulage, when a cost-effective alternative to diesel becomes available, the changeover is likely to be very rapid. The overwhelming preponderance of lifecycle impacts of trucks also comes from fuel use (Rocky Mountain Institute, 2007).

The introduction of a road user charging system for HGVs would help to encourage reductions in freight's carbon impact. Such a charging system would help level the playing field for freight operators and make European HGVs pay for their external costs on the UK road network. These systems are already in use in many European countries including Austria and Switzerland.

Airships

While not part of the core *zerocarbonbritain2030* scenario, airships are an interesting potential way of meeting transport demands, specifically semi-perishable freight. Airships use hydrogen or helium, both elements lighter than air, to provide lift. They have much lower greenhouse gas emissions than aircraft because they do not need to use energy to generate lift; they go slower; and fly lower.

Most of the modern airship designs are actually hybrids, which incorporate lighter-than-air technology with aerodynamic lift. One example is CargoLifter's proposed CL160 airship. It is estimated that this airship's greenhouse gas emissions are 80% lower than that of a Boeing 747 (Upham *et al.*, 2003). A similar figure is given by Hybrid Air Vehicles (HAV) for their SkyCat range of airships. HAV report that their SkyCat design consumes an average of 70% less fuel per tonne-kilometre than aircraft (HAV, 2008).

Furthermore, airships could conceivably be powered by hydrogen fuel cells or liquid hydrogen. When using hydrogen from electrolysis with electricity from renewable sources this would reduce emissions to almost zero. Because airships fly at a lower altitude than jets, the water vapour they give off does not have the warming effect that it does when it is released from jets, so flying them on "green hydrogen" has real benefits for the climate.

Airships are unlikely to be able to replace high-speed passenger jets on long-haul flights because they are too slow. A Boeing 747 has a cruising speed of 910 kilometres per hour (kph) and most projected airships have a cruising speed of between 100 and 150kph. An airship flying from Britain to the USA would take several days to get there. The facilities which would be required (beds, space to exercise etc) would make passenger numbers on each airship low and therefore would make it an expensive form of transport. It is more feasible to imagine that scheduled short-haul passenger services might be a possibility, but airships will find it difficult to compete with high-speed trains, which are two or three times as fast and also likely to be cheaper.

However, airships may be a really viable option for freight transport. Airships can compete in the air-freight sector on speed because air-freight is not as fast as is often assumed. The mean delivery time of air-freighted goods is 6.3 days because of the need for goods to be transported to and from the airport (Upham *et al.*, 2003). The logistics are exacerbated by the relative scarcity of suitable airports for cargo jets – in the UK there are only about five civil airports which can accept a fully-laden Boeing 747 (ibid.). Airships can carry goods "door to door" because they require very little infrastructure to dock and discharge their cargoes (ibid.). The CL160 airship has a range of 10,000km between refuelling stops (Global Security, 2005; Upham *et al.*, 2003) (see Table 5.1).

Precisely how much infrastructure is required to operate airships depends on the design of the airship. Some airships have been proposed with onboard docking systems which can be lowered to the ground, with the airship staying airborne for cargo transfers (Prentice *et al.*, 2004). This would mean no infrastructure at all would be required on the ground to load and unload cargo. Other designs do require some infrastructure, however it is clear that airship take-off and landing facilities will be far smaller, and far cheaper, than for jet aircraft (ibid.).

It is popularly believed that airships are peculiarly vulnerable to the weather. This is not the case. All methods of transport are affected by the weather. Airships, with their ability to move over land and sea, are well equipped to avoid extreme storms. "Airship vulnerability to weather extremes will likely be no greater, and probably less, than for conventional air transport" (Prentice *et al.*, 2004). Furthermore, despite a few airship accidents around a century ago, with today's engineering it is perfectly possible to make safe hydrogen-powered airships. It is also possible to use helium, which is inert.

CargoLifter's CL160 is designed to carry a cargo of 160 tonnes, whilst other companies (including HAV) say they can build airships which could carry cargos of 1,000 tonnes. This could result in significant economies of scale. There is at least one airship company which argues that very large airships could be built that could haul cargo at costs comparable to marine freight (Prentice *et al.*, 2004).

One problem linked to shifting air freight into airships is the fact that much air-freighted cargo is flown in the holds of passenger jets. However there would be some reduction in the fuel necessary for these planes as a result of the reduced weight. Additionally, about a third of air freight is carried in dedicated freight planes which airships could replace altogether (Civil Aviation Authority [CAA], 2009).

Table 5.1 highlights the huge difference in emissions from long-haul aviation to HGVs. Airships could also in theory be used to replace HGVs for freight transport over shorter distances on land. As can be seen in Table 5.1, airships are more efficient than current HGVs. However, because they are less efficient than new HGVs, a modal shift from HGVs to airships is not recommended. For this application it would be better to shift to more efficient HGVs.

Town planning

Adapting town planning is essential to facilitate the behavioural change required by the **zero**carbon**britain**2030 scenario. Dispersing services and work places over large areas makes it difficult to serve them with public transport as demand becomes very diffuse, and because they also becomes difficult to reach on foot or bicycle as distances increase. Out-of-town retail and industrial parks, offices and shopping

Table 5.1 Estimated CO_2 emissions for international freight	
Mode	**CO_2 emissions per freight-tonne-km**
Current long-haul aviation	0.6066kg (Defra)
Current HGVs	0.132kg (Defra)
New airships	0.121kg
New efficient HGV (40% saving)	0.079kg
Current maritime freight	0.013kg (Defra)

Estimated CO_2 emissions by transport mode for international freight (2008) (freight-tonne-km).
Source: Based on figures from Upham et al. *(2002) for airships and Defra data for long-haul aviation and HGVs. Note that Upham refers to a specific plane, the Boeing 747, and Defra uses a generic long-haul figure.*

centres are almost always very car dependent.

The town development layout proposed is the "hub and spoke" pattern, with core services in the centre and local service centres along the main arteries into the town (Williams *et al.*, 2000). The concentration of core services in the town centre allows them to be well served by high-frequency public transport. Meanwhile the location of local services along the "spokes" means that they are within walking distance of residential areas but also close to the main public transport lines (ibid.). To reduce transport demand it would be advisable to build up these local services, which has the additional advantage of making services more accessible to disabled, poor, senior and young citizens. For shopping, home deliveries by electric vehicles can offer a complementary role.

As well as its arrangement, the density of the built environment is important. Sprawling, low-density developments increase the distances that must be travelled and are not well suited to walking, cycling and public transport. For this reason it is preferable to increase the density of existing cities by filling in the gaps, rather than to build new developments around the outskirts (ibid.).

Clearly some sensitivity is required: cramming too many people into too small a space and building on every green site would create an unpleasant living environment which the occupiers would be eager to leave. However, there are many brownfield sites in cities and towns that can be built on with no major loss of aesthetic value. "High density" accommodation can still mean houses rather than flats, for example of the typical Victorian terrace style; and people often value the convenient access to amenities that higher density accommodation can provide.

The layout of our towns and cities is not something that can be changed overnight. However, we can start moving in the right direction immediately. Important changes that should take place include that:

- The requirement to demonstrate public transport, walking and cycling feasibility should be a much higher priority for all new developments (residential, retail, offices etc.). Local Planning Authority policies and decisions need to attach more weight to these factors, particularly when considering planning applications. National government, through the Secretary of State, and through Planning Policy Guidance should endorse this position more robustly.
- New housing developments should be built close to existing services. Where possible they should be built inside towns. Opportunities to travel by foot or by bicycle should be maximised by providing short cuts and links to existing roads and paths.
- Public buildings such as hospitals, secondary schools and shopping centres should be built inside towns on major public transport routes. The buildings themselves should be made friendly to those on foot, with entrances and directions placed on the main

road rather than in car parks, or near to public transport drop-off points.

Influencing travel behaviour

In almost any vision of a zero carbon Britain, there must be a shift from the car to more efficient forms of transport. This change requires excellent walking, cycling, and public transport infrastructure; much better integration between modes; and also requires us to confront our habitual addiction to the car.

A key problem encountered in attempts to change behaviour is the so-called "attitude-behaviour gap", described as 'one of the greatest challenges facing the public climate agenda' (Anable *et al.*, 2006). This is discussed further in the next chapter. Hounsham (2006) studied methods for motivating sustainable behaviours, and concluded that we should expect very little from information provision alone, stating that 'most of the lifestyle decisions we seek to influence are not determined mainly by rational consideration of the facts, but by emotions, habits, personal preferences, fashions, social norms, personal morals and values, peer pressure and other intangibles'.

THE STATES OF CHANGE MODEL

A range of theoretical frameworks have been developed to explain why there is often a lack of correlation between possession of environmental attitudes and environmental behaviour. Although no overarching theory can be used to explain all behaviour change, a theory often adopted in its attempts to influence travel behaviour, e.g. the TAPESTRY project,[3] uses the "States of Change" model, which is often used to explore habitual and addictive behaviour patterns such as smoking, drug addiction and weight control.

Stage 1 - Awareness of problem
Stage 2 - Accepting responsibility
Stage 3 - Perception of options
Stage 4 - Evaluation of options
Stage 5 - Making a choice
Stage 6 - Experimental behaviour
Stage 7 - Habitual behaviour

It should be noted that individuals do not necessarily progress sequentially through each stage of the model but can move backwards and forwards through the stages of changes several times with each move often increasing in duration until it becomes habitual.

As people move through the "states of change", their attitudes towards different transport modes changes, altering the perceived benefits and barriers associated with each mode. For example, Getersleben and Appleton (2007) applied the States of Change model to utility cycling, encouraging non-cyclists to cycle for a week and recording their attitudes towards cycling before and after. Before the trial 32% of respondents viewed cycling as a flexible form of transport, and after the trial this figure had risen to 57%. This shows

[3] TAPESTRY is a European project that investigated travel awareness theory and practice.

that more effort should be spent on encouraging people to "try things out", in the expectation that a proportion of them will find it a better way to travel for their needs.

SEGMENTATION AND SOCIAL MARKETING FOR TRAVEL

When implementing initiatives aimed at travel behaviour change, it is important to note that not all sections of the population should be targeted in the same manner, or will respond to the same messages. In an influential paper, Anable (2005) segmented the UK population into six distinct groups, each with varying degrees of mode switching potential.

Aspiring Environmentalists: Have a high potential to switch modes due to high moral obligation and strong perceived control. Modal switch can be encouraged by provision of information on alternatives, and reinforcing positive messages.

Malcontented Motorists: Have a moderate potential to switch modes, and can be encouraged by promoting moral obligation as well as the positive qualities of public transport and negative aspects of the car. However, they have a psychological attachment to the car, and do not perceive that their actions can make a difference.

Complacent Car Addicts: Have a low potential to switch modes due to psychological attachment to the car and lack of moral imperative. Awareness-raising activities into the positive aspects of public transport are likely to have the biggest impact on this group.

Die-Hard Drivers: Have a very low potential to switch modes due to a strong attachment to the car, lack of moral obligation, and strong behavioural norms. Steps could be taken to weaken the stereotypical images of public transport users, but fiscal measures are most likely to succeed.

Car-less Crusaders: Do not own a car out of choice.

Reluctant Riders: Are unable to own a car.

Each group represents a unique combination of preferences, world views and attitudes.

This demonstrates that different groups need to be targeted in different ways to optimise the chances of influencing mode choice behaviour. Socio-demographic factors such as age and gender were found to have little direct bearing on people's propensity to switch modes.

THE FOUR E'S MODEL

Through the UK Sustainable Development Strategy, *the Framework for pro-environmental behaviours*, and other documents, Defra promote the "Four E's" method of encouraging behaviour change. Figure 5.7 demonstrates how this can be adapted to a travel behaviour context.

SMARTER CHOICES

In 2004 the DfT commissioned the "Smarter Choices – Changing the Way We Travel" research programme. This concluded that initiatives such as travel awareness campaigns and travel plans could be very cost-effective and led to a significant reduction in trips. Unfortunately, this reduction in trips often relates to a much smaller reduction in carbon emissions as it is generally only shorter distance trips that are targeted by Smarter Choices activities.

Following on from the Smarter Choices research, "Sustainable Travel Towns" were established in Darlington, Peterborough, and Worcester. They shared around £10 million of DfT funding over five years between 2004 to 2009 in order to demonstrate the effect that a sustained package of Smarter Choices measures could have when coupled with infrastructure improvements. By concentrating interventions in a few areas the synergies between measures could be explored and the crucial role of social norms in influencing travel behaviour could be fully realised. Early results from the evaluation suggest that, on average across the three towns, walking trips increased by 13%, cycling by around 50%, public transport use by 16% whilst car driver trips fell by over 8%.

Following on from Sustainable Travel Towns, the DfT intends to designate one or two cities as "Sustainable Travel Cities" to demonstrate that the principles of sustainable travel can be embedded within a large urban area through a coordinated and intensive programme of Smarter Choices. The DfT expects to provide funding of up to £29.2 million over three years to the designated city or cities to assist them with this

demonstration. Cities are expected to provide a significant amount of match funding, and should also be willing to implement measures to lock-in the benefits of the Smarter Choices programme, such as introducing controlled parking and road space re-allocation. The successful cities are likely to maximise synergies with other non-transport measures, such as tackling obesity.

Through this project, the DfT (2009e) aims to:
- demonstrate that the principles of sustainable travel using a package of hard and soft measures can be successfully adapted to an existing large-scale urban settlement.
- fund a programme of sustainable travel measures that delivers both short-term results in number of trips made by sustainable means and long-term shifts in travel behaviour.
- collect data to build a robust evidence base to support the case for the effectiveness of Smarter Choice initiatives.
- work with the authorities to demonstrate how sustainable travel can help to meet wider objectives, particularly in relation to health, the environment, and equality of opportunity.

In parallel developments, Cardiff has recently been announced as Wales' first Sustainable Travel City, with a total funding pot of £28.5 million over two years to provide measures such as free bikes, free buses and a modern parking system. In 2008, the Scottish government also announced it will provide £15 million for seven sustainable travel towns and cities.

Fig. 5.7 Adapting the Four E's model to reduce CO_2 emissions from transport

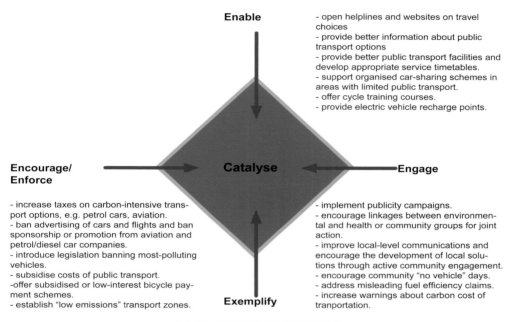

Fig. 5.7 Adapting the Four E's model to reduce CO_2 emissions from transport

Enable
- open helplines and websites on travel choices
- provide better information about public transport options
- provide better public transport facilities and develop appropriate service timetables.
- support organised car-sharing schemes in areas with limited public transport.
- offer cycle training courses.
- provide electric vehicle recharge points.

Encourage/ Enforce
- increase taxes on carbon-intensive transport options, e.g. petrol cars, aviation.
- ban advertising of cars and flights and ban sponsorship or promotion from aviation and petrol/diesel car companies.
- introduce legislation banning most-polluting vehicles.
- subsidise costs of public transport.
-offer subsidised or low-interest bicycle payment schemes.
- establish "low emissions" transport zones.

Catalyse

Engage
- implement publicity campaigns.
- encourage linkages between environmental and health or community groups for joint action.
- improve local-level communications and encourage the development of local solutions through active community engagement.
- encourage community "no vehicle" days.
- address misleading fuel efficiency claims.
- increase warnings about carbon cost of transportation.

Exemplify
- limit parking spaces, and increase cycle and shower facilties at public sector estates.
- government departments and public bodies to offer where appropriate home-working options to reduce commuting.
-government departments and public bodies to offer tele- and video-conferencing and to support appropriate technology to reduce need for business travel.
- government departments and public bodies to consider transportation policies associated with goods and services bought and provided. Where appropriate, public bodies should make efforts to source locally or to offer decentralised services, in order to reduce carbon emissions from transport.

An example of the Four E's model adapted to the challenge of behavioural change relating to transport and thus of reducing CO_2 emissions.
The Four E's model is represented by a diamond. The ultimate goal is to "catalyse" behavioural change by breaking habits. In order to reach this point, policymakers must: (1) "enable", i.e. make change easier by providing education, skills, information and alternatives; (2) "encourage/enforce", i.e. give signals through Government such as price signals, league tables, funding, regulation and rewards, that encourage and where necessary enforce change; (3) "engage", i.e. get people involved through targeted communication; and (4) "exemplify", i.e. by ensuring Government leads by example.
Source: Based on the Four E's model methodology, as discussed in Defra (n/d).

Business models

In order to reduce the overall carbon emissions of the transport sector, it is clear that new business models will be needed. For road vehicles, there needs to be a move from the upfront costs of car purchase, insurance and taxation to a system where drivers pay for each mile driven. This would make public transport costs more easily comparable with car costs, and would show that public transport is often a more cost-effective solution.

Car clubs, where drivers pay for a car by the hour is one example. Pay-as-you-drive insurance also makes drivers more aware of the single-trip costs of travel, and has been shown to cut trips by approximately 25%. However, one insurance company that pioneered the model has stopped supporting it, as it was found that as people drove less, the company's revenue decreased.

At present, vehicle purchasers want durability, reliability and fuel efficiency. Producers however simply seek increased sales. Built-in obsolescence can therefore benefit producers, who make decisions on build quality. While there is potential for increased legislation in this area, this is likely to be based around performance and would be difficult to implement.

If cars were leased and priced per mile, then incentives for durability would devolve on the leasing company. If that leasing company is also the producer, then it is also able to ensure rather than simply request build quality and durability.

This business model is already being put into practice. Riversimple, for example, has developed cars that are expected to last at least twenty years as opposed to the usual ten, and to charge per mile for their use. Producing cars which last longer is also a far better use of material resources, and is likely to substantially reduce the amount of embodied energy in car manufacture. A new car might be leased for three years, at the end of which period the user could either return the car or extend the lease. This business model rewards longevity and low running costs rather than obsolescence and high running costs.

In terms of government funding, many sustainable transport initiatives such as travel plans and intelligent transport solutions rely on revenue funding. At present the funding grant given to local authorities is heavily weighted towards capital spending, which is good for building new infrastructure, but not for encouraging more sustainable travel.

New business and economic models are needed to place the incentives back on public transport investment. Economic incentives on carbon will help all sectors including transport. In this area we have also seen the tremendous potential for aligning micro- and macroeconomic incentives. Combining carbon awareness with business model innovation can create low carbon businesses with a strategic competitive advantage.

Box 5.7 Changing motorways

The focus of the *zerocarbonbritain2030* scenario is to use a limited carbon budget to create a zero carbon transport system as efficiently as possible. There are some potential large infrastructure changes which may help decarbonise in the long term, although there would be emissions associated with their construction. These are not included in the core scenario but are mentioned briefly to help give a complete picture.

Two major possible infrastructure changes are running rails along existing motorways, or building some form of electrical pick-up to avoid the need for storage in each vehicle. Rails would decrease resistance and an electrical pick-up would reduce weight. Both would increase efficiency. However both options would require substantial feasibility studies which are beyond the scope of this report.

SAVING SUBSIDIES

Bus operators are subsided because of the public service they provide; hence it makes sense for them not to be taxed at the same time. This logic has led to bus operators receiving a rebate on fuel duty of around £413m per annum (Local Government Association [LGA], 2009). However, this decreases the incentive to save fuel or shift to electric vehicles so it would be better to rearrange this subsidy. In China they already have an electric bus with a 186km range (Thundersky, 2009).

The transport model

Energy modelling matches demand for energy (heat, electricity and fuel specific requirements) to the energy available to supply that demand.

Transport modelling conventionally examines "vehicle fleet efficiency" which improves marginally each year. This methodology does not allow for changes in mode of transport, occupancy levels or large-scale innovation. There is a huge amount of data available on individual technologies, and by combining this with UK level statistics on mode of transport, current vehicle stocks and their energy efficiency, a much more advanced model is possible.

The transport modelling for *zerocarbonbritain2030* contains two key elements: passenger transport which has been the primary focus, and freight transport.

The model combines passenger data from the Department for Transport (DFT, 2009f) and freight data (McKinnon, 2007) from the Logistics Research Centre conducted as part of the "Green Logistics" programme funded by the Engineering and Physical Sciences Research Council. This is integrated with a wide range of data concerning the efficiency of each mode of travel combined with different fuel types (diesel, kerosene, hydrogen and electric) along with current occupancy levels and capacity.

Combining all this data enables us to create a dynamic model with which we can determine the outcomes of various changes.

There are many details affecting final energy

demand. The methodology used to calculate this is summarised below.

- Energy demand per km varies on the fuel used. Hence the energy demand per km for each mode is calculated as the passenger km travelled on each fuel multiplied by the energy demand per passenger km for that particular fuel.

- There is additional potential to decrease energy demand per passenger km (all technologies) by increasing the occupancy rates of each mode of travel.

- The demand from each mode of travel is calculated as km travelled multiplied by

THE RESULTS

We have modelled many different scenarios including changing the following:

Table 5.2 The ZCB2030 transport model			
Variable	**Drivers for change**	**Action and result**	**Savings**
Change in total passenger km per person	+ A shift to working closer to home + Remote or tele-working + Climate change awareness	Decrease in passenger km provides roughly proportional decrease in energy demand and emissions, assuming equal decrease across all modes. The clear exception being reducing km walked/cycled which would not result in reduced emissions.	20% of passenger demand.
Change in average occupancy levels of cars	+ Increasing fuel prices + Climate change awareness	Increasing the current average occupancy of cars/vans/taxis (once we have changed mode) from current 1.6 (DfT, 2009h) to 2.	23% of mode.
Change in technology	+ Increasing fuel prices + Climate change awareness + Improving technology	This varies on the technology, although switching to lighter and more aerodynamic vehicles can help across vehicle type. Shifting from petrol to electricity offers significant efficiency potential. Even high performance electric cars (i.e. Tesla) are very efficient. The highest opportunity found (80% decrease in energy demand) includes savings from lower maximum speeds and lower weight in addition to fuel switching.	0–80% of mode.
Change in mode	+ A shift to working closer to home + Climate change awareness	A huge range of options are available. The proposed mode for ZCB2030 is included below.	12–23%* See below.
The potential savings in each of these case studies are dependent on a number of factors including which order the savings are applied in. For this reason we have given percentages rather than energy demand figures. For details on change in mode please see main text.			

ZCB2030 transport model variables and drivers for change.

energy demand per km.
- The final demand for electricity and liquid fuels is calculated as the sum of the total demand from each mode of travel.

This detailed methodology also ensures that we know the amount of electricity, hydrogen and biofuel demand separately.

MODAL SHIFT

Changes in mode of transport offer significant potential to decrease energy demand. However, the percentage saved is dependent on the efficiency of each mode. The technological changes in the scenario substantially increase the efficiency of private cars, which alters the effect of the modal shift.

If we run the model based on the current fuel mix and the average current efficiency of new vehicles the modal shift decreases energy demand by 23%. New vehicles have a higher average efficiency than the existing vehicle stock and if we used the average efficiency for the existing fleet instead, the modal shift would decrease energy demand even further.

If we apply the modal shift after we have applied the major changes in technology then we see only a 12% reduction in energy demand. However, it should be noted that at this point any further technology improvement is likely to be very expensive, and therefore the value of a 12% decrease is likely to be very high.

It can be appreciated from this that the most rapid way to decarbonise and move away from imported, expensive oil would be an immediate shift toward existing public transport as this has huge potential to save energy at present.

Another change that will occur over time is that as renewables are deployed, the embodied carbon of industry will decrease, therefore reducing the carbon cost of manufacturing new transport infrastructure. At present turnover rates (DfT, 2009g) the car fleet will be replaced in 14 years.

A point to note is that our methodology is based on average energy use per passenger km, which is the methodology most relevant to creating a national level end-point optimisation model like ours. However, with regard to an individual's transport decisions greater complexity arises. If a bus or train is going to run anyway, the addition of one extra person causes minimal marginal increases in fuel use. Hence it is less appropriate for an individual to make transport decisions on the basis of average figures, and they may prefer to use marginal figures instead. Further complexity arises due to various feedback loops in the system: increasing use of public transport can lead to increasing frequency, which can in turn lead to increased use. Our national model does not account for such factors which are relevant to decision making at a smaller scale, but it may be useful to consider them at an individual, community and local level.

It may help to bring about the change envisaged from the transport model if a zero carbon vehicle standard is developed. This could be applied initially to passenger vehicles, then to light goods vehicles and eventually also to heavy goods vehicles.

A methodological detail is that by adding in projected population growth (Office of National Statistics [ONS], 2010) our baseline increased by 26%.

FUTURE WORK

There is huge potential to build on this work. Two large potential areas concern the baseline, and embodied energy.

We have used a baseline for current fuel use and mode. However an accurate prediction of 2030 demand under business-as-usual would be very useful to be able to provide comparative cost savings. A degree of subjectivity would inevitably enter into such a business-as-usual calculation, and the assumptions and judgements on which it is based would need to be clearly presented for the sake of transparency.

Incorporating the embodied energy of vehicles and their infrastructure would strengthen the model. We have begun work on this area, which will be published at a later date.

TRANSPORT MODEL CONCLUSIONS

By combining modal shift, increased vehicle occupancy, wider technology improvements and fuel shifting we were able to provide the required services while decreasing predicted 2030 transport energy demand by 74% (a 63% reduction on 2008 levels) and fuelling our transport system with electricity, a small amount of hydrogen and a very small amount of biofuel.

Conclusions

In a zero carbon Britain, the transport system will look similar to today's but will sound and smell very different. Cars powered by electricity will have drastically reduced road noise and eliminated petrol fumes and exhaust gases. Towns and cities will be alive with the sound of people talking on the walk or cycle to work. Electric and hydrogen hybrid buses will compete with trams for the remaining road space, and provide excellent onward connections to railways and coaches at transport hubs. Trains will also all have been electrified, with new high-speed lines and better services eliminating the need for domestic flights.

On the nation's motorways, electric and hydrogen hybrid coaches and HGVs will be moving people and goods around the country. Many goods will also be transported by rail and boat, all sustainably powered. Cargo will be taken around the world on ships powered by solar panels, sails and sustainable fuels. Air travel will be powered by sustainably-produced biofuels and some will have been replaced by airships.

Not every vision of a zero carbon Britain must include all of these elements, but certain technological improvements are vital:

- Electrify cars and trains;
- Power buses, coaches, vans and trucks with electricity where possible and hydrogen or biofuel as needed;
- Power aviation with sustainable biofuels and/or hydrogen or replace it with other methods of long-distance transport; and
- Use solar panels, sails and hydrogen fuel cells for ships.

Even with these technologies in place however, changes in behaviour will also be needed to reduce electricity demand for running electric vehicles and producing hydrogen as transport fuel. With no such

change, the UK will need to at least double its generation capacity to meet the additional transport demand. This vision of a zero carbon Britain makes some challenging but achievable assumptions about such behavioural change:

- People will be fitter and more active, walking and cycling much more often. The distance the average Briton walks will double from 1.2 to 2.4 miles a day, and cycle use will finally stop lagging behind other European countries. With more people cycling, the average Briton will cycle six times more than before, covering 0.7 miles a day by bike.
- With better and faster train services across the country, the average distance travelled

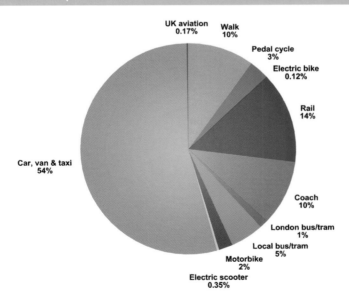

Suggested passenger transport mode split in the ZCB2030 scenario.

by train will increase by 15%, meaning 13% of all distance travelled is by rail.

- A modern and effective coach system will enable people to enjoy free wi-fi and fast connections at transport hubs provided by these super-stretch limousines. Coaches will account for 10% of all distance travelled.
- Local bus services will have improved; and people will use a smartcard to pay for tickets anywhere in the country. Elsewhere, trams and trolleybuses provide popular ways to get around the city. The average Briton will travel 50% further on local public transport than on the old buses.
- Less time is wasted travelling, with people living closer to their workplaces and working more efficiently. People will think twice before driving across the country on business or leisure. The total distance travelled drops by 20% from an average of

25 to 20 miles per day per person.

- People will also recycle more and consume less. More produce will be locally-sourced, reducing freight distance by 20%. More efficient trucks and drivers will further cut down energy demand.
- More places will be accessible by train within 2–3 hours, and reliance on domestic aviation will have all but been eliminated. People will stay closer to home for holidays, focusing on British and European destinations, greatly reducing the demand for international flights. The total amount of flying will fall to a third of the current level, powered by sustainably-produced Fischer-Tropsch biofuels.
- Smart meters will manage demand by controlling when cars and hydrogen plants operate, reducing the need for additional power generation. Many of these

Table 5.3 Transport today and in ZCB2030					
	Walk	Pedal cycles	Electric /pedal bikes	Rail	Coach
Current	4.89%	0.47%	0.00%	6.86%	0.88%
ZCB2030	10.00%	3.00%	0.12%	14.00%	10.00%
	London bus / tram	Local bus or tram	Motorbikes	Electric scooters	Cars, vans and taxis
Current	1.09%	3.85%	0.70%	0.00%	80.16%
ZCB2030	1.3%	5.00%	2.10%	0.35%	54.13%

Significant reductions in the use of cars, vans and taxis are expected by 2030, with corresponding increases in the use of local transport and walking and cycling.
Source: Data for current day based on statistics from DfT (2008e).

infrastructure changes will be achieved with sustainable construction methods. Infrastructure improvements will include the building of a small number of new railway lines, a large number of cycle lanes and transport hubs, and the redevelopment of quality public spaces when trams are introduced. This will create some additional carbon emissions, but compared to the reduction in energy demand, the net saving will be substantial.

Not only would the UK have a zero carbon transport system, but its population would be healthier and happier too.

References

ActionAid (2008) "Cereal Offenders: how the G8 has contributed to the global food crisis, and what they can do to stop it", ActionAid policy briefing, July 2008. Available at: http://www.actionaid.org.uk/doc_lib/g8report2_final.pdf [Live: March 2010].

Agrawal, R. et al. (2007) "Sustainable fuel for the transportation sector", Proceedings of the National Academy of Sciences, 104(12), pp. 4828–4833.

Anable, J. (2005) "'Complacent car addicts' or 'aspiring environmentalists'? Identifying travel behaviour segments using attitude theory", Transport Policy, 12(1), pp. 65–78.

Anable, J., B. Lane & T. Kelay (2006) "An evidence base review of public attitudes to climate change and transport behaviour: Final report", Report for DfT, July 2006. Available at: http://webarchive.nationalarchives.gov.uk/+/http://www.dft.gov.uk/pgr/sustainable/climatechange/areviewofpublicattitudestocl5730 [Live: March 2010].

Association of Train Operating Companies (ATOC) (2009) Connecting Communities: Expanding Access to the Rail Network, June 2009, London: ATOC.

Aviation Environment Federation (AEF) (2000) "From Planes to Trains: Realising the potential from shifting short-haul flights to rail", study prepared by the Aviation Environment Federation (AEF) for Friends of the Earth, October 2000. Available at: http://www.foe.co.uk/resource/reports/planes_trains.pdf [Live: March 2010].

AEF (2010) "UK Aviation CO2 Emissions Forecast", AEF [online]. Available at: http://www.aef.org.uk/?p=242 [Live: March 2010].

Baker et al. (2009) "Review of Low Carbon Technologies for Heavy Goods Vehicles", report prepared for DfT, June 2009. Available at: http://www.dft.gov.uk/pgr/freight/lowcarbontechnologies/lowcarbon.pdf [Live: March 2010].

Batterbury, S. (2003) "Environmental activism and social networks: Campaigning for bicycles and alternative transport in West London", The ANNALS of the American Academy of Political and Social Science, 590(1), pp. 150–169.

Bell, E (2006) "Why the Trolleybus?", The Electric tBus Group [online]. Available at http://www.tbus.org.uk/article.htm [Live: March 2010].

Chester, M. & A. Horvath (2009) "Environmental assessment of passenger transportation should include infrastructure and supply chains", Environmental Research Letters, 4, 024008.

Cherry, C. J. Weinert & D. Chaktan Ma, (2007) "The Environmental Impacts of E-bikes in Chinese Cities", UC Berkeley Center for Future Urban Transport, Working Paper: UCB-ITS-VWP-2007-2. Available at: http://www.its.berkeley.edu/publications/UCB/2007/VWP/UCB-ITS-VWP-2007-2.pdf [Live: March 2010].

Civil Aviation Authority (CAA) (2009) "Aviation Trends: Quarter 3, 2009". Available at: http://www.caa.co.uk/default.aspx?catid=1279&pagetype=90&pageid=9793 [Live: March 2010].

Committee on Climate Change (CCC) (2009) Meeting the UK aviation target – options for reducing emissions to 2050, London: CCC.

Cotula, L., N. Dyer, & S. Vermeulen (2008) Fueling Exclusion? The Biofuels Boom and Poor People's Access to Land, London: International Institute for Environment and Development (IIED) & Food and Agriculture Organisation of the United Nations (FAO).

Department of Energy and Climate Change (DECC) (2009) "New Car CO_2 Emissions Model Search", Act on CO_2 [online]. Available at: http://actonco2.direct.gov.uk/actonco2/home/what-you-can-do/new-car-co2-emissions-model-search.html [Live: March 2010].

Department for Environment, Food and Rural Affairs (Defra) (2008) "Guidelines to Defra's GHG Conversion Factors", Annexes updated April 2008. Available at: http://www.defra.gov.uk/environment/business/reporting/pdf/ghg-cf-guidelines-annexes2008.pdf [Live: March 2010].

Defra (n/d) "Changing behaviour through policymaking", Defra. Available at: http://www.defra.gov.uk/sustainable/government/documents/change-behaviour-model.pdf [Live: March 2010].

Department for Transport (DfT) (2007) *Low Carbon Transport Innovation Strategy*, May 2007, London: DfT.

DfT (2008a) *Transport Statistics Great Britain 2008 Edition*, London: TSO.

DfT (2008b) "Carbon Pathways Analysis: Informing Development of a Carbon Reduction Strategy for the Transport Sector", July 2008. Available at: http://www.dft.gov.uk/pgr/sustainable/analysis.pdf [Live: March 2010].

DfT (2008c) *Delivering a Sustainable Transport System: Main Report*, November 2008, London: DfT.

DfT (2008d) *Delivering A Sustainable Transport System: The Logistics Perspective*, December 2008, London: DfT.

DfT (2008e) *National Travel Survey 2007*, Transport Statistics Bulletin, London: DfT.

DfT (2009a) *UK Air Passenger Demand and CO$_2$ Forecasts*, January 2009, London: DfT.

DfT (2009b) "The Future of Rail", speech by Rt Hon Lord Andrew Adonis, Secretary of State for Transport [online]. Available at: http://www.dft.gov.uk/press/speechesstatements/speeches/futureofrail [Live: March 2010].

DfT (2009c) *Britain's Transport Infrastructure: Rail Electrification*, July 2009, London: DfT.

DfT (2009d) *Low Carbon Transport: A Greener Future – A Carbon Reduction Strategy for Transport*, July 2009, London: TSO.

DfT (2009e) "Sustainable Travel City: Information for Bidders", May 2009, DfT. Available at: http://www.gmcvo.org.uk/files/Sustainable%20Travel%20City%20Bidding%20Guidance.doc [Live: March 2010].

DfT (2009f) "Transport Trends 2009". Available at: http://www.dft.gov.uk/pgr/statistics/datatablespublications/trends/current/section2ptbm.pdf [Live: March 2010].

DfT (2009g) "Vehicle Licensing and Registration Statistics". Available at: http://www.dft.gov.uk/excel/173025/221412/221552/228038/458107/datatables2008.xls [Live: March 2010].

DfT (2009h) *National Travel Survey 2008*, Transport Statistics Bulletin, London: DfT.

Eddington, R. (2006) *The Eddington Transport Study – The Case for Action: Sir Rod Eddington's advice to Government*, December 2006, Norwich: Her Majesty's Stationery Office (HMSO).

European Network for Cycling Expertise (ENCE) (1999) "Cycling and Transport". Available at: http://www.velo.info/Library/Cycling_Transport.pdf [Live: March 2010].

Food and Agriculture Organisation of the United Nations (FAO) (2008) *The State of Food Insecurity in the World 2008. High food prices and food security – threats and opportunities*, Rome: FAO.

FAO (2009) *The State of Food Insecurity in the World 2009. Economic crises – impacts and lessons learned*, Rome: FAO.

Fargione, J. *et al.* (2008) "Land Clearing and the Biofuel Carbon Debt", *Science*, 319 (5867), pp. 1235 – 1238.

Getersleben, B. & K. Appleton (2007) "Contemplating cycling to work: Attitudes and perceptions in different stages of change", *Transportation Research Part A: Policy and Practice*, 41(4), pp. 302–312.

Global Security (2005) "CargoLifter CL60", Globalsecurity.org [online]. Available at: http://www.globalsecurity.org/military/systems/aircraft/cargolifter.htm [Live: March 2010].

GRAIN (2008) "Seized! The 2008 land grab for food and financial security", GRAIN briefing October 2008. Available at: http://www.grain.org/briefings_files/landgrab-2008-en.pdf [Live: March 2010].

Guthrie, N. (2001) "The New Generation of Private Vehicles in the UK: Should their use be encouraged and can they attract drivers of conventional cars?", MSc thesis, University of Leeds.

Heady, D. & S. Fan (2008) "Anatomy of a Crisis: The Causes and Consequences of Surging Food Prices", International Food Policy Research Institute, Discussion Paper 00831, December 2008. Available at: http://www.ifpri.org/sites/default/files/publications/ifpridp00831.pdf [Live: March 2010].

Horton, D. (2006) "Environmentalism and the Bicycle", *Environmental Politics*, 15(1), pp. 41–58.

Hounsham, S. (2006) *Painting the town green: how to persuade people to be environmentally friendly*, London: Intertype.

Hybrid Air Vehicles (2008) "SkyCat Overview", Hybrid Air Vehicles [online]. Available at: http://www.hybridairvehicles.net/products.html [Live: March 2010].

Intergovernmental Panel on Climate Change (IPCC) (2007) *Climate Change 2007: Mitigation of Climate Change*.

Contribution of Working Group III to the Fourth Assessment Report of the Intergovernmental Panel on Climate Change, 2007, Cambridge: Cambridge University Press.

Jackson, S. et al. (2006) "Road Transport", The Improving Engineering Education (ImpEE) Project, version 2: Modified by T. Bertényi. Available at: http://www-g.eng.cam.ac.uk/impee/topics/roadtransport/files/Road%20Transport%20v2%20PDF%20WITH%20NOTES.pdf [Live: March 2010].

King, J. (2008) The King Review of low-carbon cars Part II: recommendations for action, March 2008, London: HMSO.

Leturque, W. & S. Wiggins (2009) "Biofuels: Could the South benefit?", ODI Briefing Paper 48, March 2009. Available at: http://www.odi.org.uk/resources/download/2524.pdf [Live: March 2010].

Local Government Association (LGA) (2009) Securing best value and outcomes for taxpayer subsidy of bus services, London: LGA.

Mayor of London (2009) "An Electric Vehicle Delivery Plan for London", May 2009, Mayor of London. Available at: http://www.london.gov.uk/archive/mayor/publications/2009/docs/electric-vehicles-plan.pdf [Live: March 2010].

McKinnon, A. (2007) "CO_2 Emissions from Freight Transport: An Analysis of UK Data", Logistics Research Centre, Heriot-Watt University, Edinburgh. Available at: http://www.greenlogistics.org/SiteResources/d82cc048-4b92-4c2a-a014-af1eea7d76d0_CO2%20Emissions%20from%20Freight%20Transport%20-%20An%20Analysis%20of%20UK%20Data.pdf [Live: March 2010].

Mitchell, D. (2008) "A Note on Rising Food Prices", The World Bank Development Prospects Group, Policy Research Working Paper 4682, July 2008. Available at: http://www-wds.worldbank.org/external/default/WDSContentServer/IW3P/IB/2008/07/28/000020439_20080728103002/Rendered/PDF/WP4682.pdf [Live: March 2010].

Pearce, F. (2007) "Why bother going green?", New Scientist, 2630, 17 November 2007.

Office of National Statistics (ONS) (2010) "National population projections", ONS [online]. Available at: http://www.statistics.gov.uk/cci/nugget.asp?id=1352 [Live: March 2010].

Prentice, B., R. Beilock, and A. Phillips (2004) "Economics of Airships for Perishable Food Trade", Fifth International Airship Convention and Exhibition, ISO Polar. Available at: http://www.isopolar.ca/documents/isopolar_eapft.pdf

[Live: March 2010].

Rietveld, P. & V. Daniel (2004) "Determinants of bicycle use: Do municipal policies matter?", Transportation Research Part A, 38(7), pp. 531–550.

Reuters (2007) "Platinum-free fuel cell developed in Japan", 14 September 2007, Available at: http://www.reuters.com/article/environmentNews/idUSL1461117220070914 [Live: March 2010].

Rocky Mountain Institute (2007) "Profitable GHG Reduction Through Fuel Economy: Off-the-shelf technologies that bring savings to your bottom line", presentation given by Michael Ogburn. Available at: http://www.rmi.org/rmi/Library/T07-11_ProfitableGHGReduction [Live: March 2010].

Royal Commission on Environmental Pollution (2002) "The Environmental Effects of Civil Aircraft in Flight: Special Report". Available at: http://www.rcep.org.uk/reports/sr-2002-aircraft/documents/aviation-report.pdf [Live: March 2010].

Searchinger, T. et al. (2008) "Use of U.S. Croplands for Biofuels Increases Greenhouse Gases Through Emissions from Land-Use Change", Science, 319(5867), pp. 1238–1240.

Shaw, J., W. Walton & J. Farrington (2003) "Assessing the potential for a 'railway renaissance' in Great Britain", Geoforum, 34(2), pp. 141–156.

Sims R. et al. (2010) "An overview of second generation biofuel technologies", Bioresource Technology, 101(6), pp. 1570–1580.

SQM (2009) "SQM Lithium Resources and View of the Lithium Industry", presentation given by Patricio de Solminihac, Lithium Supply Markets 2009, Santiago, Chile, January 2009. Available at: http://www.galaxyresources.com.au/documents/MetalbulletinEventsPatriciodeSolminihac.pdf [Live: March 2010].

Storkey, A. (2007) "A motorway-based national coach system", Bro Emlyn – for peace and justice, http://www.bepj.org.uk/wordpress/wp-content/2007/03/motorway-based-coach-system.pdf [Live: March 2010].

Storkey, A. (2009) "The immediate feasibility of a National Coach System", paper prepared for **zero**carbon**britain**2030 Transport seminar 30 June 2009 [unpublished], 27 June 2009.

Tahill, W. (2006) "Ground Zero: The Nuclear Demolition of Ground Zero. Incontrovertible Proof that the World

Trade Centre was destroyed by Underground Nuclear Explosions". Available at: http://www.nucleardemolition.com/GZero_Sample.pdf [Live: March 2010].

Thundersky (2009) "Technical Introduction of Thundersky's super-low floor pure electric city bus", Thundersky Energy Group Ltd leaflet. Available at: http://www.thunder-sky.com/pdf/2009212153723.pdf [Live: March 2010].

TNT (2008) *Sure we can: Corporate responsibility report 2008*, Amsterdam: TNT N.V.

Transport for London (2009) "Hybrid Buses", TfL [online]. Available at: http://www.tfl.gov.uk/corporate/projectsandschemes/2019.aspx [Live: March 2010].

Upham, P., K. Anderson & L. Wood (2003) "Assessing airships for freight transport", *Freight and Transport Review*, Spring 2003, pp. 94–95. Available at: http://www.publicservice.co.uk/pdf/freight/spring2003/FT4%20Paul%20Upham%20ATL.pdf [Live: March 2010].

Vera-Morales M. & A. Schäfer (2009) "Final Report: Fuel-Cycle Assessment of Alternative Aviation Fuels", University of Cambridge Institute for Aviation and the Environment, April 2009. Available at: http://www.omega.mmu.ac.uk/Downloads/Final-Reports/10%20Final%20Report%20Sustainable%20Fuels%20for%20Aviation.pdf [Live: March 2010].

Vision Motor Corp (2009) "Vision Tyrano", Vision Motor Corp [online]. Available at: http://www.visionmotorcorp.com/maxvision.htm [Live: March 2010].

von Braun, J. (2007) "When Food Makes Fuel: The Promises and Challenges of Biofuels", Keynote address at the Crawford Fund Annual Conference, Australia, 15 August 15 2007. Available at: http://www.ifpri.org/sites/default/files/publications/2007jvbcrawfordkeynote.pdf [Live: March 2010].

Williams, K., E. Burton, & M. Jenks (eds) (2000) *Achieving Sustainable Urban Form*, London: Routledge.

Figure sources

Copyright (2010) **zero**carbon**britain**2030. Adapted from Department for Transport (DfT) (2008) *Carbon Pathways Analysis: Informing Development of a Carbon Reduction Strategy for the Transport Sector*, London: The Stationery Office (Fig. 1.3, p. 15).

Copyright (2010) **zero**carbon**britain**2030. Based on data from DfT (2008) *Carbon Pathways Analysis: Informing Development of a Carbon Reduction Strategy for the Transport Sector*, London: The Stationery Office (Fig. 3.11, p. 61; Fig 3.13, p. 63).

Copyright (2010) **zero**carbon**britain**2030. Based on data from Department for Environment, Food and Rural Affairs (Defra) (2008) *2008 Guidelines to Defra's GHG Conversion Factors: Methodology Paper for Transport Emissions Factors*, London: The Stationery Office.

Copyright Riversimple LLP.

Copyright (2010) **zero**carbon**britain**2030. Based on data from Defra (2008) *2008 Guidelines to Defra's GHG Conversion Factors: Methodology Paper for Transport Emissions Factors*, London: The Stationery Office.

Copyright (2010) **zero**carbon**britain**2030. Based on information presented in Baker *et al.* (2009) "Review of Low Carbon Technologies for Heavy Goods Vehicles", report prepared for DfT, June 2009. Available at: http://www.dft.gov.uk/pgr/freight/lowcarbontechnologies/lowcarbon.pdf [Live: March 2010]. Image of truck: Agata Urbaniak (http://www.sxc.hu/photo/1102433).

Copyright (2010) **zero**carbon**britain**2030. Based on the Four E's model methodology, as discussed in Defra (2009) *Changing behaviour through policy making*, London: DEFRA. Available from: http://www.defra.gov.uk/sustainable/government/documents/change-behaviour-model.pdf.

Copyright (2010) **zero**carbon**britain**2030.

Chapter 6
Motivation and behavioural change

> **❝ I have gained this by philosophy: that I do without being commanded what others do only from fear of the law. ❞**
>
> Aristotle

Introduction

Climate change and energy insecurity are caused by the way we live, and will be limited by the actions we take. In the UK, the energy we use in our homes and for personal transport is responsible for almost 43% of the nation's CO_2 emissions (based on data for 2008 from the Department of Energy and Climate Change [DECC], 2010). At home, people can reduce energy use and emissions by buying energy-efficient appliances; by using them less; and by insulating their homes, whether that is by supporting a government-organised retrofitting scheme or by organising a retrofit themselves. Out and about, people can adopt public transport or walking and cycling as their default transport mode; use electric cars when these modes are not applicable; and generally travel less. People can also purchase food and consumer goods that have been made using less energy or producing lower emissions; and they can support further and tougher action from government and business.

In the previous two chapters, it has been demonstrated that significant energy use reductions can be achieved in the buildings and transport sectors. Technology and legislation will play crucial roles, for example through the introduction of low carbon vehicles or the enforcement of high-efficiency building standards. As discussed elsewhere, these measures will be supported by wider policy drivers which make high carbon products and services more expensive, as well as business models which will ensure that those with limited access to capital can still access low carbon technologies and benefit from well-insulated, energy-efficient homes. Therefore the products and services produced with lower emissions will also become the cheaper options, and this will motivate many audiences to change.

The public response, direct and indirect, to the technological advances and legislative changes discussed in other chapters will affect the speed at which a zero carbon Britain can be made a reality. Because mitigating climate change involves action in numerous sectors, public attitude change will be essential for legislation to prove effective and new technology be adopted. For example, Darby (2006) notes that "consumption in identical homes, even those designed to be low-energy dwellings, can easily differ by a factor of two or more depending on the behaviour of the inhabitants". Public engagement will limit the likelihood that mitigation in one sector, enabled by regulation, will lead to greater emissions levels in another.

This chapter examines several of the strategies responsible government (at all levels) and civil society can use to motivate effective voluntary behavioural change in the adult British population, over a short- to medium-time frame (i.e. by 2030). This chapter focuses on ways to instigate behavioural change which support energy efficiency and emissions reduction strategies; in other words, it is focused on behavioural change for climate change mitigation. However it may become increasingly necessary to examine how we can influence behavioural coping strategies for a changing climate.

Lorenzoni *et al.,* (2007) define engagement as "an individual's state, comprising three elements: cognitive, affective and behavioural". In other words, effective engagement relies on knowing about climate change, caring about it, and being motivated and able to take action (ibid.). Government and organisations seeking to achieve behavioural change may do so by increasing knowledge of and changing attitudes towards the subject (or a range of interlinked subjects), including one's perception of personal responsibility, so that people voluntarily take action; or by changing behaviour itself, regardless of whether people "care" about the subject, through compulsion or incentives.

This chapter first discusses the value action gap in the UK with particular attention paid to the social and psychological determinants of behavioural change. It examines the key stated barriers to action as proposed by members of the public and the possibilities for overcoming these barriers and even turning them into motivators. It then examines in greater detail three proposed strategies to overcome these barriers and encourage a voluntary change of behaviours and attitudes: social marketing, identity campaigning, and community-led action.

The value-action gap

Numerous studies have demonstrated a widespread awareness of environmental problems generally, and of climate change specifically, amongst the UK population.

For example, in 2007 and 2009, surveys of public attitudes and behaviour towards the environment were conducted for the Department for Environment, Food and Rural Affairs (Defra)[1]. 99% of respondents in both surveys reported that they had heard the terms "global warming" and "climate change", and most respondents said they knew "a fair amount" about these terms (Thornton, 2009)[2].

Similarly, the majority of people recognise that their everyday behaviours contribute to these environmental problems. In the 2009 Defra survey, 85% of respondents indicated that they thought climate change was caused by energy use, and only 27% believed that their everyday behaviour and lifestyle did not contribute to climate change (ibid.). 55% agreed with the statement "I sometimes feel guilty about doing things that harm the environment" (ibid.).

This knowledge and concern has translated into some action. Almost half (47%) of the respondents to the Defra 2009 survey said they did "quite a few things" that were environmentally-friendly, and a quarter (27%) said they were environmentally-friendly in "most or everything" they did. Just 2% reported that they did not do anything (ibid.). Similarly, a little more than a third (36%) of respondents said they thought they were doing either "quite a number of things" (27%) or "a lot of things" (9%) to reduce their energy use and emissions. These numbers marked quite an improvement on the 2007 survey, showing progress on action. 55% said they would like to do either "a bit more" (47%) or "a lot more" (8%) to help the environment (ibid.).

Whilst many profess to care about climate change, and an increasingly large proportion of the population are undertaking some actions to reduce energy use, the vast majority are continuing with patterns of behaviour that make the problem worse. For many people there is a gap between their relatively high level of concern about the environment and their actions – the "value-action gap" (also known as the "attitude-behaviour gap"). The causes of this gap between attitude ("I agree this is the best course of action") and behaviour ("but I am not doing it") can be explained in terms of personal, social and structural barriers to action (American Psychological Association [APA], 2009; Lorenzoni et al., 2007). Different barriers often overlap or work in conjunction to limit behavioural change. However, these barriers can be tackled, and some aspects which in certain situations act as barriers to action, can even be turned into motivators of action.

Any individual's attitude and behaviour will be shaped by individual values, emotions, habits, mental frameworks, personal experiences and skills, the specific social setting of the individual, and structural constraints. Attitudes on climate change and energy security also derive to a significant extent from general societal norms. Behaviour is further mediated by individuals' understandings of personal responsibility (Jackson, 2005; Stoll-Kleeman et al., 2001).

[1] 2,009 adults were interviewed in 2009; 3,618 adults in 2007.

[2] It should be noted that these surveys are based on self-reporting of knowledge and behaviour, which may not accurately reflect the actual knowledge and behaviour of all respondents.

For example, Schwartz (1977, cited in Jackson, 2005) has suggested in his Norm Activation Theory that the intention to perform a pro-environmental or pro-social behaviour is based on the acceptance of personal responsibility for one's actions and an awareness of their consequences.

There are a number of stated rationalisations for inaction, discussed further below, that are relatively common amongst different groups of the public. These rationalisations may be interpreted as manifestations of a psychological resistance against recognising the enormity of the climate change problem and the need for major lifestyle change (Lertzman, 2008); and also as a means to reduce the anxiety, guilt and threats to self-esteem that may arise from recognition of one's personal contribution to the problem (Crompton & Kasser, 2009). They are best explained in terms of dissonance and denial.

DISSONANCE AND DENIAL

Cognitive dissonance is the uncomfortable feeling caused by holding two contradictory ideas simultaneously (Festinger, 1957). These "ideas" may include attitudes and beliefs, the awareness of one's behaviour, and facts. In general, individuals experiencing dissonance seek either to resolve it, by changing their attitudes, beliefs, and behaviours; or seek to deny or displace it, by justifying or rationalising their current attitudes, beliefs, and behaviours

(Stoll-Kleeman *et al.*, 2001). A large proportion of people have chosen to justify current behaviours and inaction rather than embrace change. To overcome the dissonance created in their minds they rely on socio-psychological denial mechanisms.

Denial is an unconscious defence mechanism for coping with guilt, anxiety and other disturbing emotions aroused by reality. Denial in this context constitutes not only active denial of the climate science but also an inability to confront the realities of its impacts and take action. It includes cognition (not acknowledging the facts); emotion (not feeling or not being disturbed); morality (not recognising wrongness or responsibility) and action (not taking active steps in response to knowledge). Cohen (2001) suggests three forms of denial:

- **Literal denial:** the facts are denied either because of genuine ignorance, calculated deception, or an unconscious self-deception or aversion to disturbing truths.
- **Interpretive denial:** the facts are not denied but the conventional interpretation is disputed either because of genuine inability to grasp meaning or because of attempts to avoid moral censure or legal accountability.
- **Implicatory denial:** there is no attempt to deny the facts or their conventional interpretation but justifications, rationalisations, and evasions are used to avoid the moral imperative to act, for example, "it's not my problem", "I can't do anything", "it's worse elsewhere".

Active denial remains a significant response to climate change science, and this is joined by several forms of interpretive denial against different aspects of the science, such as the scale and speed of its impacts. Other rationalisations for inaction or limited action demonstrate different forms of implicatory denial. These rationalisations help assuage guilt, reinforce victim status, justify resentment or anger towards others, and heighten the costs of shifting away from comfortable lifestyles (Stoll-Kleeman et al., 2001; Stoll-Kleeman, 2003). Terms such as "global warming", "human impacts", and "adaptation" are themselves a form of denial - scientific euphemisms that suggest that climate change is out of human control (Marshall, 2001).

Rationalisations for inaction

This section discusses the key rationalisations given by individuals for not taking actions which reduce energy use. These rationalisations are not exclusively used by those who refuse to take any action. Many rationalisations are also used by those who are taking some action as well, as an unconscious mechanism to limit the scope for change. Neither are each of these rationalisations used exclusively; they are often used in conjunction with each other in both complementary and contradictory combinations. Finally, this section also highlights possibilities for communications to respond to these rationalisations, and this is discussed further in terms of different behavioural change strategies later in this chapter.

At their most basic, the rationalisations for inaction highlighted below can be categorised as based on either non-conventional interpretations of various aspects of the climate science, on the diffusion of responsibility for action, or on the ability to change and desirability of that change.

REINTERPRETING THE THREAT

Lack of knowledge

"I don't know": As has been shown, many people have demonstrated a basic awareness and understanding of climate change as well as the will to do a bit more to limit their environmental impact. Yet the public has a much lower level of understanding about what they can do and especially what will make a difference. 55% of respondents to the Defra 2009 survey stated that they needed more information on what they could do to be more environmentally-friendly (Thornton, 2009). Given that information on climate change is widely available in the UK, government and environmental organisations must consider whether this information can be made more appropriate for different audiences (see Box 6.1).

Uncertainty, scepticism and distrust

"I don't believe it": A common reaction to the extreme anxiety created by the threat of climate change and the social upheaval it will engender is active scepticism and denial, either of climate change wholesale or of specific caveats of the climate science, such as the importance of anthropogenic contributions.

In the 2009 environmental attitudes and behaviours survey for Defra, respondents' opinions were divided on the comment "the so-called 'environmental crisis' facing humanity has been greatly exaggerated" (Thornton, 2009). 47% disagreed with this statement but 15% agreed with the statement and a further 15% neither agreed nor disagreed (ibid.). This shows quite a high degree of scepticism and uncertainty amongst a significant minority (15%) of the population.

People interpret new information on the basis of pre-existing knowledge and beliefs, drawing on broader discourses than simply scientific knowledge (Lorenzoni *et al.*, 2007). Sometimes this mental model serves as a filter, resulting in selective knowledge "uptake" (CRED, 2009). People unconsciously seek to reduce cognitive dissonance through a confirmation bias. A confirmation bias makes people look for information that is consistent with what they already think, want, or feel, leading them to avoid, dismiss, or forget information that will require them to change their minds and, quite possibly, their behaviour (ibid.).

The importance of mental models and the confirmation bias can be demonstrated by the rapid rise of uncertainty and scepticism amongst the UK public between late 2009 and early 2010. In February 2010, a poll of 1001 adults for the BBC showed that 25% of those questioned did not think global warming was happening, an increase of 10% since a

similar poll was conducted in November 2009 (Populus, 2010). Larger proportions also felt that global warming claims were exaggerated and doubted the anthropogenic nature of climate change (ibid.). The rapid rise in scepticism can be partially attributed to a number of high-profile stories of minor errors made by climate scientists, a prolonged cold snap in the UK, and the Copenhagen climate summit which took place between the two polls. These events may have contributed to the "confirmation" of scientific uncertainty and political disagreement amongst those who were already uneasy about the climate science, the rate of societal change the science suggests is necessary, and the proponents of such change.

This case also demonstrates the importance of the media's representation of the issue. The media tends to highlight the areas of scientific and political disagreement, rather than the significant levels of consensus, and this suggests to laypeople that scientific evidence is unreliable.

Some groups intrinsically distrust messages from scientists, government officials, the media, or other information sources. Communications should therefore be delivered by sources or spokespersons deemed trustworthy and credible to the audiences targeted. It will be essential for the environmental movement to forge links with all sections of the media. As discussed in Box 6.1, there are a number of ways to improve the presentation of climate science communications generally.

Communicators should consider the pros and cons associated with combating high-profile proponents of climate denial directly. It will also be necessary for communicators to reflect on the psychological motivations underlying active denial.

The belief that the climate change threat is distant

"It won't affect me": Another common reaction is the argument that climate change is not relevant to the individual now: the impacts will happen in another place, to other people, in another time. For example, just over a fifth of respondents (21%) to the 2009 Defra survey agreed with the statement that "the effects of climate change are too far in the future to really worry me" (Thornton, 2009).

The American Psychological Association (2009) suggests that individuals are often less concerned about places they do not have a personal connection to. If conditions are presumed to be worse elsewhere, individuals might also be expected to have less motivation to act locally (ibid.). In a multinational study, members of environmental groups, environmental science students, and children were asked about the seriousness of, and their sense of responsibility for, various environmental problems at the local, national, continental and global level. Uzzell (2000) found that people ranked environmental problems as more serious at increasing areal scales. Yet feelings of responsibility for the environment

were greatest at the neighbourhood level and decreased at increasing scales. Although people felt that they were responsible for the environment at the local level, they perceived relatively few problems here.

The lesson for communicators may be to frame where possible climate change as a local and near-term problem (see Box 6.1). It may also be appropriate to highlight the losses associated with inaction rather than the benefits offered from action, as people have a natural tendency to undervalue future benefits against the present, and are generally risk-averse, more concerned with limiting damages than exploiting opportunities (CRED, 2009). Communicators must however understand that the role of place attachment is complex, and can be contradictory. For example, it can be deployed to gain strong support for pro-environmental policies but can also lead to local opposition to essential environmental infrastructure such as wind farms (APA, 2009).

Fatalism and the "optimism bias"

"It's too late"; "It's out of my hands": Some people's inaction is due to a belief that whatever happens will be the will of God or Mother Nature (APA, 2009), or that technology will solve the problem (Spence & Pidgeon, 2009). For others, inaction is due more to a fatalistic attitude; that is they think it is too late to do anything about climate change, and argue that it is therefore a waste of time to try and mitigate climate change (ibid.). Appropriate

Box 6.1 Improving the communication of climate science

There are many ways of improving climate change communications to encourage a more positive response from a wider spectrum of the population. Climate science information presented on its own often does not impart a sense of urgency in most audiences (Center for Research on Environmental Decisions [CRED], 2009). For example, effort spent deciphering scientific jargon can prevent the public from concentrating on the actual message. Certain terminology can therefore be used in communications which are both easier for the public to understand and have more appropriate connotations. For example, "carbon pollution" evokes connotations of dirtiness and poor health, whereas "carbon dioxide emissions" is more scientific but does not evoke strong connotations (Platt & Retallack, 2009).

Similarly, it is common for the public to overestimate the uncertainty of climate science. For example the Intergovernmental Panel on Climate Change (IPCC) uses likelihood terminology when discussing the effects of climate change. However the probability range assigned to each level does not necessarily correlate with the probability range the public imagine is associated with each level, with the effect that laypeople feel that the climate science is more uncertain than it actually is (Budescu et al., 2009).

Moreover, it is hard for many to really comprehend how dramatic the effects of global temperature increases of a few degrees will be, given that every day far greater temperature variations occur (CRED, 2009). The "weather" frame of reference suggests to many that climate change is out of human control (APA, 2009). Additionally, the risk appears distant in time and in space, encouraging the view that climate change will not affect them (ibid.).

Climate change communications should grab the attention of the audience, support them to have a fuller understanding of the causes and effects of climate change, and motivate them to take action. This requires more vivid descriptions of the problem, by trusted spokespersons, which can be achieved for example through clear comparisons, the use of personal anecdotes of the impacts of climate change, and local or national examples (CRED, 2009; McKenzie-Mohr & William, 1999). When the impacts of climate change are discussed at the level of their home or locality, the issue is more clearly "felt". In other words, climate change moves from being a scientific concern to a local/personal problem; or, from a cognitive issue to an affective issue.

Feeling vulnerable and at risk is critical to moving people to action (APA, 2009). Psychological literature on this point indicates substantial evidence that "fear framing" will initiate action, provided that individuals feel that the issue is directly relevant to them and that they have some degree of control to act in response to the problem (see APA, 2009; Stern, 2005). When control is absent, internal psychological defences, such as denial, come into play (APA, 2009; Spence & Pidgeon, 2009). Climate communicators should therefore seek to frame emotive messages alongside positive, credible steps which people themselves can take (McKenzie-Mohr & William, 1999; Spence & Pidgeon, 2009).

At the same time however, communicators must be aware that the juxtaposition of discourses highlighting the awesome scale of climate change with discourses emphasising small, mundane responses implicitly raises the question of how the latter can really make a difference (Retallack et al., 2007). This type of framing may ultimately be counterproductive by encouraging audiences to switch off or become habituated to the messages that they receive (CRED, 2009; Retallack et al., 2007). Hulme (2008) suggests that fear framing may play into the hands of climate sceptics claiming that such messages are "alarmist", and increase many people's perception that climate change is exaggerated.

The links between the climate science and the actions necessary to mitigate climate change should be made more explicit. One way of making solutions more clearly relevant is to provide information at the point of energy use, for example, with smart meters (Boardman and Darby, 2000, cited in Lorenzoni et al., 2007). Explaining how each sustainable action relates to climate change mitigation and the relative importance of different actions in terms of reduced energy use, should increase people's understanding of the issue generally and could assist the adoption of more challenging but significant behaviours.

spokespersons can go some way to undermine these arguments, however, both fatalism and the optimism bias can be seen as psychological tools to ignore the dominant discourse and limit exposure.

REINTERPRETING RESPONSIBILITY

Scapegoating, disempowerment and projection

"It's other people's fault"; "Others should lead": Because climate change is a global problem, it has a large social dimension, and this lends itself to the denial of personal power and the blaming of others. Some people attribute principle blame for the causes of climate change onto others: "The south blames the north, cyclists blame drivers, activists blame oil companies, and almost everyone blames George Bush" (Marshall & Lynas, 2003). They argue that their individual impact is not as great as others, and therefore that they should not be held responsible for taking mitigation action.

Many accept a level of responsibility for the causes of climate change but feel that others should bear responsibility for instigating action. The global interconnected nature of climate change means that many believe they cannot influence it. Whilst it is certainly true that any individual's influence is limited, group inaction is reinforced through the psychological response of diffusing responsibility (Cohen, 2001; Marshall & Lynas, 2003). In this way, climate change is susceptible to the "passive bystander effect". This describes a failure of people to act in emergency situations when they are in a group. Individuals assume that someone else will intervene and so each individual feels less responsible to take action (Marshall & Lynas, 2003). Additionally, individuals also monitor the reactions of others to see if they think it is necessary to intervene, and because everybody is doing the same thing, nobody acts (ibid.).

Similarly, projection is a psychological strategy by which the individual's own powers and abilities are projected onto others who, it is hoped, will take care of the problem and can be criticised and attacked if they do not (Randall, 2005). In the UK, people have demonstrated an eagerness for government and business to lead by example, and are hence less impelled to act on their own. Respondents to Defra's environmental survey were asked to say what they thought were the most important issues the Government should be dealing with. "Environment/Pollution" was the third most frequently cited response to the question in 2009 (it was the fourth in 2007), with more respondents mentioning this as a more important issue for the Government than crime (Thornton, 2009). This indicates that the Government has a popular mandate to undertake strong action on climate change.

Dissatisfaction with lack of action by government, business and industry

"Others aren't doing enough": The lack of a visible public response reinforces the passive bystander effect, by offering a rationale for inaction: 'Surely', people reason, 'if it really is that serious, someone would be doing something' (Marshall, 2001). Many people are de-motivated by the lack of action taken so far by governments and businesses, especially given the pre-existing distrust that some have towards such actors. This demonstrates the great importance of demonstrating collective public action and government leadership to develop new social norms.

Freeriders

"I'm not doing anything unless enough others do it too": The collective action problem describes a situation where individuals in any group attempting collective action will have incentives to "freeride" on the efforts of others if the group is working to provide or conserve public goods (see Olson, 1965). Freeriders gain the benefits of others' actions without the costs associated with it. Because climate change involves costs, a key concern preventing meaningful action by many (individuals, organisations and governments) is of others freeriding. In the Defra 2009 survey, 35% agreed with the statement "it's not worth me doing things to help the environment if others don't do the same" (Thornton, 2009).

People report that they will follow action by government and business in the UK. In 2009, 58% of respondents agreed to the statement "If government did more to tackle climate change, I'd do more too" (Thornton, 2009). 58% also agreed with the statement "If business did more to tackle climate change, I would too" (ibid.).

People are especially concerned about free-riding at an international level. 45% agreed with the comment "it's not worth Britain trying to combat climate change, because other countries will just cancel out what we do" in 2009 (although this marked a significant improvement from 2007 when over half of respondents (54%) agreed with the statement) (ibid.).

Freeriding is a genuine concern, because the changes necessary to limit climate change and reduce energy insecurity cannot take place without global collective action. However, a large number of people have a highly distorted understanding of the distribution of global emissions contributions, especially on a per capita basis. Dominant communications often implicitly or explicitly support the view that emissions from other countries and other users are chiefly "responsible" for climate change. A concern about freeriding may also be used by some as an excuse for inaction, and an attempt to deny individual moral responsibility. The combined result of freeriding, and the more general diffusion of responsibility, is a mass paralysis of action (see Box 6.2).

Box 6.2 Dispelling blame through communal responsibility

People require strong social support and the validation of others to undertake significant behavioural change. Rather than debating who is to blame, communications can emphasise the value of communal efforts, and government can support action within communities and social networks. Communications should not seek to assign blame to any individual group or nation. These will promote resentment, inaction and even reaction. Rather, they should be forward-looking at the solutions, and evoke a collective spirit.

Movements such as 10:10, which asked individuals and organisations to pledge to reduce their carbon footprint by 10% in 2010, are based on high participation. Whilst people make individual voluntary commitments, which can easily be reneged on, the power of the movement is based on the psychological benefit associated with communal effort. On the other hand, the diffusion of responsibility effect is much less significant in smaller groups, so simultaneously supporting local action groups, could fortify action.

Efforts by government to engage the public will be most effective if they are integrated as part of a coherent and consistent response to climate change. Government must act on climate change, and ensure that this action is visible to the public. To limit concerns about freeriding, the benefits of "leading the way" can be emphasised at all scales. On the international scale, the UK can gain by investing in renewable energy industries and by decarbonising before fossil fuel scarcity and energy price increase the challenges associated with it. Within the UK, economic incentives and public congratulations can encourage "early adopters", and help foster new social norms, which show that mitigation behaviours are both economically efficient and high status.

DOUBTING THE DESIRABILITY OF CHANGE AND ABILITY TO CHANGE

Social norms and expectations

"It's not normal": Another important type of potential barrier relates to dominant social and cultural norms, whether national or specific to an ethnic, religious or lifestyle group. Social norms are customary rules of behaviour, implicit and explicit, that coordinate our interactions with others (Durlauf & Blume, 2008). Norms can be enforced through the simple need for coordination amongst large groups of people, through the threat of social disapproval or punishment for norm violations, or through the internalisation of norms of proper conduct (ibid.). Through internalisation, socially-acceptable ways of behaving become ingrained as unconscious habitual behaviours – unquestioned and intractable.

Social and cultural norms strongly influence individual attitudes on climate change (Stoll-Kleeman et al., 2001), and their willingness to change. Relevant social (interpersonal) norms to climate change mitigation might include widespread social expectations about what kind of house or car one should have to be seen as successful (APA, 2009). In today's society, ownership and consumption are important status symbols (Lorenzoni et al., 2007), whilst green living has traditionally been seen by some as undesirable, "weird", or "hippy" (ibid.). The lifestyle change necessary to create a zero carbon Britain is divergent to the current aspirations held by many.

The perception of what the individual should do, if anything, depends on whose opinion is important to the individual, and what their opinion is (APA, 2009; Smith & Strand, 2008; Stern, 2005). For example, when homeowners are told the amount of energy that average members of their community use, they tend to alter their use of energy to fit the norm (Schultz et al., 2007 cited in APA, 2009), increasing or decreasing their energy use accordingly.

It is possible to influence norms to promote positive actions, so that they are a motivator for positive behavioural change. If certain actions and behaviours can be "socially normalised", then the potential for widespread adoption is significant. For example certain pro-environmental behaviours such as recycling or not littering have become internalised social norms amongst large segments of the UK population; in other words, they are seen as the "right thing to do".

Lyons et al. (2001) undertook a major study of attitudes towards waste minimisation in Surrey. Focus group members associated recycling with undesirable role models from bearded old men to eco-warriors and "outdoors types" to simply "someone boring". Four years later however there had been a shift in the image of a recycler. Whilst recyclers were still largely considered to be "do-gooders" and left-wing, they were also seen as likeable, energetic people; typified by an older, female, locally-employed person with a family, car and a garden (Nigbur et al., 2005). As the urgency and acceptability of such environmental action continues, negative stereotypes are likely to diminish further. This should also prove the case for other pro-environmental behaviours.

It is important for communicators to be aware of the implications of environmental behaviours on self-image and identity, so that stereotyping may be built on, combated or incorporated into communications and interventions (Spence et al., 2008). Communicators should also be aware of the enormous value of role models and opinion leaders in fostering new social norms (Collins et al., 2003). The opportunities for supporting new norms are discussed further later in this chapter.

Reluctance to change and low prioritisation of climate change

"I don't want to"; "other things are more important": People tend to be very reluctant to make major changes to their lifestyle. 48% of the Defra survey respondents agreed that "any changes I make to help the environment need to fit in with my lifestyle" (Thornton, 2009). People take a risk when they make changes to lifestyle, especially to those elements closely associated with a sense of self-identity. The change may not work, it may waste time and money, and it may be mocked by others (APA, 2009). In this way, individual behaviour interacts strongly with dominant social norms.

Climate change offers a typical "tragedy of the

commons" scenario. The classic example of the "tragedy of the commons" involves a common grazing area. Each family adds more cattle to its own herd to increase its own wealth, but the common area eventually becomes overgrazed and everybody suffers (see Hardin, 1968). With climate change, it is in many individuals' rational short-term interest to continue emitting high levels of carbon emissions. However the results, for everybody, of the resultant increased global temperatures, will be devastating.

Of course it is not simply hard-nosed short-term rationality preventing widespread, deep action. Some people attempt to suppress thought about the issue so that they do not have to confront the reality (Marshall, 2001). Apathy, limiting exposure, keeping thoughts in the present, and seeking pleasurable diversions are all psychological defence mechanisms for supplanting anxiety-arousing information with other material (Crompton & Kasser, 2009; Marshall, 2001). Others may deliberately indulge in wasteful activities as a misplaced reaction against knowledge of the climate science.

Even when a willingness to change exists, many habitual behaviours are extremely resistant to change (APA, 2009). This is exacerbated by the fact that most people have more pressing priorities relating to family and finances, and even local environmental issues, which take priority over consideration of the impacts of lifestyle on the climate.

Structural constraints and habit

"It's too hard": Structural barriers to change are those that exceed an individual's influence. Such barriers include economic barriers, such as a lack of credit, which prevents poorer households from retrofitting their homes or buying more energy-efficient vehicles. Working patterns and demands on time can also act as structural barriers to certain behaviours (Defra, 2008). Institutional barriers are also significant. These include regulatory restrictions and "split incentives" in which one actor pays the costs of action while another gets the benefits, such as energy efficiency retrofits in rental housing (APA, 2009). Structural barriers to action may also be based on geography and infrastructure, for example it is particularly difficult to reduce car use in rural areas where public transport is limited (ibid.). Overcoming many of these structural barriers are discussed with specific reference to different sectors within other chapters of the report, and so will not be elaborated on here.

Of course, people may cite structural constraints whereas in reality they are not as significant as imagined, and are more the product of habit. As well as interventions to remove or reduce structural constraints, policymakers can support people to actively break habits, and create new ones. Tackling habits may involve getting people to consciously examine their habits, or to change activities for a length of time so that new habits are formed. Periods of transition offer particularly good opportunities to help people develop new, more sustainable habits, for example, when moving house, people are more likely to be interested in low carbon retrofitting for their new properties as well as in new modes of travelling around their new neighbourhood (Defra, 2008; Spence & Pidgeon, 2009).

FROM BARRIERS TO MOTIVATORS

Clearly, without a sophisticated understanding of the psychological and emotional reactions to change, the transition to a zero carbon society could be slowed or significantly hampered. Running (2007) draws parallels between the major upheavals involved in mitigating climate change and the grieving process, which involves several stages including denial, bargaining and the eventual acceptance of the change. Running suggests that psychologists can help people to accept the necessary lifestyle changes using similar tools to those used to support the grieving process. The psychological and emotional effects of mitigating climate change (and possibly of climate related disasters) are so significant that the American Psychological Association (2009) recently called for the development of materials for psychologists and councillors specifically to help them deal with patients who are experiencing stress and anxiety.

An understanding of how people respond emotionally to requests for major behavioural change can also help us understand how

to design effective communications and policy interventions. Traditional behavioural change strategies have often focused solely on removing structural barriers to behavioural change and have overlooked social and personal (psychological) barriers. The UK Government has increasingly attempted to design interventions which reflect a broader understanding of the barriers to and motivators of behavioural change. The Four E's model devised by the Government attempts to respond to several of these critical barriers (Defra, n/d). The model envisages four stages which together catalyse public behaviour change:

1. **Enable:** providing education, skills and information so that people can make responsible choices, and making these choices easy with easily accessible alternatives and suitable infrastructure.
2. **Encourage:** using regulation, price signals, taxes, league tables and rewards to encourage and where necessary enforce appropriate behaviour.
3. **Engage:** encouraging others to get involved through targeted communications.
4. **Exemplify:** Government taking the lead by applying strategies proactively in government policies and on public estates.

The "enable" and "encourage" stages reflect traditional policy to effect behavioural change. For example, it recognises the need for structural barriers to be removed in the enabling stage and the use of regulatory mechanisms in the encourage stage. However the model also reflects a greater understanding of the social and personal barriers to change. Through the "engage" and "exemplify" stages it recognises the need for better and more targeted communication as well as for government leadership. Whilst the Four E's model is a positive step towards a more holistic approach to public behaviour change, it would benefit from closer attention to the psychological barriers and motivators of action.

The results of studies examining the socio-psychological elements of the value-action gap need to be carefully translated into appropriate policy action (Stoll-Kleeman et al., 2001). Policies to mitigate climate change, in both the private and public sphere, may compete with important values, such as the right to choose or freedom of expression. Therefore, policy measures designed to mitigate climate change must be framed with sensitivity to pre-existing cultural frameworks, to limit the reinforcement of existing prejudices and the resultant resistance and hostility (ibid.). Insights from the behavioural sciences can further advise the discourses and strategies required for society to debate the economic and structural changes required (Spence et al., 2008). Social marketing strategies are based on responding to the barriers discussed above, by adopting the same "ways of thinking" that individuals or groups use to express these barriers.

Communications should also acknowledge the emotions underlying the coping strategy, and respond to these empathically (Crompton & Kasser, 2009). Stoll-Kleeman et al., (2001) consider the possibilities of working directly with groups to address their dissonances and denials, with the goal of eventually producing a more participatory and ethically-centred citizenry. This is one methodology advocated by proponents of the identity campaigning approach.

Behavioural change strategies

Attempts by government to affect public behaviour have traditionally been based on providing knowledge through big publicity campaigns and changing behaviour through regulation and economic incentives (taxes and grants) (Defra, n/d) (Retallack et al., 2007). These are powerful and necessary tools, but to engender rapid and significant behavioural change, they should be supplemented by other behavioural change strategies which more appropriately target the social and personal barriers to action.

Michael Rothschild (2009) argues that there are three classes of behavioural change strategies, which should be used in combination: regulation, education, and marketing. Rothschild's term "education" might be better termed "information" to avoid confusion with the formal education process. Rothschild (1999) hypothesises that the more significant the behavioural change required, and the more essential it is for the good of society, the more necessary it will be for regulation to enforce action[3]. However, regulation is not in itself very effective at altering attitudes (the affective element of engagement) (Lorenzoni *et al.*, 2007). Given the complexity of energy use, regulation on its own will not be effective in enforcing public behaviour change.

Information (the cognitive element of engagement) on the other hand will tend to alter both attitudes and behaviour, but usually only when the required behavioural change is minor and the benefits to the individual are significant and immediate (Rothschild, 1999). Climate change mitigation behaviours do not fall into this category, because whilst taking action against climate change offers enormous long-term societal benefit, the immediate benefits to individuals are less tangible (CRED, 2009). Moreover, the level of behavioural change required is major; climate change challenges almost every aspect of modern lifestyle (Lorenzoni *et al.*, 2007).

Legislation and technology will be most effective if there is a simultaneous shift in public mindset to reinforce change in government and business (see Box 6.3). The UK government has increasingly attempted to use some social marketing methodologies to combat intractable social and environmental problems, including climate change. Social marketing attempts to alter specific behaviours, rather than knowledge or attitudes per se. This is primarily by offering incentives (economic and non-economic) appropriate to the person targeted. Through social norms, individual actions can accumulate to such a degree as to foster changes in attitudes, which in turn fosters wider and deeper behavioural change amongst society as a whole.

More recently, an identity campaigning approach to dealing with climate change has developed. This critically examines the relationship between affluence, materialistic values, well-being, community engagement and environmentally-damaging behaviours (Uzzell, 2008). Identity campaigning is focused on the affective element of engagement, and aims to change behaviour by appealing to intrinsic values and directly altering the way people "feel" about the environment and social and environmental problems.

Whilst both social marketing and identity campaigning approaches recognise the advantages of action within community settings, they are principally aimed at the activities of third parties leading a behavioural change strategy, whether that is government or environmental organisations. However, there has been a simultaneous grass roots community-led counter movement, often called "transition culture", which has recognised that effective change can only come about when people themselves want it and are willing to work for it. The section on community-led action examines the benefits and challenges associated with community-led action, and the opportunities for government and other external parties to assist these movements.

[3] Of course legislation may also be used to create opportunities for voluntary behavioural change, for example, by establishing education and marketing campaigns.

BOX 6.3 Rationing. Public acceptance of regulation: learning from history

As is demonstrated throughout the report, the Government can influence choices in the personal, business and government sectors. One of the most significant actions recommended in this report for government to take, in terms of its direct impact on the general public, is carbon pricing, so that the true costs of emissions are accounted for. Efforts to internalise the cost of carbon, whether through trading or taxation, will impact individual purchase decisions by altering the relative cost of different options. Carbon pricing will provide a significant impetus to active behaviour change, as lower carbon choices will also become the cheaper choices.

Communications can seek to not only change specific values and behaviours directly relating to energy consumption, but also foster social demand for, and acceptance of regulation (Ockwell *et al.*, 2010). Communications can also draw from the lessons learnt from the management of and communication surrounding the rationing system in World War Two.

In World War Two, and following it, the public accepted that rationing of basic goods was a temporary but necessary measure. Communications reinforced the necessity and economic fairness of rationing. These were assisted by the underlying trust in central government, and positive memories of rationing during the First World War (Roodhouse, 2007). Black markets in goods and ration stamps existed but these were limited (ibid.).

Trust in government can no longer be taken for granted, yet it is still possible for government to assure the public that the ration or price levels of any carbon rationing or pricing scheme implemented are fair; that the system is administered transparently and fairly; and that evaders will be caught and penalised (i.e. that freeriding will not be permitted) (ibid.). Placed alongside "positive" communications which reinforce the benefits of decarbonisation, whether these are moral, social or financial, these will contribute to the necessary cultural shift towards a zero carbon Britain.

Social marketing

Social marketing is rooted in behavioural science and utilises marketing tools traditionally used in the commercial sector to effect long-term behavioural change for the benefit of society. Fundamentally, social marketing is about understanding people's reasons for behaviour, and on the basis of that understanding, offering something, whether it is information, fun, money, or a feeling of belonging, so that they change their behaviour (Smith & Strand, 2008). It is also action-oriented. Social marketing seeks behavioural change. Awareness, unless accompanied by behavioural change, constitutes failure of the programme (ibid.).

Critical aspects of the social marketing approach include targeting, engaging and embedding action. These tools are now used in many disciplines. The following sections discuss these in the context of the UK and efforts to change behaviour on environmental and climate change mitigation actions.

AUDIENCE TARGETING IN THE UK

Any behavioural change strategy must respond to the key concerns held by different people – a "one size fits all" approach may be of limited impact. Segmentation according to shared characteristics proxy for the dominant mix of concerns, motivations and behaviours held by each individual within the group. Segmentation therefore aims to break up the entire audience into smaller groups for better targeting of strategies and messages.

Rather than creating lists of actions which follow on from one single message, segmentation can help guide the targeting of messages and promotion of actions that are most appropriate to the views, values and constraints felt by different groups of people. For example, reducing domestic carbon emissions need not only be couched in terms of "saving the planet": it can also be marketed to different audiences as a way of reducing fuel bills, keeping up with the Joneses or even taking back power from electricity companies (Rose, 2009).

Segmentation also leads to prioritising behavioural change in some groups over others. Groups which are particularly resistant may not be targeted specifically given the limited resources available, but they may grow less resistant to change when they see others adopting the new practices (Uzzell, 2008). The diffusion of innovation theory states that an "innovation", whether it is a new technology or a new behaviour, spreads among different parts of the community beginning with "early adopters" and moving to "late adopters" (Smith & Strand, 2008).

Traditional segmentation has occurred according to socio-demographic group, for example, on the basis of the audience's

education level, gender, age or income, or according to geography, for example, by region or community size. The Energy Saving Trust (EST, 2007) has segmented its audience by socio-demography and by geography to better tailor their advice packages. Belief in climate change does broadly vary by socio-economic status and location, as do the social and structural barriers to action. For example, belief in climate change amongst respondents to a poll in February 2010 was 80% amongst the AB socio-demographic group and 70% amongst the DE group (Populus, 2010).

Other segmentation models focus more specifically on the behaviours that practitioners seek to change or get adopted. The "states of change" model helps explain how people's behaviour changes, from contemplation, to action and maintenance, and it can also be used as a way of segmenting the population (APA, 2009). Segmentation may also take place along willingness and ability to take action, by defining groups in terms of "would, could, can't, don't and won't" (Uzzell, 2008).

Segmentation models can also be focused on specific issues. Defra has developed a segmentation model based on people's responses to its 2007 attitudes and behaviours survey. The segmentation model, "The Framework for pro-environmental behaviours", divides the public into seven different audience segments, each sharing a distinct set of attitudes and beliefs towards the environment, environmental issues and behaviours (Defra,

Fig. 6.1 The Defra segmented strategy for pro-environmental behaviours

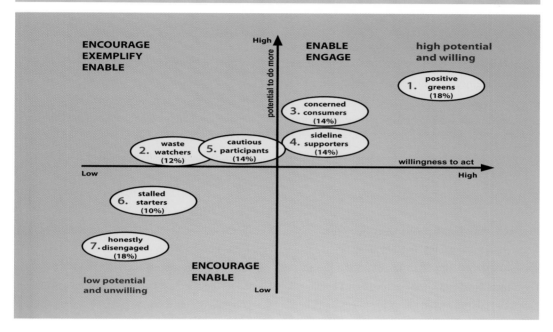

The Defra pro-environmental behaviour segmented strategy model (2007).
People within segments 1, 3, and 4 are expected to have quite a high potential and willingness for action and therefore the emphasis of interventions should be on those that enable and engage by tackling external barriers such as a lack of information, facilities and infrastructure and motivating action through appropriate communications and community action (Defra, 2008). People within segments 2 and 5 also seek government and business to lead by example. Segments 6 and 7 are generally less willing to act and therefore some level of choice editing in product availability or regulation is likely to be necessary to instigate action (ibid.).
Source: Adapted from Defra (2008).

2008) (Figure 6.1).

The Defra researchers identified the types of sustainable behaviour members of each segment are already likely to engage in, the types of behaviour that they could be encouraged to engage in, and the motivations and barriers to this behaviour. For each segment, Defra suggest the most appropriate mix of broad interventions, based on their Four E's framework.

It therefore distinguishes between those groups which are largely willing and able to act and require only facilitation, those which require more active support to adopt new behaviours, and those which will follow behaviours only once they have become normalised. This research has inspired the ACT ON CO_2 campaign (Box 6.4).

Another popular national-scale segmentation

Box 6.4 The ACT ON CO$_2$ campaign

The Government launched the ACT ON CO$_2$ campaign in July 2007. It aims to provide clear and trustworthy advice on climate change to the public and to provide easy, achievable ways for everybody to reduce their carbon footprints (ACT ON CO$_2$, 2008). It also aims to demonstrate Government leadership on the issue. The campaign aims for action on 12 headline behaviour goals in the areas of personal transport, eco-products, and energy, water and waste in the home. These include a range of low- and high-impact behaviours as well as easy and hard behaviours (ibid.).

Low-impact but easy behaviours were included to potentially engage large numbers of people not previously concerned by climate change, whilst higher impact but harder behaviours were more appropriate for targeting particular population groups (ibid.). Targeting of behaviours is based on the segmentation model produced by Defra, with the current focus on segments 1 to 5, representing 72% of the population (ibid.). The campaign also envisages six steps of engagement with the issue (disengagement, contemplation, preparation, action, maintenance, embedded) based on the states of change model.

model is based on the values underlying behaviours. The segmentation model, developed by research organisation Cultural Dynamics Strategy & Marketing, consists of three broad "motivational groups", each of which covers four more specific "value modes" (Figure 6.2). Values are distinct from attitudes – they are "more central to the self, transcend objects and situations, and determine attitudes and behaviour" (Crompton, 2008).

This three-level segmentation is broadly based on three of the five tiers of the hierarchy of needs identified by the American humanistic psychologist Abraham Maslow (Rose & Dade 2007):

- "Pioneers" (inner-directed, concerned with ethics, exploration and innovation, and comprising approximately 40% of the UK population),
- "Prospectors" (outer-directed or esteem-driven, concerned with wealth, position and glamour, and comprising approximately 40%), and
- "Settlers" (security-driven in Maslow's terms, concerned with home, family and community, and comprising approximately 20%).

There has been a gradual fall since the 1970s in the proportion of Settlers and a consummate rise in the proportion of other groups, which has led to a shift away from traditional values (Rose, 2007). In terms of the adoption of new behaviours in society, Pioneers lead, Prospectors follow, and then Settlers follow the Prospectors (ibid.). Pioneers are currently the largest motivational group, and Prospectors seek to emulate them by adopting their behaviours, although not their underlying motivations. Nonetheless, Rose points to qualitative research which suggests recent shifts in attitudes amongst Prospectors to those that might be typified as belonging to Pioneers (ibid.).

Fig. 6.2 Value modes segmentation model

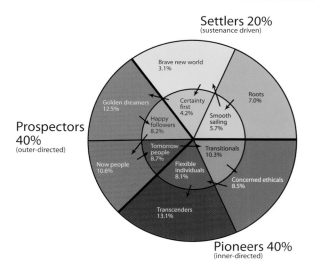

The Defra pro-environmental behaviour segmented strategy model, with percentages of the adult British population for each segment (2007).
There are 12 specific "value modes", which fall into three broad "motivational groups". Individuals tend to move across value modes segments over the course of their lifetime. Arrows show how people typically move across these value modes segments.
Source: Adapted from Rose & Dade (2007) and Rose et al. (2008).

ENGAGING AND MOTIVATING ACTION

Social marketing aims to remove the barriers to action. The aim of the social marketing practitioner is to make the behaviour appear fun, easy, and popular to the audience. This relates to three of the key constraints and motivations affecting behaviour: the perceived consequences of the action; self-efficacy (an individual's belief that he or she can do a particular behaviour); and social norms (Smith & Strand, 2008). Obviously, what is felt to be fun,

easy and popular will vary by audience group. Techniques from the commercial marketing sector can be adopted that are appropriate for each group. The marketed behavioural change also needs to be considered against "competing behaviour". This includes current behavioural patterns, inertia, alternative behaviours, and commercial marketing itself where this promotes negative behaviours (ibid.; MacFadyen *et al.*, 1999).

Social marketing theory suggests that both the climate science and the appeal and action experience should be personal and local; visual, engaging and memorable. People have also been shown to respond well to face-to-face contact and in particular when approached by others from a similar background.

In California, home assessors were trained to present information about energy efficiency in people's homes vividly, for example by adding up the cracks around doors and windows and comparing it to a football-sized hole in the wall (Gonzales, 1988, cited in McKenzie-Mohr & William, 1999). This very powerfully demonstrated the scale of the problem. During home assessments, householders can also be encouraged to become actively involved, for example, by being invited to feel levels of loft insulation and so on. The results from such efforts were extremely positive (McKenzie-Mohr & William, 1999). Where actions are entertaining, they will be more memorable, and more likely to be repeated.

Targeting Prospectors

We now consider broad strategies for targeting action amongst the Prospector group. Experts recommend targeting the Prospector group to adopt climate mitigation behaviours, because they "turbo-boost whatever they do" (Rose, 2007)[4]. They are representative of "Middle England": a key group of consumers who also tend to be swing voters and are therefore disproportionately important to societal change (Platt & Retallack, 2009) (Rose et al., 2007).

Traditional approaches to communication on environmental issues are often devised by

Pioneers and have been information-driven and alarm-sounding (Platt & Retallack, 2009; Rose et al, 2008). These tend to appeal to other Pioneers, for whom the promise of future societal benefit is sufficient to engender action. However the majority of the population do not hold the same values as this group and have not been engaged in significant action thus far.

Prospectors are primarily concerned with improving their status, and are therefore attracted by "value for money, convenience, cachet and tangibility" (Rose et al., 2007). Any environmental benefits arising from the actions they take, or products and services they buy, are a welcome consequence of their actions rather than the motive for it.

Actions should therefore be marketed as easy, quick and cost-effective. Cost-effective does not necessarily mean cheap: the cost of an action needs to be considered as referring not only to the financial cost, but also to the time, effort and psychological cost associated with it. The more uncertainty and possible downsides involved, and the more effort implied, the greater the incentive to find a way to ignore the call for action (Rose, 2009). Actions could also be reformulated into status-enhancing products and services.

The status of an action is linked to its visibility. Prospectors in particular, respond well to rewards and competition, and both Prospectors and Settlers want to see action, and endorsement of their own action, from others, whether from their peers, celebrities,

* It should be noted that the Prospector group encompasses four more specific motivational groups, and several authors have focused on specific strategies to target each of these groups.

governments or corporations. Government has an important role to play by leading by example as well as by sponsoring marketing campaigns and generally by incentivising and removing the barriers to effective action, for example by promoting "green" products and services or by reducing the financial cost of decarbonisation.

EMBEDDING BEHAVIOURAL CHANGE

The social marketing approach adopted by government and environmental organisations may be partially responsible for the significant increase in the number of people stating that they undertake some actions on the environment between 2007 and 2009 (as based on Defra's pro-environmental attitudes and behaviours survey). There are a number of ways in which the social marketing discipline aims to build upon initial, generally small actions; from providing reminders, targets and rewards, to building on and developing new social norms.

A number of very simple strategies can move people from the initial take-up of a new behaviour to its maintenance. Prompts are a simple strategy to help individuals remember to perform specific actions such as turning off a light, recycling more or buying greener goods. Making recycling bins more attractive, for example, by having them painted by local schoolchildren, and located conveniently, will act as a positive visual reminder for recycling.

Providing goals or targets, and offering rewards, whether they have a monetary value,

or simply involve praise, can further motivate action (Genovese, 2008). Oral and written pledges or promises to change a specific behaviour have been shown to be very effective in the maintenance of behaviour, especially if publicised, and if the person is already pre-disposed to undertake the new behaviour (McKenzie-Mohr & William, 1999). The more often new behaviours are performed, the more they are ingrained and reinforced until becoming automatic.

There are a number of ways of supporting people while they adopt these new behaviours. People learn best by watching the behaviour of others. Therefore modelling new behaviours through simple, step by step demonstrations of sustainable behaviours either in person or through the media can help disseminate these behaviours (Genovese, 2008; McKenzie-Mohr & William, 1999). Similarly, by offering opportunities to "try things out" with appropriate support, and by providing feedback on actions, people are more likely to overcome anxiety and mental barriers to action (CRED, 2009; Genovese, 2008).

These strategies work to embed specific actions. However several theories suggest that undertaking one action can lead to further consistent actions, and wider behavioural change in individuals as well as in society (see Jackson, 2005). This is known as "positive spillover". The "foot-in the-door" effect is when behavioural change increases an individual's likelihood to adopt a second and more ambitious behavioural change (ibid.). The cognitive dissonance theory suggests that when people act responsibly in one area, they may feel a strong internal pressure to behave "consistently" through responsible actions in other areas (Crompton & Thøgersen, 2009) (McKenzie-Mohr & William, 1999) . The more actions people undertake, the greater the internal pressure they feel to undertake deeper behavioural change, rather than rationalising wasteful behaviour.

Changing a specific behaviour also allows individuals to acquire knowledge or learn skills that make the adoption of other pro-environmental behaviours easier, both of which may influence future behaviour (Crompton & Thøgersen, 2009). A key aim of every requested action then is to encourage people to see themselves as environmentally-concerned, and to encourage further commitments to action (McKenzie-Mohr & William, 1999).

The development of new social norms is another way in which behavioural change can become embedded within society. The passive bystander effect stops operating as soon as sufficient people become involved (Marshall & Lynas, 2003). Programmes can attempt to actively affect norms by involving high status individuals, giving recognition, prizes and awards to those who are engaging in positive behaviour, and by publicly demonstrating the desired behaviour (Genovese, 2008). The process of social diffusion occurs people introduce family or peers to new behaviours. Those who are already heavily engaged in climate mitigation behaviour have an important function to play by acting as role models and sharing their personal experiences with others (ibid.). Communicators may also directly target opinion leaders for more rapid diffusion of new social norms. The "pester power" of children was the only incentive found to work across all motivational groups (Rose et al., 2007).

DO MOTIVES MATTER?

The social marketing approach in the UK involves appealing to the values and attitudes that different segments of the population currently hold, rather than espousing the values and attitudes that environmental organisations and policymakers may want them to hold. As such, pro-environmental actions may be promoted using reasons which do not directly relate to the environment, such as social status or financial self-interest.

Critics of the approach argue that whilst appealing to non-environmental motives for undertaking pro-environmental actions may be the most effective way of motivating the greatest number of people to adopt easy, cheap behaviours, "it seems less clear that this approach will engender public appetite for radical changes in how we live – and a commensurate popular acceptance of, or demand for, far-reaching policy change" (Crompton, 2008). They point to evidence which demonstrates that for long-term, deep behavioural change, it matters not only what people do but also why they do it.

The "rebound effect" suggests that an individual undertaking one pro-environmental behaviour may act in a less pro-environmental manner in other areas if that individual is not doing the behaviour for primarily environmental reasons (Crompton, 2008), for example, someone may buy a hybrid car for status, but then drive it further, or use an energy saving light bulb but because it is cheaper, keep it on when they leave the room, undoing some of the benefits of the initial action. If people are doing something because they care, they will do it better and more consistently.

Moreover, because mitigating climate change will involve more than one or two actions by individuals, the effects of taking one pro-environmental action on taking another needs to be considered carefully. The "single action bias" (or contribution ethic) suggests that people are willing to undertake just one or two actions and then feel that they have "done their bit" (CRED, 2009; Crompton & Thøgersen, 2009). Since most people do easy and cheap actions first, these may in practice be justified over doing more difficult and costly but also more significant actions, especially if environmental communications or campaigns serve to exaggerate the environmental benefits of these small steps (Crompton & Thøgersen, 2009).

Self-determination theory distinguishes between the motives for engaging in a particular behaviour, and the types of goals that an individual pursues through this behaviour.

The willingness of an individual to suffer inconvenience and difficulty in engaging in pro-environmental behaviour is related to their motivation for doing so (Crompton, 2008). When an activity is pursued to uphold a set of "intrinsic" values (for example, personal growth, emotional intimacy, or community involvement), engagement is likely to be more energetic and persistent than when the activity is pursued to uphold a set of "extrinsic" values (such as the acquisition of material goods, financial success, physical attractiveness, image and social recognition) (ibid.).

According to critics of the social marketing approach, this means that communications encouraging pro-environmental behaviour by appealing to extrinsic goals, such as financial benefit or status, may be of limited effectiveness when it comes to motivating someone to undertake hard actions such as flying less. When people are concerned with the underlying issue, they are more likely to undertake difficult actions (Crompton, 2008).

The above critiques can inform better social marketing strategy. Indeed, in recent years there have been efforts to ensure social marketing goes "upstream" and is used much more strategically to inform both policy formulation and strategy development. This is called "strategic social marketing". Here the focus is on using a strong customer understanding and insight to inform and guide effective policy and strategy development over long time periods and at a variety of scales (see Macgregor, 2007).

Box 6.5 Consumption, identity and pro-environmental behaviours

Many people today gain their identity partly through consumption, much of which requires energy. Although psychological needs drive consumption, consumption is often a poor method of satisfying those needs. Self-identity is not permanently satisfied, nor anxiety permanently relieved, by new purchases. New aspirations are formed and perpetuated in discourses about quality of life, becoming interpreted as "needs" rather than "wants" (Crompton, 2008; Lorenzoni et al., 2007; Randall, 2005).

Materialism in general is associated with less social cohesion and more ecological degradation, and it has been demonstrated that materialistic people are less altruistic and less concerned about human and animal welfare and the environment (Crompton & Kasser, 2009). As highlighted in the Policy and economics chapter, in which a move away from using GDP as a key national measure is discussed, once basic needs are met, increased levels of income do not correlate with life satisfaction. Indeed, at European levels of wealth, increased economic activity leads to lower levels of subjective well-being. This may be due to the exclusion of other areas of activity, which are more closely associated with happiness and satisfaction (see Kahneman et al., 2006).

On the other hand, there is evidence that an intrinsic value orientation leads to higher levels of subjective well-being, and that such orientations also lead to greater engagement with pro-environmental behaviour (see Crompton, 2008; Crompton & Kasser, 2009). When we distinguish between our basic psychological needs, for example for safety and security, competence, connectivity and autonomy (Kasser, 2003), and the actions taken to reach those needs (consumption), we can see that the objective can be met in other ways. We can have the same, or even a better, quality of life with less material goods. One strategy for dealing with the environmental implications of materialism is therefore to work with people to prioritise intrinsic values, and create new identities based on these rather than on materialistic, "extrinsic" values (Crompton, 2008).

Green consumerism

A more substantive critique of the social marketing approach is that implicitly or explicitly it condones and even encourages materialism and consumerism. To appeal to many segments of the population, and especially to the Prospector groups, forms of "green consumerism" have been advocated, from new products, to share-schemes, to green and ethical labelling schemes (Platt & Retallack, 2009). These techniques offer obvious opportunities to collaborate with manufacturers and retailers and disseminate a green message widely, which should act as a gateway step toward significant action.

But there are several problems associated with this approach. Firstly, green consumerism is unlikely to lead someone to choose to spend money on inconspicuous measures like loft insulation (Crompton, 2008). Secondly, it also raises problems of "greenwashing", where companies overstate the environmental and ethical benefits of their products, to sell more.

More significantly however, advocating green consumerism, is still advocating consumerism. In practice, green consumerism does not necessarily result in simple product substitution (people buying more environmentally friendly versions of the same things). Nor does it necessarily encourage less overall consumption, because the underlying motivations behind consumption are not challenged (Crompton, 2008) (see Box 6.5); although it might have that effect if "green" goods are more expensive.

Identity campaigning

In response to the critiques of social marketing discussed above, and based on political campaign ideas, "identity campaigning" has evolved. Identity campaigning seeks to develop a clearly articulated moral vision, based on the values held by the base of the movement, rather than the people the movement is trying to reach. As Schellenberger and Nordhaus (2004) argued in their highly influential book, *The Death of Environmentalism*, "we need to create a consistent vision, working with others, based on our shared values."

As well as a critique of traditional marketing approaches, this approach is greatly influenced by research by George Lakoff and the political campaign ideas utilised successfully in the 2004 U.S. Republican campaign (see Lakoff, 2004). Here it was shown that having a strong sense of values helped the candidates and was even successful at attracting people who held different values in some areas but who could understand the consistent values-based message of the candidate.

Like social marketing then, identity campaigning places a high emphasis on values. However, rather than segmenting populations according to the dominant values shared by different groups, the identity campaigning approach recognises that everybody is influenced to differing extents by the same types of values, and aims to appeal to the intrinsic types of values. By motivating behavioural change through appeals to intrinsic values, deeper and more sustainable change can be achieved than through appeals to extrinsic values such as status or wealth (see Box 6.5). For example, motivating people to save energy by awakening or re-awakening a genuine concern for the environment and the environmental and social repercussions of

> **The transition to a sustainable society cannot hope to proceed without the emergence or re-emergence of some kinds of meaning structures that lie outside the consumer realm.** (Tim Jackson cited in Crompton, 2008)

climate change and fossil fuel depletion, will limit the rebound effect and is more likely to inspire positive spillover.

Within an identity campaigning approach therefore, the challenge for policymakers and communicators is to draw upon the intrinsic values held by all, and to challenge the promotion of extrinsic values by business and industry seeking profit, but also by organisations seeking positive social change.

CHALLENGING EXTRINSIC VALUES

Extrinsic values include a focus on goals such as the acquisition of material goods, financial success, physical attractiveness, image and social recognition (Crompton, 2008). Extrinsic values can be challenged for example through tackling advertising and by highlighting the ways in which the marketing industry manipulates motivations. They can also be challenged through redefining social progress, for example by highlighting the negative implications of materialism and by challenging the assumption that economic growth as it is currently defined is positive for society (Crompton, 2008; Crompton & Kasser, 2009). As well as behavioural change in the personal sphere, identity campaigning seeks people to become politically engaged with the issue and to push for strong action by government and business.

Communicating and campaigning from an identity perspective also involves not confusing or contradicting any message by appealing to competing values, which creates cognitive dissonance. Corner *et al.* (2009) gives the example of an email encouraging car sharing stating economic, social, and environmental reasons together invokes opposing values, thrift or status for example, and so gives a feeling the overall argument is weak.

FOSTERING INTRINSIC VALUES

Government and NGOs can also support the fostering of intrinsic values and goals such as self-acceptance, affiliation and community feeling. This will involve engaging with psychological responses to climate change in a much deeper way: in order to help activate positive environmental behaviours, environmental organisations will need to understand and allow the expression of people's anxiety at climate change (Crompton & Kasser, 2009).

Supporting the flourishing of intrinsic values across society requires a sustained programme of repeating these values over and over – through short-term campaigns, and through the discussion of intrinsic values in non-environmental campaigns. Marshall (2009) calls on us to frame environmental communications in terms of gender, equality, and resource or freedom issues, all of which also appeal to intrinsic values.

Research suggests that people who consider themselves part of nature, or see nature as part of their "in-group", also exhibit more positive environmental attitudes and behaviours. For example, one large cross-cultural study of residents in 14 countries found that connectedness to nature emerged as one of the strongest and most consistent motivational predictors of pro-environmental behaviour (Crompton & Kasser, 2009). It is therefore important for people to gain experiences of "nature" (Box 6.6).

Social support groups have been used to help people live by intrinsic values, so supporting certain types of community projects may be beneficial for fostering not just individual actions but also new norms. Government and other interested organisations can support audiences to think for themselves about what they can do, rather than suggest actions, by providing technical expertise and the appropriate infrastructure and institutions necessary to support such participatory problem-solving (Crompton & Kasser, 2009; Kaplan' 2000). Reflecting on the reasons for current sustainable behaviour may be a key way in which related values can be changed (Spence & Pidgeon, 2009). WWF-UK, through their "Natural Change" project, have encouraged people to engage with nature and reflect on their behaviour within natural environments to instigate a deep level of engagement and behavioural change (see Harrison, 2009).

The ultimate aim is to achieve a heightened consciousness and feeling of connectedness with wider ecological and social processes, leading individuals to take responsibility for lifestyle changes and stimulate change and awareness in others (APA, 2009).

CRITIQUES OF THE IDENTITY CAMPAIGNING APPROACH

Of course, attempting to draw out intrinsic values and bring them to dominance is a much greater challenge than appealing to different groups on the basis of extrinsic values.

Tackling the promotion of extrinsic values in society should have a positive effect on the effectiveness of communications which promote intrinsic values, helping to release currently suppressed values and aspects of identity. Nonetheless, communications appealing to intrinsic values have generally failed to appeal to those outside the Pioneer audience group. Creating a societal shift in dominant values therefore, is likely to be slow and time-consuming.

However, it may be a very effective way of communicating with people who might be categorised as "light green" - in other words, already undertaking a few actions and with some concern about climate change, resource depletion and similar issues - as a means of supporting not just one or two actions, but of supporting a much deeper level of behavioural change and a level of engagement with the issues that leads to public support for stronger government action and public mobilisation.

BOX 6.6 Putting "nature" into formal education

As we begin to decarbonise the country we will also need to examine how the formal education system can begin to assist in this process. Concepts of sustainability are increasingly being built into the curricula of all subjects. As well as being a channel for conveying basic information about possible mitigation activities education also plays a crucial role in shaping the attitudes, values and behaviours of children in later life. We must therefore ask what kinds of attitudes and values citizens will need, to live in and maintain a zero carbon Britain.

Recent research provides some insights into how education can create citizens likely to be responsible and concerned for the natural environment. In a study of approximately 2000 adults, Wells and Lekies (2006) found that childhood participation in activities such as playing in the woods, camping, hunting and fishing led to positive environmental attitudes in later life. There is clearly a case for starting immediately to build more wild and outdoor play activities into the national curriculum in order to engender positive environmental behaviours later down the line.

Community-led action

Community action usually appeals to intrinsic values and is an excellent way of rapidly developing, diffusing and embedding new social norms. Community action promotes behavioural change across several strands of sustainability, not just on single isolated behavioural steps. Yet many current environmental campaigns engage with the community in only a fairly shallow way; promoting communities as the settings for change, but not reflecting sufficiently on their capacity to constitute the drivers of change (see Table 6.1).

Despite this, there are already many community-led initiatives acting on climate change, energy use and other socio-environmental issues. Some of these follow guidelines, models or schemes developed elsewhere and promoted by non-governmental organisations (NGOs), such as Transition Towns, CRAGs (Carbon Reduction Action Groups), The Greening Campaign, and Camps for Climate Action. Other communities find their own unique way forward. In this short section we will briefly summarise the benefits and pitfalls of working in this way as well as how government can support this community-inspired action[5].

Our communities are often places of trust, sharing and learning (EST, 2007; Preston *et al.*, 2009). Community-led initiatives are therefore more likely to be successful in the long-run than schemes imposed from the "outside". Community action offers a trusted resource base. Local actors, whether neighbours, friends, social networks, local councils, independent agencies, are generally the most trusted sources of information and advice (EST, 2007; Roberts *et al.*, 2004). This aids the momentum of projects, and helps the social diffusion of new ideas and norms. Freeriding is also limited in smaller social groups. There is a vested interest in success when the time and effort to start and run the project comes from local people's input and the

Table 6.1 Approaches to community participation

Approaches to participation	Energy related examples
Informing communities	Traditional EEAC activities
Consulting with communities	Wind energy development or other large energy project development
Deciding together (delivery community)	Traditional warm zone or area-based independent of activities
Acting together (delivery partnership with community)	Isolated examples of energy supplier activities e.g. Scottish & Southern Energy (as part of smart meter trials) and British Gas (Green Streets)
Supporting individual community-led initiatives	East of England Development Agency (Cut your Carbon), NESTA (Big Green Challenge), local "Climate Friendly Community Initiatives" and NGOs e.g. Marches Energy Agency, The Greening Campaign
Solely community-led initiatives	Examples include Transition Towns, Carbon Rationing Action Groups (CRAGS), and some isolated communities

Approaches to community participation with examples from energy provision and efficiency programmes.
There is a continuum in terms of the extent of community participation. Government should move from primarily informing and consulting with communities to also supporting community-led initiatives.
Source: Adapted from Preston et al. (2009).

outcomes directly effect the community in a positive way.

Engagement and participation are likely to be high at the local level when the issues and actions are presented as locally relevant (Action with Communities in Rural England [ACRE], 2009; Luna, 2008; Marshall, 2009). Of course, the links between climate change and local-scale impacts should not be overstated, given that exaggeration could lead to dismissal of the climate science (Centre for Sustainable Energy [CSE] & Community Development Xchange [CDX], 2007). The issue of climate change differs significantly from the subject of most community-based initiatives, which tend to be based on local and immediate known beneficiaries and have a clear sense of agency. Nonetheless, issues relating to energy security and other community benefits associated with decarbonisation, for example linked to health and safety, remain locally significant.

Furthermore, people are more likely to take responsibility as a citizen at the local scale (Nash & Lewis, 2006; Uzzel, 2008). Being part of a wider movement offers a level of participation which behavioural science touts as a key motivation for environmentally-responsible behaviour (De Young, 2000; Kaplan, 2000) and connection

> **Community-led initiatives add significant value to sustainable energy activity, enhancing levels of trust, empowerment, engagement, longevity and the capacity to evolve and progress to encompass all aspects of sustainable living. In particular, such initiatives are not usually solely driven by the 'quick wins' associated with installing measures, as per local authority and energy agency-led schemes, but strive for long-term sustainable living.**
>
> (Preston *et al.*, 2009)

to social identities beyond that of individual action. The local scale offers a middle ground between (slow moving) national and global politics, top-down policies and official rhetoric; and individual actions which can seem too insignificant (Segnit & Ereaut, 2007; Transition Network, 2010). Individuals gain satisfaction from group achievements and from benefits and gains, whether these are personal or to someone else (CSE & CDX, 2007). Some people are also motivated by knowing that they have recognition and support from authority (ibid.).

THE DIFFICULTIES OF COMMUNITY-LED ACTION

However, community-led action does not hold all the answers and there are lessons to be learnt from experiences on the ground so far as to how they can be made more effective. Firstly, it is essential for any sustained action or project to be able to measure or gauge its success so that it is able to adjust strategies accordingly and remain enthusiastic and realistic. This is often overlooked in community-led action (Preston *et al.*, 2009).

"community-driven activity is often heavily reliant on volunteer time and a few local enthusiasts, the danger being that without the required support or visible achievements, activity and interest will wane. As such, … whilst 'energy and enthusiasm' are a notable strength of the 'bottom-up' grass roots climate change community groups, measureable outputs are key to delivering change, and this may require support (financial and/or 'tools') from a higher level."

Preston *et al.* (2009)

Secondly, such action frequently involves large amounts of time commitment and energy from volunteers, which regularly comes from a small number of enthusiasts leaving the action susceptible to "volunteer fatigue" and dependent on a few individuals who are already engaged and active. One "remedy" to these problems is for outside organisations (such as NGOs, local or national government bodies) to provide additional support.

HOW CAN GOVERNMENT HELP?

Government at all levels can assist the efforts of communities. Care must be taken by both the "giver" and "receiver" of this support so as not to jeopardise the original aims and values of the project (Chatterton & Cutler, 2008). With careful consideration of roles and direction from the community, NGOs and the state can have an important supporting role to play that does not threaten the empowerment and autonomy of the project.

The UK government, through DECC, now plans to capitalise on some of the benefits of working at the community scale through the new Community Energy Saving Programme and the Low Carbon Community Challenge, both of which are exciting developments and which recognise previous success and research at this level. However, whilst demonstrating alternatives through pilots is one important way to engage the public, support needs to be presented as being accessible to all communities, and not dependant on some "special" feature of the community or particular funding opportunity. In particular, where funding has been withdrawn, it has had negative effects on communities, beyond the scope of the initial community group participants (CSE & CDX, 2007).

As at the individual level, an affirmative national policy context which shows how the actions of communities are aligned with government and business, inspires and motivates stronger action. More specifically, support can be offered through the removal of restrictions or objections to innovative ideas. The feed-in tariff offers gradual financial support and therefore might be a very effective support for community-level renewable technology.

Community actors will have most interaction

with local government, and the actions of local authorities can be particularly beneficial in facilitating action and behavioural change. Local authorities can provide resources, technical support and guidance. Members of community action groups have suggested introducing "carbon ambassadors" in local authorities, who would act as a single contact for local groups, limiting the extent to which communities have to negotiate different departments and conventional working hours (CSE & CDX, 2007). Preston *et al.,* (2009) also suggest providing easily available external support on completing funding applications, which currently can consume significant amounts of volunteer time.

Research by the Energy Saving Trust (2007) has found that there are four main types of people, having varying amounts of influence within their communities: Community Changer, Armchair Advocate, Teatime Solvers and Self-contained Singles. These different types of people require different types of support to contribute effectively to community action. Government should support tools and mechanisms which promote wide levels of engagement within communities.

For community action to be truly successful it needs to develop within the context of wider local, regional and national change towards a radically different way of living as suggested by the other chapters in this report. Community action can support these changes, locally, nationally, and even internationally by demonstrating to others that "We have… Now you."

Conclusions

In ***zero**carbon**british**2030*, a huge array of measures will be implemented in every sector to address climate change. Responsibility for many of these measures lies with government and business, although they will obviously impact on individuals and influence their lifestyles. For example, carbon pricing will influence the prices of goods and this will motivate new consumption patterns amongst the population. Individuals and communities must also play an active part in decarbonisation, by accepting, supporting and indeed calling for the societal change that the climate science shows is necessary. This chapter has therefore examined strategies to foster change in the personal sphere, based on a sound understanding of the psychological and social barriers to action.

To move beyond inaction and tokenistic action, we need to recognise that change is challenging. It is critical that policymakers remove structural barriers to action, but we also need to recognise that there are a whole host of personal and social mechanisms which "lock" us into unsustainable actions. Good communications can limit the anxiety we feel towards change, and can inspire us into taking action. Further research within the behavioural sciences, for example into what influences or "motivates" altruism and activism, and how we respond to social and environmental change, can support the design of more focused and supportive communications and behavioural change strategies.

How do we best change behaviour; and to what

extent do we want or need to change attitudes as well? Gardner and Stern (2002) have reviewed evidence concerning strategies focused on changing the information available, changing incentive structures for individuals and groups, changing values, and developing community management programmes. They find that none are sufficient on their own to significantly change environmental behaviour, but that they all contribute, and that the value of each depends on the context.

Social marketing theory suggests that government and NGOs must develop communication strategies focused on the audiences they want to reach, rather than the problem they want to solve. This can be achieved by the promotion of a series of entertaining, tangible and achievable action experiences. Reaching out to those not traditionally engaged with "green" or "ethical" issues can foster new social norms and encourage widespread adoption of new behaviours across society. Legislation and financial tools should be used in conjunction to alter motivations relating to particularly "difficult to change" behaviour.

These techniques are arguably of less value in scaling-up the level of action amongst those who are already committed to a cause, and are unlikely to lead to positive affective engagement. So a simultaneous process of challenging extrinsic values in society, as recommended by identity campaigning proponents, must take place. Social marketing tools are vital, but communicators should consider the long-term ramifications of multiple individual appeals to extrinsic values relating to wealth and social status.

Programmes to help draw out intrinsic values using fun, participatory methodologies amongst important role models and norm leaders may be one way of amalgamating lessons from the social marketing and identity campaigning approaches. Supporting local programmes which attempt to achieve specific behavioural objectives but also foster intrinsic, community-oriented values, is another way.

Wider societal debates on the value of economic growth and traditional measures of societal progress should also be encouraged. We need to fundamentally examine the implications of our dual roles as consumers and citizens in society. In this way, we will achieve more than just limiting the damage currently posed by climate change and fossil fuel depletion. We will also challenge the values, structures and processes that led to this case of overconsumption and resource depletion, and which might otherwise lead to more.

References

Action with Communities in Rural England (ACRE) (2009) "Climate Change: Policy Position Paper", ACRE. Available at: http://www.acre.org.uk/DOCUMENTS/publications/Policypositionpapers/ClimateChange.pdf [Live: March 2010].

ACT ON CO2 (2008) "Act on CO2 Toolkit", Act on CO2. Available at: http://actonco2.direct.gov.uk/actonco2/home/aboutus/toolkit/columnBParagraphs/0/content_files/file0/actonco2toolkit.pdf [Live: March 2010].

American Psychological Association (APA) (2009)

"Psychology and Global Climate Change: Addressing a Multifaceted Phenomenon and Set of Challenges, Report of the American Psychological Association Task Force on the Interface Between Psychology and Global Climate Change". Available at: http://www.apa.org/science/about/publications/climate-change.pdf [Live: March 2010].

Budescu, D.V., S. Broomell & H. Por (2009) "Improving Communication of Uncertainty in the Reports of the Intergovernmental Panel on Climate Change", *Psychological Science*, 20(3), pp. 299–308.

Center for Research on Environmental Decisions (CRED) (2009) *The Psychology of Climate Change Communication: A Guide for Scientists, Journalists, Educators, Political Aides, and the Interested Public*, New York: CRED.

Centre for Sustainable Energy (CSE) & Community Development Xchange (CDX) (2007) *Mobilising individual behavioural change through community initiatives: Lessons for Climate Change*, London: Defra.

Chatterton, P. & A. Cutler (2008) "The Rocky Road to Transition: the transition towns movement and what it means for social change", Trapese: Popular Education Collective. Available at: http://www.trapese.org/ (select About Us tab) [Live: March 2010].

Cohen, S. (2001) *States of Denial: Knowing about Atrocities and Suffering*, Cambridge: Polity.

Collins, J. *et al.* (2003) "Carrots, sticks and sermons: influencing public behaviour for environmental goals", a Demos/Green Alliance report produced for Defra. Available at: http://www.green-alliance.org.uk/uploadedFiles/Publications/CarrotsSticksSermons.pdf [Live: March 2010].

Corner, A. with G. Maio & U. Hahn (2009) "Promoting values for a sustainable Wales", Life Change for a One Planet Wales: Viewpoints, Sustain Wales/Cynnal Cymru. Available at: http://www.sustainwales.com/home/downloads/viewpoints/adamcorner.pdf [Live: March 2010]

Crompton, T. (2008) *Weathercocks & Signposts: The environment movement at a crossroads*, Godalming: WWF-UK.

Crompton, T. & T. Kasser (2009) *Meeting Environmental Challenges: The Role of Human Identity*, Godalming: WWF-UK.

Crompton, T. & J. Thøgersen (2009) *Simple and Painless? The limitations of spillover in environmental campaigning*, Godalming: WWF-UK.

Darby, S. (2006) "The effectiveness of feedback on energy consumption: A review for Defra of the literature on metering, billing and direct displays", April 2006, Oxford Environmental Change Institute. Available at: http://www.eci.ox.ac.uk/research/energy/downloads/smart-metering-report.pdf [Live: March 2010].

Department of Energy and Climate Change (DECC) (2010) "2008 UK final figures – data tables" [spreadsheet]. Available at: http://www.decc.gov.uk/en/content/cms/statistics/climate_change/gg_emissions/uk_emissions/2008_final/2008_final.aspx [Live: March 2010].

Department for Environment, Food and Rural Affairs (Defra) (2008) *A Framework for Pro-Environmental Behaviours*, January 2008, London: Defra.

Defra (n/d) "Changing behaviour through policy making". Available at: http://www.defra.gov.uk/sustainable/government/documents/change-behaviour-model.pdf [Live: March 2010].

De Young, R. (2000) "Expanding and evaluating motives for Environmentally Responsible Behaviour", *Journal of Social Issues*, 56(3), pp. 509–526.

Durlauf, S.N. & L.E. Blume (2008) *The New Palgrave Dictionary of Economics*, 2nd edition, Basingstoke: Palgrave Macmillan.

Energy Saving Trust (EST) (2007) *Green Barometer 3: Communities – The power of one*, November 2007, London: EST.

Festinger, L. (1957) *A theory of cognitive dissonance*, Stanford: Stanford University Press.

Gardner, G. and P. Stern (2002) *Environmental Problems and Human Behaviour*, 2nd Edition, Boston: Pearson Custom Publishing.

Genovese, J. (2008) "Behaviour change for combating climate change", created for the DEC community education branch, January 2008. Available at: http://learningfundamentals.com.au/wp-content/uploads/behaviour-change-for-combating-climate-change.pdf [Live: March 2010].

Harrison, S. (2009) "Natural change: psychology and sustainability", WWF-UK. Available at: http://www.naturalchange.org.uk/wp-content/uploads/NaturalChange_Report_finallowres.pdf [Live: March 2010].

Hardin, G. (1968) "The Tragedy of the Commons", *Science*, 162(3859), pp.1243–1248.

Hulme, M. (2008) "The Conquering of Climate: Discourses of Fear and Their Dissolution", *The Geographical Journal*, 174(1), pp. 5–16.

Jackson, T. (2005) *Motivating Sustainable Consumption: a review of evidence on consumer behaviour and behavioural change*, London: Policy Studies Institute.

Kahneman, D. *et al*. (2006) "Would You Be Happier If You Were Richer? A Focusing Illusion", *Science, 312(5782), pp. 1908–1910*.

Kaplan, S. (2000) "Human Nature and Environmentally Responsible Behavior", *Journal of Social Issues* 56(3), pp. 491–508.

Kasser, T. (2003) *The High Price of Materialism*, London: MIT Press.

Lakoff, G. (2004) *Don't think of an elephant! Know your values and frame the debate – The essential guide for progressives*, Vermont: Chelsea Green.

Lertzman, R. (2008) "The myth of apathy", *The Ecologist*, 19 June 2008.

Lorenzoni, I., S. Nicholson-Cole & L. Whitmarsh (2007) "Barriers perceived to engaging with climate change among the UK public and their policy implications", *Global Environmental Change*, 17(3–4), pp. 445–459.

Luna, M. (2008) "Out of sight, out of mind: Distancing and the geographic relationship between electricity consumption and production in Massachusetts", *Social Science Quarterly*, 89(5), pp. 1277–1292.

Lyons, E., D. Uzzell, & L. Storey (2001) *"Surrey Waste Attitudes and Actions Study: Final Report"*, Report to Surrey CC & SITA Environmental Trust, Social Psychology European Research Institute, University of Surrey. Available at: http://www.surrey.ac.uk/Psychology/EPRG/files/wastestudy.pdf [Live: March 2010].

MacFadyen, L., M. Stead & G. Hastings (1999) "A Synopsis of Social Marketing", Institute for Social marketing, University of Stirling. Available at: http://www.ism.stir.ac.uk/pdf_docs/social_marketing.pdf [Live: March 2010].

Macgregor, E. (2007) "Strategic social marketing: how social marketing can support policy, strategy and implementation", National Social Marketing Centre, 13 March 2007. Available at: http://www.nsmcentre.org.uk/component/remository/func-startdown/67/ [Live: March 2010].

Marshall, G. (2001) "The Psychology of Denial: our failure to act against climate change", *The Ecologist*, 22 September 2001.

Marshall, G. & M. Lynas (2003) Why we don't give a damn, *New Statesman*, 01 March 2003.

Marshall, G. (2009) "Problems with polls, poles, plastic bags and peers", Life Change for a One Planet Wales: Viewpoints, Cynnal Cymru/Sustain Wales. Available at: http://www.sustainwales.com/home/downloads/

viewpoints/george%20marshall.pdf [Live: March 2010].

McKenzie-Mohr, D. & S. William (1999) *Fostering sustainable behavior: An introduction to community-based social marketing*, Gabriola Island, B.C.: New Society.

Nash, N. & A. Lewis (2006) "Overcoming obstacles to ecological citizenship: The Dominant Social Paradigm and Local Environmentalism", in Dobson, A. & D. Bell (eds) (2005) *Environmental Citizenship*, London: MIT Press, pp. 153–184.

Nigbur, D. *et al*. (2005) "Increasing Recycling Through Community Action: Summary Report", Environmental Psychology Research Group, University of Surrey. Available at: www.surrey.ac.uk/Psychology/EPRG/files/SurreyScholarSummaryreport.pdf [Live: March 2010].

Ockwell, D., S. O'Neill & L. Whitmarsh (2010) "Strong climate legislation and public behaviour change – the role of communication", Sussex Energy Group policy briefing 6, January 2010, University of Sussex. Available at: http://www.sussex.ac.uk/sussexenergygroup/documents/behaviour_changeweb.pdf [Live: March 2010].

Olson, M. (1965) *The logic of collective action: Public goods and the theory of groups*, London: Harvard University Press.

Platt, R. & S. Retallack (2009) *Consumer Power: How the public thinks lower-carbon behaviour could be made mainstream*, London: Institute for Public Policy Research (ippr).

Populus (2010) "BBC Climate Change Poll – February 2010", BBC. Available at: http://news.bbc.co.uk/nol/shared/bsp/hi/pdfs/05_02_10climatechange.pdf [Live: March 2010].

Preston, I. *et al*. (2009) *Best practice review of community action on climate change*, Bristol: Centre for Sustainable Energy.

Randall, R. (2005) "A new climate for psychotherapy?", *Psychotherapy and Politics International*, 3(3), pp. 165–179.

Retallack, S. & T. Lawrence with M. Lockwood (2007) *Positive Energy: Harnessing people power to prevent climate change – a summary*, London: ippr.

Roberts, S. with H. Humphries & V. Hyldon (2004) "Consumer Preferences for Improving Energy Consumption Feedback", Report to Ofgem by the Centre for Sustainable Energy. Available at: http://www.cse.org.uk/pdf/pub1033.pdf [Live: March 2010].

Roodhouse, M. (2007) "Rationing returns: a solution to

global warming?", policy paper 54, History and Policy: Connecting historians, policymakers and the media [online]. Available at: http://www.historyandpolicy.org/papers/policy-paper-54.html [Live: March 2010].

Rose, C. (2009) "Climate Change, Warnings & The Car Alarm Problem", Campaign Strategy Newsletter 55, September 2009. Available at: http://www.campaignstrategy.org/newsletters/campaignstrategy_newsletter_55.pdf [Live: March 2010].

Rose, C. & P. Dade (2007) "Using Values Modes", Campaign Strategy.org: modest suggestions for anyone trying to save the world. Available at: http://www.campaignstrategy.org/articles/usingvaluemodes.pdf [Live: March 2010].

Rose, C. with P. Dade & J. Scott (2007) "Research Into Motivating Prospectors, Settlers and Pioneers To Change Behaviours That Affect Climate Emissions", Campaign Strategy.org: modest suggestions for anyone trying to save the world. Available at: http://www.campaignstrategy.org/articles/behaviourchange_climate.pdf [Live: March 2010].

Rothschild, L.R. (1999) "Carrots, Sticks and Promises: A Conceptual Framework for the Management of Public Health and Social Issue Behaviours", Journal of Marketing, 63, pp. 24–37.

Rothschild, M.L. (2009) "Separating Products and Behaviors", Social Marketing Quarterly, 15(1), pp. 107–110.

Running, S.W. (2007) "The 5 Stages of Climate Grief", Numerical Terradynamic Simulation Group, University of Montana. Available at: http://www.ntsg.umt.edu/files/5StagesClimateGrief.htm [Live: March 2010].

Shellenberger, M. & T. Nordhause (2004) The Death of Environmentalism: Global Warming Politics in a Post-Environmental World, New York: Breakthrough Institute.

Segnit, N. & G. Ereaut (2007) Warm Words II: How the climate story is evolving and the lessons we can learn for encouraging public action, London: ippr and EST.

Smith, W. A. & J. Strand (2008) Social Marketing: A Practical Resource for Social Change Professionals, Washington: Academy for Educational Development.

Spence, A. & N. Pidgeon (2009) "Psychology, Climate Change & Sustainable Behaviour", Environment Magazine, November-December 2009.

Spence, A., N. Pidgeon & D. Uzzell (2008) "Climate change – psychology's contribution", The Psychologist, 21(2), pp. 2–5.

Stern, C.P. (2005) "Understanding Individuals' Environmentally Significant Behavior", Environmental Law Reporter, 35(11), pp. 10785–10790.

Stoll-Kleemann, S., T. O'Riordan & C.C. Jaeger (2001) "The psychology of denial concerning climate mitigation measures: evidence from Swiss focus groups", Global Environmental Change, 11(2), pp. 107–117.

Stoll-Kleeman, S. (2003) "Integrating social psychological theories for interdisciplinary global change research", GAIA, 12(4), pp. 325–326.

Thornton, A. (2009) "Public attitudes and behaviours towards the environment – tracker survey: A report to the Department for Environment, Food and Rural Affairs", London: Defra.

Transition Network (2010) "Introduction: Cheerful disclaimer", Transition Towns Wiki. Available at: http://transitiontowns.org/TransitionNetwork/TransitionNetwork [Live: March 2010].

Uzzell, D. (2000) "The psycho-spatial dimension to global environmental problems", Journal of Environmental Psychology, 20(4), pp. 307–318.

Uzzell, D. (2008) "Challenging assumptions in the psychology of climate change", The Australian Psychological Society. Available at: http://www.psychology.org.au/inpsych/challenging_assumptions/ [Live: March 2010].

Wells, N.M. & K.S. Lekies (2006) "Nature and the Life Course: Pathways from Childhood Nature Experiences to Adult Environmentalism", Children, Youth and Environments, 16(1), pp. 1–24.

Figure sources:

Adapted from Department for Environment, Food and Rural Affairs (Defra) (2008) A Framework for Pro-Environmental Behaviours, January 2008, London: Defra (p8; p10).

Adapted from Rose, C. & P. Dade (2007) "Using Values Modes", Campaign Strategy.org: modest suggestions for anyone trying to save the world. Available at: http://www.campaignstrategy.org/articles/usingvaluemodes.pdf (p12). Group population percentage figures from Rose, C., Higgins and Dade (2008) "Who Gives A Stuff About Climate Change and Who's Taking Action?", Campaign Strategy.org: modest suggestions for anyone trying to save the world. Available at: http://www.campaignstrategy.org/whogivesastuff.pdf (p3).

"Meat is a wasteful use of water and creates a lot of greenhouse gases. It puts enormous pressure on the world's resources. A vegetarian diet is better"

Lord Nicholas Stern of Brentford,

Former Chief Economist of the World Bank; Professor and Chair of the Grantham Institute for Climate Change and the Environment at London School of Economics; and author of the Stern Review Report on the Economics of Climate Change.

landuse

Chapter 7
Land use and agriculture

Introduction

This chapter explores a low carbon scenario for land use and agriculture in the Britain of 2030. The **zero**carbon**britain**2030 land use scenario follows the same logical pattern as the rest of the report:

- It looks at all the sources of emissions related to land use and proposes ways to minimise them ("PowerDown");
- It identifies how the demand for land use goods and services can be met with low carbon supply systems ("PowerUp").

There is, however, one key difference: the land use sector has the unique capacity to deliver not only zero carbon, but negative carbon processes. It can do so by capturing and storing CO_2 in soils, plants and products. In all sectors, there are some emissions that cannot entirely be eliminated. These residual emissions must be balanced by equivalent "negative emissions" or "sequestration" processes to achieve zero carbon. In fact, it might even be possible to achieve a "sub-zero Britain" that actively cleans up the atmosphere rather than simply reducing its emission levels to zero. This chapter aims to show how this might be done.

The basic approach is straightforward, and relies mainly on product switching. The agricultural product mix gradually shifts away from high-emitting sectors, mostly grazing livestock, towards nutritionally-equivalent crop products that emit far less. This alone can reduce emissions by 60–70%. But the shift has another crucial effect. It releases large areas of land for energy and sequestration crops. The decarbonisation of the energy and transport system detailed in the other chapters reduces agricultural emissions by 10%, and the remaining emissions are balanced out to zero or beyond by dedicated sequestration crops.

This very simple concept is summarised in Figures 7.1a and b, representing the present situation and the **zero**carbon**britain**2030 scenario proposals respectively.

This "product switch" approach releases a surprising wealth of hidden resources. This chapter shows how, in principle, the land use sector can completely decarbonise itself, mop up the residual emissions from the rest of the UK economy, and at the same time deliver improved food security, healthier diets and enhanced biodiversity.

Fig. 7.1 Emissions from the land use and agriculture system

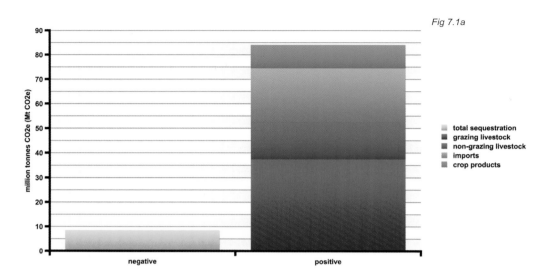

Fig 7.1a

Legend:
- total sequestration
- grazing livestock
- non-grazing livestock
- imports
- crop products

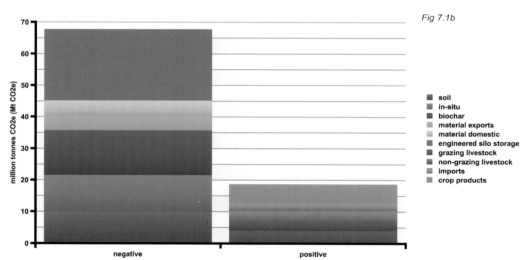

Fig 7.1b

Legend:
- soil
- in-situ
- biochar
- material exports
- material domestic
- engineered silo storage
- grazing livestock
- non-grazing livestock
- imports
- crop products

Balance of positive and negative emissions in a) the current land use and agriculture system and b) the ZCB2030 land use and agriculture system, by product type (million tonnes CO_2e).

Negative emissions, i.e. sequestration, are shown on the left and positive emissions on the right. Currently, sequestration accounts for only a small portion of emissions. In ZCB2030, sequestration will exceed emissions.

METHODOLOGY

The **zero**carbon**britain**2030 project aims to eliminate greenhouse gases from the British economy while delivering at least an adequate, and preferably abundant, level of customary goods and services such as energy, buildings, transport and so on. In the agriculture, food and land use sector, the dominant services are food, biodiversity, energy and carbon sequestration. However, the scenario also has implications for employment, skills, farm economics, rural life, landscape, diet and general culture. All of these need to be considered in the context of decarbonising the sector.

In the present globalised world, Britain has no strict economic need to produce food at all. Agriculture currently contributes less than 1% of GDP, and is possibly even a net loss to the economy if all subsidies and externalities are taken into account (Atkinson *et al.*, 2004) (Hartridge & Pearce, 2001). It is possible to imagine an economically-globalised "zero carbon world" where the UK imports most of its goods and services, including food, and simply pays in cash for all the carbon debits that accompany them.

We have not chosen this route. We note the extensive concerns and burgeoning literature on food security (Biotechnology and Biological Sciences Research Council [BBSRC], 2009) (Department for Environment, Food and Rural Affairs [Defra], 2006) we agree that food security is important; and finally, we believe that this

can be delivered without undue difficulty (Tudge, 2007). We therefore take the view that Britain should be able to feed itself, at least in principle, even though it imports a proportion of low carbon staples and high carbon (but low volume) culinary "luxuries" from overseas.

To simulate what is taken to be a realistic level of imports, it is assumed that about 15% (by volume) of food consumed is sourced from the EU, and about 7.5% from the tropics. Nearly all of this is constituted by items for direct human consumption. Other biomass-based imports – limited quantities of imported livestock products, feedstuffs, bioenergy and wood or fibre products – are all assumed to be balanced by carbon-equivalent exports.

Apart from this small amount of trade, the landmass of mainland UK has, for the purposes of this analysis, been treated as an entity that can be separated from the rest of the world. This is necessary because the analysis is based on creating an "end-point model" for optimum land use. There is, however, discussion of how to approach the possible indirect effects of the UK's domestic actions on other countries, in Box 7.2 on international land use change.

SOME PRELIMINARY REMARKS ABOUT LIVESTOCK AND LIVESTOCK PRODUCTS

The specific point of the **zero**carbon**britain**2030 exercise is to develop zero carbon scenarios. In the case of agriculture and land use, no way

Box 7.1 Some common assumptions within the scenario

The time horizon

In contrast to many other proposals to reduce emissions from the land use sector, *zerocarbonbritain2030* is projected about 20 years ahead, i.e. 2030. Its purpose is first to demonstrate that decarbonised worlds are physically possible, and then to create provisional targets for trajectories of change. Some of the proposals put forward here are unfeasible in the present context, but it is believed that measures of this scale are required to match the demands of climate change, and also that they could be achieved within 20 years, given the appropriate incentives. This is one scenario; there are many ways to get there.

Trade and carbon pricing

The assumption of "normal", liberalised trade based on comparative advantage does pose a difficulty for the scenario exercise. Assuming complete self-sufficiency would make the modelling simple, but is highly unrealistic. On the other hand, once trade is introduced the model could quickly lose its internal coherence.

This problem is partially addressed by supposing that, at the scenario date of 2030, there will be a binding worldwide treaty that will effectively regulate the flow of agricultural (and other) goods, and internalise the "carbon costs". Some international agreement is unavoidable in any serious engagement with the climate problem (Stern, 2007; Helm & Hepburn, 2009). Such an agreement would almost certainly entail an effective "carbon price" far in excess of contemporary business-as-usual projections. Carbon prices in 2030 are routinely expected to be in the region of £70 per tonne (Department of Energy and Climate Change [DECC], 2009), but this relates to the slower carbon reductions envisaged by current policy. Rapid and deep reductions imply much higher levels. For example the UK Energy Research Centre (UKERC, 2009) considers that:

"A market signal of around £200/ tonne CO_2 by 2050, 15 times the current EU carbon price, is needed to hit the long–term target. This rises to £300-350/tonne CO_2 if action is delayed or more stringent targets are set."

Our targets *are* more stringent, and delayed action is, sadly, the default presumption (Giddens, 2008). Prices as high as £500 a tonne are therefore possible, should the global community decide to tackle the climate question with due resolution. It is assumed that such prices will in fact drive most of the changes described in the scenario, and that the new low carbon land use sector will emerge in an orderly and rather "ordinary" fashion, with a minimum of regulation. The prices would of course affect all involved, from farmers to consumers. The signals would be strong but not coercive. As an approximate illustration, at a price of £500 per tonne, a retail kg of beef would be about £7 more expensive, chicken £1.75, cooking oil 37p, legume products 20p. All food types would be readily available, but their relative prices will drive changes in both production and consumption (Hedenus, 2009).

has been found to achieve this with the present level of grazing livestock. Innumerable recent studies have come to the same conclusion (Audsley *et al.*, 2009; Friel *et al.*, 2009; Garnett, 2007a; 2007b; 2008; Reijnders & Soret, 2003; Stehfest *et al.*, 2009; Steinfeld *et al.*, 2006; Tukker *et al.*, 2009; Wirsenius, 2008).

It must be acknowledged that this proposal goes against very strong preferences, powerful vested interests, and an almost universal

The "carbon-price effect"

Two of the main factors that currently frustrate decarbonisation measures are the present cost structure, and the lack of well-developed technologies. These reinforce each other, and make it very difficult to "start from here". Things simply "can't be done", either economically or technically, and the future tends to be judged by what is possible and economical today. The exercise of jumping to 2030 and its high carbon prices liberates **zero**carbon**britain**2030 from this problem because so many things now considered "unrealistic" will become the economically "realistic" default. It is important to emphasise that this supposition about carbon prices is not simply idle speculation or an economic silver bullet. It is, as the UK Energy Research Centre (2009) points out above, an absolute requirement for delivering a sustainable world.

The carbon-price effect allows plausible projections to be made about, for example, research priorities, yields of various crops, management of ecosystems, food technology and so on. The presumed carbon price is simply used to predict how people, institutions or markets are likely to behave, and which technological pathways are likely to be pursued. It does not rely on the presumption of the existence of unproven technologies, as some other scenario exercises have done (e.g. Audsley et al., 2009). In consequence, the present approach is regarded as more realistic.

The carbon-price effect has a corollary: techniques of measurement and inspection of greenhouse gas flows will be greatly increased, as will the effort put into verification. This is especially important in modelling the effects of diffuse "best practice" measures such as optimising carbon sequestration in agricultural soils (Smith, 2004).

historical trend towards higher consumption of livestock products. A reduction in grazing livestock is proposed because logic and evidence compel it, not for any other reason. As it happens, many different benefits emerge from this basic,

and from the present perspective, unavoidable measure.

Some of the common assumptions behind the scenario are discussed in Box 7.1. One in particular deserves emphasis. Throughout this chapter, repeated use is made of the assumption that high prices for carbon emissions in 2030 (in the hundreds of pounds per tonne) will render certain activities, products and technologies highly profitable and desirable, even though they are at present marginal or barely thinkable.
If the world of 2030 is indeed a low carbon world, or at least well on its way to becoming one, carbon prices *will* be very high. If they are not, then the global community will essentially have failed to engage strongly enough with the problem, and exercises such as this will be irrelevant. The point then, is that the "carbon-price effect" as it is here referred to, is an inevitable aspect of successful world decarbonisation; it is therefore appropriate, and indeed necessary, for local scenarios (such as this one) to assume it.

PRESENT GREENHOUSE GAS EMISSIONS FROM THE LAND USE SECTOR

While CO_2 derived from fossil fuels is the primary greenhouse gas in other sectors, in the land use and agriculture sector the principal gases are different. They are:
- Nitrous oxide (N_2O),
- Methane (CH_4), and
- CO_2 released from soils.

Box 7.2 International land use change

*zero*carbon*britain*2030 is an end-point scenario for the UK, demonstrating what can be done with British natural resources. When creating such an end-point scenario, it is necessary to isolate the UK to a degree, but the international implications of the scenario have been considered throughout the creation of the scenario.

At present, about 18% of global greenhouse gas emissions arise from land use change, primarily deforestation. The causes of deforestation are disputed, but based on estimates from the Food and Agriculture Organisation (FAO), Audsley *et al.* (2009) suggest that commercial agriculture is responsible for 58%.

Imports of food or biomass that have been grown on recently-deforested land may be directly implicated in international land use change. Major current examples are soybeans and palm oil, which are often grown on deforested land in Brazil and South East Asia. In *zero*carbon*britain*2030, we will avoid causing direct land use change abroad through the restriction of imports. All animal feed needs are met domestically, and only a small amount of food and biomass imports are allowed, under the assumption that they will be subject to stringent sustainability certification. For this to become reality would require significant reform of international trade legislation.

In addition to "direct" land use change, there has recently been much discussion of "indirect" change that occurs due to displacement or price effects. If a farmer switches from growing food to growing biomass, there may be no land use change directly associated with the biomass. However, the gap in the global food market may then be filled by a different farmer growing food on deforested land. Through such indirect market mechanisms, it is possible for products to be implicated in land use change abroad even if they are grown domestically.

Attempts to include such indirect global market effects have introduced new methodologies by which responsibility for international land use change can be allocated to different products. One method is to divide up responsibility among all global land use products on the basis of how much land they use (ibid.). This method abstracts completely from what is actually causing land use change on the ground, and also ignores the different substitutabilities and price elasticities of different products, and thus fails to reveal the real effects of different actions. It also fails to differentiate between products on the basis of whether or not they are necessities, so is also of limited use in determining how land use change might be tackled. It attributes much of the responsibility for land use change to the consumption of subsistence food, which cannot be (desirably) reduced.

An alternative method for determining indirect land use change is to use economic modelling to try to estimate the real effects of actions (Searchinger *et al.*, 2008). However, a considerable amount of subjectivity can enter into such calculations, and it can be hard to avoid double counting (Brander *et al.*, 2008).

As can be seen from these examples, the concept of international indirect land use change is based on the assumption of a global market and is therefore inconsistent with the *zero*carbon*britain*2030 methodology. For this reason, calculations of indirect land use change have not been included in the *zero*carbon*britain*2030 greenhouse gas accounting, or in the more detailed decisions about how best to use British land for climate mitigation. However, one of the crucial aspects of the scenario is that overall, it causes a decrease in the total quantity of land required to supply British consumption of food, fibre and energy. The British land use footprint is therefore reduced at an international scale in *zero*carbon*britain*2030.

Methane in the agricultural sector is produced mostly by ruminant livestock (including sheep, cattle and deer) in their digestive processes. Most of the rest is from animal manures (Defra, 2010).

Nitrous oxide is primarily released from agricultural soils. To increase yields of crops and grass it is customary to spread nitrogen-containing materials on the land, or to grow nitrogen-fixing crops that are incorporated into the soil by ploughing. Not all of this nitrogen is taken up by plants, and some of the residue is oxidised to N_2O. Nitrous oxide is released disproportionately from fertilised grazed grassland and manure handling (60%), and relatively little from arable cropland (15%) (Brown & Jarvis, 2001). Grazing greatly increases N_2O emissions (Saggar *et al.*, 2004).

Soil CO_2 is usually released as a consequence of soil disturbance or long-term change in land use, particularly in the conversion of forest or grassland to arable use. Undisturbed soils tend to build up "reservoirs" of carbon in the form of organic matter that can be released by changes

Box 7.3 Greenhouse gases in the agriculture system: background

Although smaller quantities of nitrous oxide and methane are released than CO_2, they have a much larger effect per unit emitted. Over a 100-year period, a tonne of N_2O emitted has a global warming potential 298 times that of a tonne of CO_2, while methane is about 25 times greater. There is some debate about whether the 100-year time-horizon is the most appropriate one to use, but for purposes of comparability the calculations are all based on the 100-year horizon. Further discussion of this potentially significant question can be found in Technical appendix* 1.

in external circumstances (Dawson & Smith, 2006).

It can be seen that emissions of both methane and nitrous oxide are strongly associated with the livestock side of agriculture, while soil CO_2 emissions are associated with the crop side. Livestock and crops behave so differently that they are analysed separately throughout this study. This follows practice elsewhere (e.g. Williams *et al.*, 2006).

Although not all greenhouse gases actually

Fig. 7.2 The food supply chain

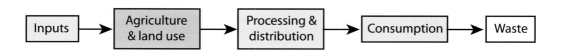

The supply chain for food and agricultural products.
In this chapter we focus on the second step (shown in green). Other steps are discussed further in other chapters.

* See www.zerocarbonbritain.com

contain carbon, all can be converted to "CO_2 equivalents" (CO_2e). Thus, "carbon emissions" is used here as a general shorthand. Emissions and sequestration throughout this section are given in tonnes of CO_2 equivalent (CO_2e). The breakdown of CO_2e from UK land use and agriculture in 2007 was about 5% CO_2, 55% N_2O and 40% percent CH4 (DECC, 2008).

In this chapter we concentrate specifically on the agriculture, forestry and land use system rather than on the whole supply chain for food and agricultural products. The reason for this is that emissions from other parts are nearly all due to energy and fossil CO_2, which have been dealt with in other chapters. This means that the analysis can focus more clearly on the land sector with its unique mixture of emissions. Figure 7.2 shows the links between the land use

Table 7.1 CO_2 emissions from Great Britain crop and livestock production and imports	Quantities (1000 Tonnes)	Area (1000 Hectares)	Emissions (1000 Tonnes CO_2e)
GB crop production for direct consumption	26356	2121	9855
GB crop production for livestock feed	13179	1890	(5975)
Exports	3500	250	(1653)
All GB crop production	43035	4584	15828
GB production livestock products	5775	10930	52298
Total GB products	**48810**	**13550**	**68125**
Imported crop products for direct consumption	24412	4882	5371
Imported livestock feeds (estimated)	10141	3264	(4000)
Imported livestock products	1883	1150	13871
Total imports	**36436**	**9269**	**19242**
Total attributed to British consumption	**57678**	**22846**	**82392**
All crop consumption	50786	8179	18006
All livestock consumption	7658	172234	64386
Estimated annual sequestration			8000

Estimated greenhouse gas emissions from British crop and livestock production and imported products, 2007 (CO_2e). *Data for this table have been drawn from various sources and recalculated. Owing to numerous uncertainties and different reporting conventions, figures should be treated as reasonable approximations. Generally the figures sum to totals, but numbers in brackets are excluded to avoid double-counting. The carbon flows for timber, paper and other biomass products are difficult to assess and attribute, and are discussed in Technical Appendices 2 and 9. A best estimate figure of 8 million tonnes from wood products and other sequestration processes is included for completeness, in both graph and table. Deducting this from the total would give a figure for overall emissions of 76.4 million tonnes attributable to the land use sector in its widest sense.*
Source: Based on data from Audsley et al. (2009), Defra (2008a) Williams et al. (2006).

Fig. 7.3a Agricultural production, land intensity and greenhouse gas emissions

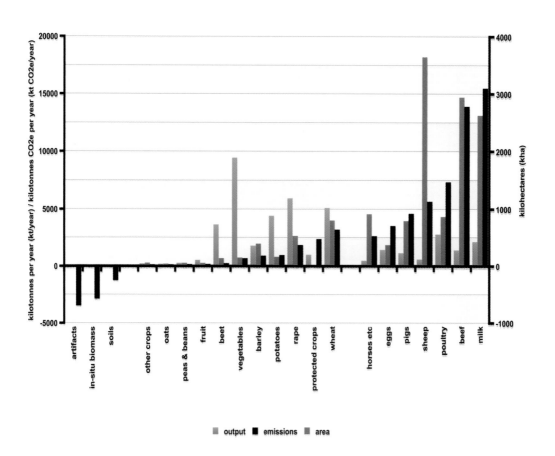

The graph compares greenhouse gas emissions (black), land area used (red) and nutritional output (green) of the main groups of products from the present agricultural system in Britain. For clarity the groups are separated into three classes (livestock products, crop products, and sequestration processes), each ranked in order of its emissions. Sequestration processes are equivalent to 'negative emissions' and so have negative scores. Data are principally derived from Williams et al. (2006) and include an adjustment for land quality. In each case the raw tonnage of product is adjusted to allow for differences of nutritional quality, following the Nutritional Density Score index developed by Maillot et al (2007). Imports are not included.

It is immediately obvious from the graph that the livestock sectors produce most of the emissions. They also require 70-80% of the land, either for grazing or feedstuffs. In contrast, their adjusted nutritional output is relatively low. This means that in general their 'carbon intensity' and 'land intensity' are remarkably high. 'Intensities' are useful measures of environmental impact, and are used for an alternative representation of the same data in Figure 7.3b.

Fig. 7.3b

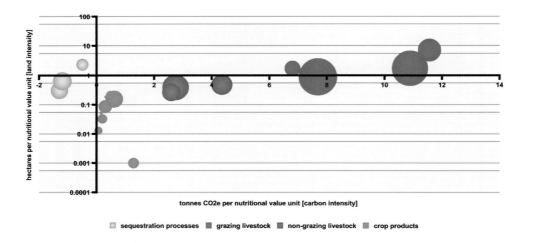

This graph shows similar data to 7.3a but in the form of 'intensities'. The horizontal axis shows 'carbon intensity', i.e., emissions of greenhouse gases per unit of nutritional output. The vertical axis shows 'land intensity', i.e., land used per unit of nutritional output. Note that the vertical scale is logarithmic. The data points are plotted as 'bubbles', where the areas are proportional to the total emissions for that product class. This gives a quantitatively accurate representation of the relative sources of greenhouse gases from different parts of the agricultural sector. Data sources are as for Figure 7.3a.

Four clusters of products are shown, including sequestration processes on the negative side of the carbon-intensity scale, from wood products stored in buildings and other artefacts, and carbon sequestration in forests. Further graphs of this type are shown in Technical appendix* 3.

sector and other parts of the food system.

Table 7.1 shows a numerical summary of the current emissions within the agriculture sector from production up to the farm gate, together with the food produced and the land area involved, plus imports. As can be seen from both Figure 7.3 and Table 7.1, by far the largest share of UK greenhouse gas emissions in the agriculture, food and land use sector can be attributed to the production and consumption of livestock products. The same is true of land usage, although to a lesser extent. This would

be broadly expected on the basis of well-established ecological principles (Odum, 1959) or of known biomass conversion efficiencies (Wirsenius, 2008).

Figure 7.3a shows absolute greenhouse gas emissions from the principal agricultural products, their outputs adjusted for nutritional value, and the areas used. Figure 7.3b plots the same data in a different way.

In both these graphs, the imbalance between positive and negative, and the disparities between productivity and land-take, is clear.

Fig. 7.4 Land use decarbonisation

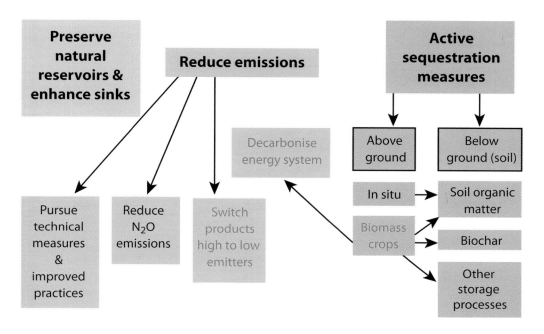

How land use management can reduce greenhouse gas concentrations in the atmosphere.
Emissions can be reduced through decarbonisation of the agricultural sector and of the energy system. The land and biosphere also acts as a carbon sink. Better land use management can help preserve natural carbon reservoirs and can be supplemented by active sequestration measures. The most effective measures are displayed in red.

These differences are indicative of the strong pressures that would accompany high carbon or land prices. It is important to emphasise that the graphs do not reflect current economic value, which is generally much higher per tonne for livestock products. These higher current values would however be nullified by a carbon price above £200 per tonne (see the discussion on carbon-pricing in Box 7.1).

Planning the scenario

A logical approach to decarbonising the land use sector entails action on three fronts, summarised in Figure 7.4.

- Conserve natural stores of carbon,
- Reduce emissions across the sector by a variety of means,
- Pursue active capture and storage of atmospheric carbon using natural systems and products.

The most significant and effective measures are shown in red. They will be discussed in turn.

RESERVOIRS

A great deal of carbon is locked up in various "pools", constituting long-term stores or "reservoirs" within the territory of the UK. Any decarbonisation strategy must ensure that its efforts are not being negated by releases, possibly unmeasured, from these pools. The largest pools are soils, especially peatlands; woodlands, mostly in living trees (Dawson & Smith, 2006); and biomass products in use within the human economy (Timber Research and Development Association [TRADA], 2005). Estimates of the size of these pools, and the background flows into and out of them, vary widely. Our baseline assumptions are shown in Technical appendix* 2.

In **zero**carbon**britain**2030, we deploy two principles with respect to reservoirs:
- Minimising any disturbance or activities that might release carbon,
- Promoting activities or processes that will encourage natural uptake.

Certain land use changes can result in severe carbon loss, particularly the cultivation of peatlands and conversion of forest or grassland to cropland (Dawson & Smith, 2006). In ZeroCarbonBritain, cropland, grassland, forest and peat will all retain their present character as far as possible, except for some net increase in forest cover. Tillage of previously untilled land has no net effect in the scenario simply because the scenario contains no such changes. However, with appropriate management peatlands can be converted from net sources to net sinks. We invoke the carbon-price effect to justify an annual sink of 500 kilotonnes of CO_2e per year ($ktCO_2e/yr$), following estimates by Worrall *et al.* (2003).

EMISSIONS REDUCTION

This is potentially the most powerful of the three classes of decarbonisation measures. There are four principal methods.

Decarbonisation of the energy system

This is dealt with in detail in the rest of the **zero**carbon**britain**2030 report. Its effect on the food system as a whole is substantial (Audsley *et al.*, 2009) but in the strict agriculture and land use sector it is smaller, because fossil-CO_2 is a relatively small proportion of the sector's emissions. This reduction of emissions has been incorporated in the scenario by adjusting the CO_2 element of the carbon-intensities for each product, following data in Williams *et al.* (2006). The effect is approximately a 20% reduction for livestock and about 45% for crops.

The **zero**carbon**britain**2030 land use scenario includes the production of energy from biomass in various forms, with a total energy content of around 315TWh. This is to supply the needs of other sectors where they cannot be served in other ways, including kerosene for aviation,

Fig. 7.5 Miscanthus and short-rotation coppice willow

Fig 7.5a

Fig 7.5b

**Images of (a) miscanthus, and
(b) short-rotation coppice willow.**
*Both miscanthus and short-rotation coppice willow
can grow very tall as these images demonstrate.
Source: University of Illinois (2006) and Silvanus Nursery (2008).*

diesel for shipping and biomethane to back-up and balance the predominantly wind-based electricity system (see the Renewables and Transport chapters for details).

We utilise perennial crops such as miscanthus and short-rotation coppice (SRC) willow for energy (see Figure 7.5). Unlike the conversion of grassland to growing annual crops, converting grassland to growing perennials need not cause a loss of soil carbon (St Clair *et al.*, 2008). These perennial crops are also low nitrogen users and do not require fertilisation after establishment. Nitrous oxide emissions from these crops are therefore also very small and negligible in comparison with sequestration effects (Borzecka-Walker *et al.*, 2008) (St Clair *et al.*, 2008) calculate the pre-harvest emissions from converting grassland to miscanthus or short-rotation coppice willow at between 0.16 and 0.2 tonnes CO_2 equivalent per hectare over the whole first five years. This can be compared to converting the same land to growing oil seed rape (used as feedstock for first generation transport biofuels), which would emit about 3.5 tonnes of CO_2e over the same period, mostly in soil carbon and nitrous oxide.

Finally, decarbonisation of the energy used in the production and transport of the proposed energy crops means that overall, their adoption would cause minimal greenhouse gas emissions.

Product-switching

This is the most important single measure, and its implications are discussed at length. Production of foodstuffs from grazing livestock is reduced by 80–90%, that from non-grazing livestock by 10–60%. Imports are reduced from 40% to about 20% of consumption. Production of crop-based foodstuffs is increased by 60%. These measures alone reduce the sector's emissions by 60%. Details of individual product values are found in Technical appendix* 11.

N$_2$O reduction

Based on data from Brown & Jarvis (2001), it is expected that in **zero**carbon**britain**2030, N$_2$O emissions will be reduced by about 65% (see Technical appendix* 8). The net effect is to reduce the final scenario emissions by about 10 million tonnes CO$_2$e.

Good practice and technical innovations

The literature generally expresses expectations that efficiencies will improve and carbon intensities will decline over time due to practice and technical innovations. Indeed this is *the* cornerstone of contemporary carbon policy,

---

Box 7.4 General management of land and agriculture

Efforts have been made not to place too many extra constraints on the **zero**carbon**britain**2030 land use scenario, and it has been assumed that things will not change unless for decarbonisation reasons or through the assumed price incentives. One of the main questions is whether "organic" practice should be presumed, ruled out, or simply ignored.

We share the widespread (but not universal) view that, other things being equal, organic farming is preferable, especially with respect to biodiversity (Hole et al., 2005). In some areas, organic practice has carbon benefits (Azeez, 2009). Unfortunately however there is often a higher land-intensity, and sometimes a higher carbon-intensity for organic products (Williams et al., 2006), so there cannot simply be an assumption of generalised organic practice.

The recommendations of a recent Soil Association report (Azeez, 2009) are broadly accepted, that there should be an "expansion and development of organic farming, and a parallel approach to improve non-organic farming".

Some sub-sectors might be entirely organic. For example in a general shift from quantity to quality, virtually all the scenario's livestock products could be organic. Perhaps intensive production in urban areas would be organic as well, taking advantage of volunteers, trainees, and interested customers (Groh & McFadden, 1997). It is widely agreed that organic matter should be incorporated into soils wherever possible, and the scenario makes this a matter of routine policy to encourage the sequestration of carbon in soils as well as improving the quality of the soil. At the same time the scenario minimises chemical inputs in order to reduce emissions of nitrous oxide and other chemicals that might adversely affect climate and other environmental factors. **zero**carbon**britain**2030 will certainly be more "organic", but in a pragmatic rather than literal, fashion.

---

* See www.zerocarbonbritain.com

and the principal bulwark against involuntary behaviour-change (Harper, 2007). The carbon-price effect can be expected to raise the currently rather feeble declines in carbon intensity and to encourage targeted research into cost-effective greenhouse gas-reducing measures such as nitrate oxidation inhibitors and means of reducing enteric methane (Audsley *et al.*, 2009). "Best Practice" would be profitable, monitored and routine. It is difficult to assess the quantitative effect of such measures by 2030, but it is more credible to suppose it will have a positive effect than none at all. A 10% improvement in total CO_2e emissions has been chosen as a conservative adjustment.

ACTIVE SEQUESTRATION MEASURES

If decarbonisation consists only of emissions reductions a "zero" state can never be achieved because there are always "residuals" of one kind or another. It is mathematically essential to develop net-negative processes to balance the residuals. Various kinds of net-negative processes, often described as "geo-engineering" (Broecker & Kunzig, 2008; Fox, 2009; Royal Society, 2009) have been widely discussed, for example "artificial trees" designed to remove carbon dioxide from the air, after which it could be buried underground (Lackner *et al.*, 2001).

While there is an obvious case for research into such measures, ***zero**carbon**britain**2030* restricts itself to the proven technology of land-based Carbon Capture & Storage using natural

photosynthesis. The scenario attempts to show that, provided there is a sufficient reduction of emissions, this will indeed be adequate to absorb the residuals. The embodied carbon would then be stored in three natural sinks:

- below-ground storage in soils,
- above-ground "in-situ" storage as biomass, and
- long-life storage in biomass products and in engineered "silos".

These are briefly discussed here, with further details and references in Technical Appendices 7 and 9.

Below-ground storage

The quantity of carbon stored in the world's soils (15,000 billion tonnes) is twice that in the atmosphere. Thus theoretically, only a trivial proportion in annual additions would be needed to counteract the global emissions of around 32 billion tonnes. This does not mean that such an addition is possible, but the numerical observation has attracted strong interest in soil storage.

Soil carbon exists mostly in the form of living biomass (roots and other organisms) and various forms of non-living organic matter. It can be increased (but not indefinitely; see Jenkinson, 1988; Smith *et al.*, 1997) by growing plants in it – especially perennials – and by adding organic matter. In a recent report, the Soil Association (Azeez, 2009) argues strongly for increased attention to both of these methods, and claims that appropriate practices can guarantee a net addition of about 0.5 tonnes CO_2e/ha/year for at least 20 years in both arable land and grassland.

These arguments are accepted by this report and the proposals have been incorporated into *zerocarbonbritain2030*, based on the assumption that they might be ramped up quickly after 2020. With the incentive of the carbon price effect and a rigorous inspection regime (Smith, 2004), it is likely that the above sequestration rate could be both increased, and extended by several decades, although not all these expectations are relied on in the scenario.

In the longer term it is believed that gains from a change in land management practice will tail off as a new equilibrium is reached. Furthermore, if the management practices are reversed the carbon may be released again, often in a far shorter time than it took to accumulate (Smith *et al.*, 1997)

Because of this, many soil scientists have reservations about treating soils as permanent sinks, although they are prepared to accept the existence of a 20-year "window" during which they may be effective (Smith, 2004). Using conservatively-weighted readings of the literature, we adopt soil sequestration values that it should be possible to achieve by 2030 and probably for some decades thereafter. The

Table 7.2 Soil sequestration estimates from better land management	
Changing to best practice management on arable land	0.5t/ha/y (Smith, 2004; Weiske, 2007)
Changing to best practice management on grazed grassland	0.5t/ha/y (Soussana *et al.*, 2007)
Changing to best practice management on ungrazed grassland	1t/ha/y (St Clair *et al.*, 2008; Klumpp, 2009; Borzecka-Walker *et al.*, 2008)
Changing to best practice management of existing woodland	0.5t/ha/y (Brainard *et al.*, 2003)
Using best practice to establish woodland on land that had previously been grassland	2–4t/ha/y (FAO, 2010)

Soil sequestration estimates under various "best practice" land management options for a period of approximately 20 years following the change.
The calculations on which the figures in this box are based can be seen in Technical appendix* 5. The values shown here are representative.
Source: Based on data from Borzecka-Walker et al. *(2008); Brainard* et al. *(2003); FAO (2010); Klumpp (2009); Soussana* et al. *(2007); St Clair* et al. *(2008); Smith (2004); Weiske (2007).*

* See www.zerocarbonbritain.com

actual values adopted vary according to the type of land, but are typically as shown in Table 7.2.

It is worth remarking at this point that if the 20-year window is as significant as some have argued (Azeez, 2009; Smith, 2004), then the appropriateness of using such a long (100-year) horizon to compare greenhouse gases could be disputed. Over shorter time periods methane has a proportionally greater warming effect. As methane is predominantly produced by livestock, using a shorter time frame to compare greenhouse gases would greatly reinforce the importance of reducing livestock numbers. Further remarks on this question are found in Technical appendix* 1.

Biochar: The crucial problem with most forms of organic matter applied or returned to soil is that they are unstable. They are high-energy "food" materials easily attacked by decomposer organisms, mostly microbial, which readily break them down and release the stored CO_2.

In view of the uncertainties in enhancing carbon sequestration by adding organic matter, alternative means of increasing soil carbon stocks have been sought. One of the most promising approaches utilises charcoal or "biochar", a natural but non-organic form of carbon that cannot be broken down by decomposers (Lehmann & Joseph, 2009) and so should last indefinitely (see Figure 7.6).

Biochar may have further benefits if used as an agricultural additive. Charcoal has the

Fig. 7.6 Biochar

An example of biochar.
Source: Carbon Gold.

ability to retain nutrients and water. There is evidence that in many circumstances, it may increase the efficiency with which plants use fertiliser, decrease N_2O emissions from soil and enhance plant growth (Sohi *et al.*, 2009). Biochar is still under research and there remain many uncertainties. However, it is considered sufficiently promising to warrant incorporating around 4.3 million tonnes into the **zero***carbon***britain***2030* scenario and allocating some biomass resources to make it, in addition to the use of biomass process-wastes. More details can be found in Technical appendix* 7.

Above-ground sequestration in biomass

Production rates for various kinds of biomass, along with references, are given in Technical appendix* 9. There are two approaches:

• "In situ" sequestration, where the carbon is stored in the plant that produced it, invariably a tree; and

• harvested crops turned into a permanent form.

In situ storage: Growing trees convert atmospheric CO_2 into wood. Over the years, this can build up into a reservoir of thousands of tonnes per hectare. Eventually the process slows down, but given a rolling replacement regime there can be a reasonable balance of long-term in situ storage and storage-crop production (Read *et al.*, 2009). Once established, trees can continue to absorb and store carbon for many decades, and it is reasonable to suppose that the efficiency of this process will improve when suitably incentivised. For new plantings, the scenario takes a figure of between 5 and 15 tonnes of CO_2e per hectare per year (tCO_2e/ha/y) for uncropped forest, depending on land type. The model developed by Read *et al.* (2009) suggests that under favourable circumstances this sequestration rate could be maintained even if there is a regular harvest, but the scenario assumes a progressive decrease in wood yield when managing for in situ sequestration.

Biomass crops: Most biomass crops in the scenario are harvested on a rotational basis and used in the "technosphere" the world of human artifacts. Their uses include energy, industrial feedstocks, building materials, biochar, and compost (that is, for the deliberate incorporation of organic matter into soils). The last three uses involve potential sequestration, although putting a value on this requires assumptions about how long they will last in their bound-carbon forms. The main biomass crops are:

• Straws, arising as by-products from food crops and needing no land of their own;

• "Energy-silage", standard agricultural grasses harvested for energy, usually via anaerobic digestion and biogas;

• Hemp, an annual crop with an enormous variety of uses, used for building materials such as "Hemcrete®" (Bevan & Woolley, 2008);

• Miscanthus, a very high-yielding perennial grass, for energy and for structural and other materials;

• Short-rotation coppice – closely-planted stands of willow and poplar, harvested every 3 years, mostly for energy;

• Short-rotation forestry, tree crops harvested every 5–7 years, also for energy;

• Plantation tree crops, grown for structural timber and other wood products.

Long life storage in biomass products and silos

In **zero***carbon***britain***2030* around 36 million tonnes of biomass are made into permanent materials, mostly for the building industry, in silos or are exported for similar uses abroad.

One million tonnes of miscanthus plus other forestry wastes and co-products is converted into biochar. The biochar also produces useful fuel oils as a co-product.

Box 7.5 Biomass crops

The term "biomass" refers to organic matter created by living organisms. It is created initially by plants, using solar energy to combine CO_2 and water into sugars and starch. The formula for the cellulose monomer, $C_6H_{12}O_6$, is sometimes used as a kind of proxy formula for biomass, although $C_5H_7O_2N$ is considered more accurate. A molecule of biomass takes nearly 2 molecules of CO_2 to make, so theoretically every tonne of biomass can "sequester" nearly two of CO_2. In practice it is not so straightforward to calculate the sequestration value, and this study has generally used a value of 1.3 for "oven-dry biomass" and 1.2 for air-dry wood products (following MacMath & Fisk, 2000).

If biomass is burned, the chemistry is more or less reversed, and the original energy and raw materials (CO_2 and water) are released. There is then no net gain or loss of CO_2, which is why biological fuels are considered to be "carbon neutral".

Typical yields of biomass crops in various circumstances are given in Technical appendix* 9. The allocation of biomass output to various functions is shown in Table 7.5.

This leaves around 18 million tonnes of raw materials for pulp, paper and other chemical and industrial products. Probably half of these may eventually come back into the agricultural system as compost or as energy used within the agricultural sector. Recovered digestate from anaerobic digestion is particularly valuable as a fertiliser because it contains a high level of plant nutrients (Banks, 2009).

Although the UK economy absorbs (and of course, discharges) very large quantities of materials, there must be a question mark over whether it could actually absorb nearly 40 million tonnes of industrial biomass material a year and accumulate it on a permanent basis. We assume that in **zero**carbon**britain**2030, the building industry in particular will design new structures with the specific aim of incorporating large quantities of biomass. Builders and developers would receive a credit for sink services. At £500/tonne, 8 tonnes of biomass material (9.6 tonnes of CO_2) for a house would be worth £4800 in credits, quite apart from its actual value as a building material, although this would have to be shared between farmers and builders.

It may eventually be possible to sequester carbon by simply dumping biomass in the deep ocean. This sounds as bizarre as many other geoengineering proposals, but the economics appear to be quite attractive (Strand & Benford, 2009). Ecologically the idea seems rather more questionable, and the scenario strives to find positive uses for its sequestration crops.

However, in view of the crucial importance of net-negative processes, the scenario acknowledges the possibility of biomass carbon-storage in engineered "silos" (Zeng, 2008). This might well be practical in the next 20–30 years, since it is already happening in an uncontrolled manner and on a suprisingly large scale: Fawcett et al., (2002) estimate that as much as 24 million tonnes of CO_2e per year is currently being sequestered in UK landfill sites in the form of wood and paper products.

In **zero**carbon**britain**2030, there will be an almost complete phasing out of the landfilling of food wastes. Along with greatly increased efficiency of gas-capture this will reduce residual landfill emissions of methane to a small quantity. It is well-established that degradation of woody wastes and paper under dry anaerobic conditions is extremely slow (Rathje & Murphy, 2001; Ximenes et al., 2008), so there is a clear technical possibility to use existing techniques and systems to achieve carbon-negative rather than net-emitting effects.

Our overall assumption is that for many years, the UK will be able to absorb and maintain some tens of millions of tonnes of cellulosic biomass material, in various ways. As time goes on, uncertainties about the properties of soil storage may be resolved, and the likelihood is that, with appropriate management or the development of biochar technology, soils will be able to act as a much larger proportion of the sink.

Altered functions for land in **zero**carbon**britain**2030

Given the purpose of the **zero**carbon**britain**2030 project, it is logical to use grassland areas for dedicated decarbonisation activities as far as possible, and concentrate on the arable areas for producing food, including feed for livestock. Table 7.3 shows a basic classification of land in mainland Britain, its current principal uses, and proposed alternative uses. The categories are simplified to clarify the argument.

LIVESTOCK

In **zero**carbon**britain**2030 , livestock will play an important but smaller role than at present. The greatest reductions will be in grazing animals – cattle, sheep and horses. This is required to release land for other decarbonisation purposes, but it also targets the groups with the highest carbon-intensities. There would be smaller reductions in housed livestock, while egg production is not reduced at all.

Overall, output of livestock products is approximately halved, and there are no imports of livestock products or feeds. Grazing is reduced from around 11 million to under 2 million hectares, feed-growing from around 2 million to about 0.5 million hectares. Carbon emissions of the whole livestock subsector are reduced from 65 million to less than 13 million tonnes.

The scenario incorporates the following levels of ruminants relative to the present day:
- 20% of sheep, with those remaining mostly in hill and upland areas;
- 10% of beef cattle, in lowland pastures and some upland areas;
- 20% dairy cattle (also supplying some meat), in rotational grazing and improved grassland.

With a major reorganisation of land use

Table 7.3 Land use in Great Britain

	Current GB Total (million hectares)	Principal existing uses	Principal scenario uses
Total crops	**4.87**	Arable crops	Arable crops, N-fixing legumes
Of which is used for feeding livestock	2.10	Livestock feed	Mostly direct consumption, livestock feed, hemp, N-fixing legumes
Fallow and set aside	**0.20**		As above
Total grassland including rough grazing	**11.20**		
Of which is temporary leys (grass under 5 yrs old)	1.14	Milk cattle	Hemp, milk cattle, energy silage, clover
Of which is improved permanent lowland grassland	4.49	Milk & beef cattle	Energy silage, miscanthus, milk & beef cattle
Of which is unimproved permanent lowland grassland	0.92	Beef cattle sheep	Miscanthus, SRC willow, beef, sheep
Of which is upland hill farms	1.25	Beef cattle sheep	SRC willow, short-rotation forestry, reforestation, sheep
Of which is upland peat moorland	1.36	Sheep	Sheep, minor reforestation
Of which is other upland grassland	2.04	Sheep, beef cattle	short-rotation forestry reforestation, sheep
Woodland	**3.24**	Wood products	Wood products, sequestration management
Of which is farm woodland & hedgerows	0.50	Wood Products	Wood products, seasonal grazing
All other agricultural land	**0.50**	Intensive livestock units	Arable, hemp, intensive livestock units, fish farms, protected crops
Urban land	**3.28**		
Of which is potentially agriculturally-productive land in urban areas	1.00	Derelict recreation under-used	Intensive horticulture, intensive livestock units, fish farms, protected crops
Total land	23.09		

Current land use modes in Great Britain (million hectares) and description of principle current and scenario uses.
Source: Defra (2004).

patterns, there might in some cases be different choices for grazing or browsing stock, possibly including goats, camelids, ostriches, geese, deer, buffalo, and horses. Requirement for hay/ silage and winter forage would be met locally, and small amounts of concentrates would be provided from the national crop sector.

Non-grazing livestock have lower carbon-intensities (Williams *et al.*, 2006) so the scenario includes higher proportions relative to present production: 100% laying poultry (for eggs), 80% pig meat, 50% table poultry. We do not specify how these would be reared, but for animal welfare reasons it is supposed that a larger proportion than today would be low-input, "free-range" and/or organic, many in small operations serving local markets. There might well be novel and productive ways of combining livestock with woodlands and the "new" perennial crops.

Non-ruminant outputs would be complemented by a fivefold increase in farmed fish to about 50,000 tonnes (Defra, 2008b). Fish can convert grain and plant proteins at a good rate, often better than 2:1, and appropriate feed is available from the arable sector (Barclay, 2008). It is assumed that there will also be some supply of wild sea fish. The current supply of 600,000 tonnes (Marine Fisheries Agency, 2008) is however unlikely to be sustainable, and it would be imprudent to assume similar future levels (Defra, 2007).

The feed industry would probably be similar to today's, but inevitably smaller and using different feedstocks. The UK currently imports around half the concentrate feedstuffs for its livestock (Defra, 2008a). Much of this is high-protein soya products from tropical areas. Soya is both cheap and an excellent protein source, but the ultimate consequences of its use are under suspicion and it cannot be assumed that in a decarbonising world, these supplies will be available.

In order to maintain its purposes as an "in principle" demonstration, the scenario does not permit imports of grain or soya meal for livestock feed. Instead we increase the acreage of legume crops such as peas and field beans, and of oil crops which provide both oil and high-protein presscake. Research is needed to develop indigenous feedstocks that are as good as soya (ADAS, 2009), but under an "incentivised" regime this should not prove too difficult.

These feeds could be combined with suitable food wastes. Domestic, commercial and industrial food wastes would be collected, processed and combined with specially-grown feedstuffs from the crop sector to generate the required range of feed products. Naturally, the present EU restrictions on such processes would need to be lifted, and methods developed to minimise health and other risks. The scenario's biomass industry also provides abundant by-products for low-grade forage and for bedding. In many low carbon energy scenarios, food waste is processed by anaerobic digestion (AD) to generate biogas. However, the present scenario is not short of energy, and AD is an inefficient use of high-quality food. Instead, in the *zerocarbonbritain2030* scenario, the bulk of food waste is used for feeding non-ruminant livestock. It is calculated that food wastes could provide about half the necessary feed for non-grazing livestock. However, AD does enter the picture at the end, to process the manure, bedding and slurry and to generate stable compost.

We presume increased multi-functionality in agriculture. There are always several potential parallel yields from a given farm or area of land, and they should all be taken into account and if possible given an economic value.

In these circumstances it is likely that the livestock sector shifts from cheap bulk production to high-added value, local, "slow" products of the highest quality, with much better standards of animal welfare being observed (Jones *et al.*, 2003). This anticipates the recommendations of the Soil Association's *Soil Carbon* report (Azeez, 2009).

By putting some slack into the system, livestock plays a role as a "cushion" against unexpected shifts in world trade or politics, and allows for population growth. Although much reduced in the **zero**carbon**britain**2030 scenario, the livestock sector still emits half the greenhouse gases and still requires 3 million hectares of land, with relatively low nutritional returns. It is a luxury that society can, and wishes to, afford. However there is always the option of improving total output by reducing the livestock sector still further. Such a shift could easily accommodate the expected 16% growth in population. An extended discussion is provided in Box 7.6.

Box 7.6 Livestock and livestock products: more detail

It might be asked how the envisaged reductions in livestock would come about. What are the drivers? It is assumed that these will be mostly of an economic nature. If carbon prices in the 2020s are above £200 a tonne and rising (see Box 7.1), this will strongly favour low-intensity products and penalise high-intensity ones. To give a crude example, a price of £400/tonne would amount to a penalty of around £4800 per tonne of beef, negating all but the highest added value. Meanwhile the three hectares that produced this tonne of beef could be producing, say, 50 tonnes of sequestration crops, worth up to £20,000 in carbon credits. It is unlikely to be so brutally simple in practice, but the example shows how carbon pricing could invert the present order of things and drive completely different choices for farmers. At the same time, consumers too would be reorienting their food choices in response to unmistakable price signals.

It might then be asked whether, under these conditions, grazing livestock can survive at all. It is assumed that in reality, the price of scarce, "niche" beef, lamb and milk products will rocket and make it worthwhile for a proportion of very high added-value products to flourish alongside the carbon crops. Clever farmers will certainly find ways of doing both.

The necessary reduction of the livestock sector has substantial cultural implications, and not just for farmers. Deliberate cultural adaptations can be envisaged. For example, there might be many advantages in increasing the population of livestock in urban areas, complementing the proposed growth in urban crop production (Garnett, 1996). The City Farms movement has proved successful in regenerating run-down areas in many cities, and in bringing young people into direct contact with farm livestock (Whitfield, 1987). This could be greatly expanded, developing skills and stimulating interest in farming. At the same time, the high value of livestock products could prompt a revival of backyard poultry and even pig rearing. Perhaps encouraged by official policy, such trends could have the paradoxical result that city people have more, rather than less, interaction with farm animals.

MAIN CLASSES OF LAND

Arable land

As can be seen in Table 7.3, about 5 million hectares are currently described as "arable" or "cropland" and tilled for arable crops. This is the best land, found mostly in the east of Britain. Of this, about half is used to grow food directly for humans, and half grows feed for livestock. In **zero**carbon**britain**2030, livestock numbers are reduced so less feed is needed, while extra crops are required to replace the lost input from livestock products, and also to replace some imports. It is assumed that crops would be rotated in the "organic" manner, with legumes to provide nitrogen, and livestock where appropriate.

There is also land in and around urban areas that could be used for especially-intensive food production and semi-recreational or educational livestock (Garnett, 1996) (Urban Agriculture Programme, 2003). This is estimated to be as much as a million hectares, although it would not be practical or desirable to use all of it (London Assembly, 2006). 380,000 hectares of this have been allocated, which could include a greatly increased volume of protected crops, taking advantage of the decarbonised energy supply, heat from Combined Heat & Power (CHP) and the potential availability of composts, CO_2 enrichment and other inputs. Further discussion of this matter is to be found in Technical appendix* 6.

Woodland

There are currently over 3 million hectares of woodland of various kinds, including farm woodland and "linear features", principally hedgerows. Just over 1 million hectares is planted coniferous woodland. In **zero**carbon**britain**2030 existing woodland would be carefully managed to optimise its many functions, including carbon sequestration in both soils and above-ground standing biomass.

In addition to the existing forest land, the scenario incorporates an additional 1.37 million hectares of appropriately-sited afforestation, extending the principles outlined by Read *et al.* (2009).

Grassland

About 11 million hectares, more than half the total agricultural area, are currently described as grassland, and devoted principally to grazing. In addition, an uncertain (and possibly considerable) area of grassland and cropland is used for non-food livestock, horses, pets and other uses.

The basis of the **zero**carbon**britain**2030 land use scenario is to change the principal functions of this very large area, while reserving a proportion for existing uses. Future uses must therefore be matched, at least approximately, to the various types of grassland. The principal grassland types are:

• Rotational grass and leys. This is highly

productive, regularly tilled and reseeded, often heavily fertilised, mainly used for dairy cattle and the best quality beef. In organic systems it is often sown with clover/grass mixes or other legumes.

- Improved permanent pasture. This is drained, seeded with high-yielding grasses and fertilised. It is mostly lowland, used for beef cattle and some dairy.
- Unimproved lowland permanent pasture is not so productive, used for beef cattle and some sheep.
- Hill farms have higher, often sloping terrain and poorer land. They can still carry out improvements, fertilise the fields and grow forage crops etc. They currently produce beef and lamb.
- Other upland areas are largely grassland, grazed but unmanaged, mostly used for sheep.
- Peat moorlands are a special case, very "unproductive" but often grazed by sheep.

A distinction is sometimes made between managed grassland and "rough grazing". "Rough" includes areas of many farms everywhere, but mostly in the western and northern uplands. It is principally used for sheep grazing at low density.

USES FOR THE RELEASED GRASSLAND

Because of the reduction in livestock, much of this grassland is "released" in **zero**carbon**britain**2030. Bearing in mind that there are endless local peculiarities, and that "multifunctional use" is generally presumed, the following discussion identifies principal uses for each category in the context of decarbonising the sector.

Rotational grass and leys

The best quality rotational leys and grazing land is currently used largely for dairy production. We reserve about 20% for the same use, but in rotation with other crops and patterns of use. Although as far as possible, the aim is to keep arable land arable and non-tilled land non-tilled, there is an impressive potential for agroforestry to deliver a more resilient suite of goods and services overall.

Agroforestry typically involves planting trees and shrubs in specially-designed ways on arable land, while maintaining production of field crops and some livestock (see Figure 7.7). It might also be tried on grassland, and carefully monitored for outcomes. Preliminary data indicate that agroforestry has the potential to combine sequestration with moderately high multi-crop yields (Gordon & Newman, 1997; Wolfe, 2004; 2009).

Rotations would include hemp as a major

crop, generating high-quality biomass for sequestration and building purposes, as well as many other useful products including oils and animal feed. Hemp is an extremely valuable and versatile crop (Bevan & Woolley, 2008) and it would be desirable to produce more than is envisaged in **zero**carbon**britain**2030. The reason for restricting the acreage devoted to hemp is that, as an annual, it requires the ground to be tilled. One of the "rules of thumb" is that only tilled land should be tilled, in order to avoid the CO_2 release penalties that would follow the conversion of grassland to cropland for hemp. Hemp is therefore only grown on current rotational grassland.

Improved permanent pasture

Better-quality permanent grassland would largely be used for perennial grasses for energy production and sequestration. Some could be in the form of "energy silage" – forage-type grass that is mowed regularly and stored as silage for generating biogas (Kadziuliene et al., 2009). The advantage is that the agricultural procedures are similar to those that already exist, and it could synergise well with livestock. Livestock could be grazed on these areas at some times of the year, and be fed some of the silage in winter. The principal market for the crop would however be in a regional anaerobic digestion (AD) or gasification plant rather than for livestock, on-farm or otherwise. In energy and carbon terms this is several times more efficient than using manure or slurry from housed livestock (Banks, 2009; Holliday, 2007).

It is also more efficient in terms of nutrient recycling. As an organic fertiliser, the residual solid waste from AD plants is equivalent to farmyard manure, but more stable and predictable, and with lower emissions of methane, nitrous oxide or ammonia (Hobbs & Chadwick, 2009). In any case, grass grown for its energy rather than protein content needs less nitrogen fertilisation, consequently reducing N_2O emissions (see Technical appendix* 8).

Where appropriate, a different kind of crop could be obtained through planting high-yielding grasses such as miscanthus or switchgrass, giving 10–35 oven-dried tonnes per hectare per year (odt/ha/yr) depending on conditions (Borzecka-Walker et al., 2008) (Lovett et al., 2009). These have several uses including energy, building materials, paper production, chemical feedstock and high-carbon compost material. Once planted, such crops last for around twenty years before renewal.

Clearly this option would involve disturbance of previously untilled land. There might be an initial penalty in terms of CO_2 emissions during site preparation and establishment of the new perennial crop, but such evidence as there is suggests that in this special case, the opposite is true (Richter et al., 2007).

Unimproved pasture

In areas of unimproved grassland, woody species would be more appropriate, such as willows in the form of short-rotation

Fig. 7.7 Agroforestry

An example of agroforestry.
Source: Burgess/Cranfield University.

coppice (3-year rotations) and larger species as short-rotation forestry (5–15 years). These are generally regarded as energy crops, but advances in materials and building technology may be expected to turn them, at least partially, also into sequestration crops.

There are of course some areas of unimproved pasture (e.g., calcareous grassland) with important biodiversity value, which appear to require grazing livestock for their maintenance. These should be prioritised for use by the limited remaining number of grazing livestock.

There are also, however, opportunities for enriched biodiversity among perennial crop plantings, in that there is a great deal of cover, abundant senescent biomass, and relatively little disturbance (Game and Wildlife Conservation Trust, 2009a; 2009b; Haughton *et al.*, 2009). Intelligent planting geometries could amplify these benefits. Seasonal grazing might also be possible, perhaps using unusual species such as alpacas or geese.

These fast-growing crops would need to be planted where there is easy access for harvesting machinery, mostly on flatter land. On steeply-sloping ground it would be better simply to reforest and harvest according to whichever regime suits the local circumstances. However, one of the effects of high carbon-prices will be to increase the cost of materials and equipment relative to labour. Some labour-intensive operations that are now uneconomic might become viable. There might also be a greater demand for working horses (Gifford, 1998).

Peatlands

As described, peatlands are already very substantial carbon reservoirs, and as such must be carefully managed. These areas can also be active carbon sinks, and this sink effect can be enhanced in various ways such as sensitive reforestation and the blocking of ditches (Wallage et al., 2009). All upland areas would continue to provide very important ecosystem services in hydrology and biodiversity. The best use for peatlands is probably very light grazing by sheep and deer. Licensed hunting would continue, and possibly increase, as a source of venison and game birds.

Implications and results

The basic aim of the scenario is the decarbonisation of the land use sector. But other requirements must also be met, as described in Box 7.1. The two most important are the provision of adequate diets and the maintenance of biodiversity. The scenario can claim not only to satisfy these requirements, but to deliver significant improvements.

DIETS

It might be thought in some quarters that such a severe reduction in livestock products would cause problems in the supply of a balanced diet. The evidence does not support this, and if anything suggests the opposite. The product outputs shown in the tables and graphs (see Technical appendix* 3, Figure 11) are adjusted to be nutritionally equivalent according to the Nutrient Density Score Index introduced by Maillot et al. (2007).

A possible approach to the question would be to construct an "optimum carbon/land use diet" and an "optimum health diet" and see how far they match. One answer, resulting in a rationale for a healthy and globally-sustainable diet, has been provided by Tudge (2007), which after much analysis reduces the answer to nine words: *Plenty of plants; not much meat; and maximum variety*.

Potentially, this matches the balance of the scenario's output rather well. There is plenty of protein, but the animal: plant ratio shifts from 55:45% to 34:66%, which is in line with recommendations for improved dietary health (Walker et al., 2005). It is consistent with the UK Food Standards Agency recommendations for levels of protein intake at about 50g per day for adults (Crawley, 2007). The proportions of food products available in ***zero*carbon*britain*2030** closely match the Healthy Eating proportions recommended by the Harvard School of Public Health (see Box 7.7).

The mixture of food products generated from UK territory in **zero**carbon**britain**2030 creates a healthier balance than today's mix and guarantees food security. To the basic mix is added a certain amount of wild fish and imported crop products from both Europe and the tropics, amounting to about 20% of the total volume. Although bulk livestock imports are disallowed for the purposes of the scenario, it is expected that there would remain a fairly vigorous European trade in high-value regional products such as pickled herrings, Parma ham, halloumi, salami etc. The food mix envisaged within the **zero**carbon**britain**2030 scenario provides a healthy diet. Further details are discussed in Box 7.7.

BIODIVERSITY

The major changes envisaged in **zero**carbon**britain**2030 are a shift from grazing to perennial crops, with lower levels of disturbance and lower fertiliser inputs. There is no reason to expect this to result in an overall biodiversity loss, although there would inevitably be a shift in balance.

The scenario still contains a significant proportion of grazed land and mixed farming, and it can be assumed that special habitats, Sites of Specific Scientific Interest, protected areas etc will continue more or less as now. Grazing activity would be concentrated where it has the most benefit. We do not envisage an all-organic Britain, but a greater proportion of

certified organic farms and a far higher level of what might be termed "organic in spirit". This will in itself favour increased biodiversity (Hole *et al.*, 2005).

Plantations of energy crops are fairly recent arrivals in the British landscape, and little research has been done on their biodiversity effects. The evidence that does exist suggests a strongly positive effect relative to the replaced grassland, largely as a result of increased micro-habitat diversity, available biomass for food, complex edge effects, lower inputs of agrochemicals, and reduced physical disturbance (Haughton *et al.*, 2009). This appears to be true both of miscanthus (Game and Wildlife Conservation Trust, 2009a; Semere & Slater, 2005) and short-rotation coppice (Cunningham *et al.*, 2006; Game and Wildlife Conservation Trust, 2009b; Rich *et al.*, 2001). All these effects can be enhanced by optimising the geometry of plantings. For these reasons it is believed that overall the scenario should have positive rather than negative effects on biodiversity.

THE NITROGEN CYCLE

As described earlier, nitrous oxide is the largest agricultural contributor to greenhouse gas emissions (Pathak, 1999), with most coming from grazed grassland fertilised with chemical nitrogen (Brown *et al.*, 2002). In **zero**carbon**britain**2030 grazed grassland will largely be replaced with ungrazed grassland,

Box 7.7 Dietary implications

Fig. 7.8 The healthy eating food pyramid

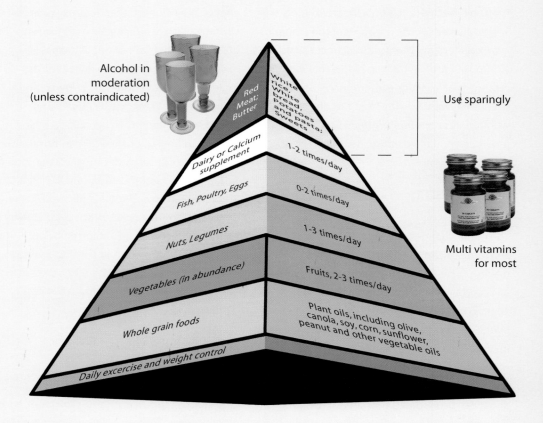

Alcohol in moderation (unless contraindicated)

Red Meat; Butter

White rice, White bread, potatoes, and pasta; Sweets

Use sparingly

Dairy or Calcium supplement

1-2 times/day

Fish, Poultry, Eggs

0-2 times/day

Nuts, Legumes

1-3 times/day

Vegetables (in abundance)

Fruits, 2-3 times/day

Whole grain foods

Plant oils, including olive, canola, soy, corn, sunflower, peanut and other vegetable oils

Daily excercise and weight control

Multi vitamins for most

The healthy eating food pyramid, *devised by the Harvard School of Public Health. Source: Willett & Skerrett (2005).*

The product mix generated by the scenario closely matches the so-called "food pyramid" devised by researchers at the Harvard School of Public Health (Willett & Skerrett, 2005) after many years of collecting epidemiological statistics. It is devised entirely from the perspective of optimising long-term human health. The pyramid shape is chosen to emphasise larger quantities of the items at the bottom, and smaller quantities of items at the top.

The healthy eating food pyramid is reproduced in Figure 7.8. It is notable that animal products do not appear until the fourth level. Even then, they are optional. These are the non-grazing livestock products that we provide in (relatively) larger quantities. On the next level are dairy products, provided by the scenario at about 20% of current supply: apparently about right for optimum health. At the top level are items understood to be "optional extras" that can be eaten sparingly: they contribute little to health, and in fact are associated with create well-known risk factors (Singh et al., 2003). We have reduced these to 10–20%, although there is a good supply of pork at 80% of current British output. In terms of proteins, the present ratio of livestock-based to plant protein is about 55:45. In the scenario it is 34:66.

It is not possible to match up the carbon and dietary optima in a precise quantitative way, but the congruence is undoubtedly striking. The implication is that, although at first sight the **zero**carbon**britain**2030 scenario appears to conflict with dietary requirements, it in fact moves society further towards a dietary optimum, better than the typical diet of today.

It must however be acknowledged that most people prefer a diet richer in animal proteins and fats. It is difficult to provide these in a zero carbon scenario. There is however a potential role for the food processing industry. Food technology could do remarkable things with the abundant supply of starch, sugar, oil and protein flowing from the cropland sector. It already makes high-protein plant foods like TVP, tofu, oatmilk, miso and mycoprotein. High carbon prices will drive innovations and could create novel foods with traditional tastes, textures and cooking qualities.

Of course, in a market system, albeit a regulated one, the "real thing" would always be available, but at a considerable price. It would acquire a cachet, and a genuine value, commensurate with its real (i.e. carbon) costs. It would be used for special occasions, feasts, treats and gifts, not for items of "fast food" and ready meals. For these, "generic meat" is more than adequate, and which the new meat alternatives could easily supply at lower carbon, land and monetary cost.

Currently, the UK produces about 25 million tonnes of crop products from about 2 million hectares of land, and imports a similar amount. In **zero**carbon**britain**2030, in addition to the 4.8 million hectares of existing cropland, a further 400,000 hectares or so of land in and around urban areas is added for intensive vegetable production or livestock rearing. The output of crop products is much higher: around 40 million tonnes. In addition to this, there would be 6 million tonnes of various livestock products, 100,000 tonnes of wild fish, 50,000 tonnes of farmed fish, about 7 million tonnes of imports from Europe, and about 3 million tonnes of imports from the tropics – plenty of wholesome, healthy food.

and with crops that need almost no fertilisation. This alone will reduce both emissions and demand for artificial nitrogen.

The scenario has a far higher conversion rate of soil nitrogen to protein, and also assumes a more efficient recycling of organic materials and better reclamation of nutrients. This will further reduce the need for extra nitrogen inputs, and will also conserve scarcer nutrients such as phosphorus (Hahn, 2002). Further, it will greatly reduce other malign effects of excess nitrogen in the system: ammonia, run-off, eutrophication etc.

Ideally, the nitrogen balance can be maintained by clover leys, legume crops and assiduous recycling in the scenario, but it is difficult to be certain that losses will not outweigh gains. It is calculated (see Technical appendix* 10) that possibly 100,000 tonnes of extra nitrogen might be required. If so, Haber-Bosch ammonia could be created without further greenhouse gas emissions, by a decarbonised electricity supply using hydrogen or biomethane feedstock. Subsequent N_2O emissions could be minimised by the simultaneous addition of organic materials (Kramer *et al.*, 2006) and possibly biochar (Singh *et al.*, 2010).

OVERALL RESULTS

In order to present a coherent case, the scenario must show that:

- Substantial emission reductions are feasible;
- The land required is not greater than that available;
- An adequate supply of food is maintained;
- Plausible sequestration processes can offset residual emissions.

Technical appendix* 11 contains spreadsheets with numbers and calculations. Summaries are presented here.

Table 7.4 summarises the initial results in terms of nutritionally-adjusted quantities, areas and emissions. Import derivations are in Technical appendix* 12. The following paragraphs expand on the raw data given in Table 7.4.

Production

The average nutritional value of each tonne of food produced is improved in the scenario, compared to the present day, so the total nutritional value of the food produced in *zerocarbonbritain2030* is higher than it appears to be if merely the raw tonnage is considered. The total available is actually 25% greater than at present, giving a reasonable allowance for 16% population growth, and potential food exports in the event of emergency shortages elsewhere in the world (Evans, 2009).

Land area

The land required for food production is only 29% of that previously used. 600,000 hectares overseas seems a reasonable level of demand and could be viewed as a healthy contribution to overseas development and trade.

Carbon-intensity

Overall, this is reduced to about half in all product classes through decarbonisation of the energy supply and other measures.

Land-intensity

This is also reduced, largely through product-switching in the livestock and import categories.

Emissions

These are reduced to a total of 28 million tonnes, one third of the present level, through product switching and reduction of intensities. This is reduced still further by two other considerations:

- First, N_2O emissions will be lower by about 10 million tonnes CO_2e, because the product mix has lower requirements for fertiliser, and converts nitrogen into biomass more efficiently.
- Secondly, it is assumed that by 2030, the carbon price effect will have stimulated technical improvements in nitrogen handling and other aspects of the land use sector. It is therefore more plausible to postulate an improvement of, for example, 10% than 0%. For present purposes, a figure of 10% is used. Taken together, these reduce the total emissions to 17 $MtCO_2e$. Workings are given in Technical appendix* 8.

Although this represents a dramatic reduction, the food production system in **zero**carbon**britain**2030 still produces 17 million tonnes of CO_2e, which will need to be offset with other crops, mostly non-food crops.

Having released a substantial amount of land through reduced land intensities, this remains to be allocated. The area allocations for these crops are shown in Table 7.5b, along with allocations for livestock grazing (see breakdown in Table 7.5a).

Net-negative processes

In contrast to emissions, the permanence of sequestered carbon is uncertain. Carbon stored above and below the ground may be released at a latter date by a future shift away from best practice land management; wooden objects may be burnt. To allow for the uncertainty concerning the ultimate fate of the carbon we have adjusted each of our sequestration figures by an estimated uncertainty figure. The figures shown in the paragraphs below are prior to the uncertainty discount.

The carbon-negative processes assessed by the scenario are as follows. These subjective assessments (derivations given in Technical Appendices 2, 7 and 9):

- A moderate sink of 500,000 tonnes CO_2e per year in peatlands achieved by carbon-sensitive management (Worrall *et al.*, 2003; see Technical appendix* 5).
- A non-peat soil sink of 15 million tonnes (Mt) CO_2e per year achieved through best practice on all soil types (Brainard *et al.*, 2003; Klumpp *et al.*, 2009; Weiske, 2007; see also Technical appendix* 5).

Estimated certainty for all soil sequestration is 60%.

Table 7.4 Land use intensity and emissions from agriculture

		Output (1000 tonnes)	Nutritional equivalent	Area (1000 hectares)	Greenhouse gas intensity per nutritional unit	Land-intensity (hectares per nutritional unit)	Total emissions (1000 tonnes CO_2e)
Livestock products	Now	5673	9119	11972	5.74	1.31	52298
	Scenario	2451	4232	2760	3.08	0.65	13033
Crop products	Now	25865	31162	2121	0.31	0.068	9597
	Scenario	50809	81179	4150	0.14	0.051	9942
Imports	Now	35795	35795	10750	0.61	0.3	21815
	Scenario	10000	10000	600	0.38	0.06	3800
Great Britain production	Scenario	53260	85411	6910	0.44	0.081	22975
Great Britain consumption	Scenario	63260	95411	7510	0.31	0.079	26775

Land and greenhouse gas intensity of the land use and agriculture system, by sector, current, and within the ZCB2030 scenario.
Source: Defra (2004).

- Deliberate incorporation of 4 Mt/year of Biochar into soils (Sohi et al., 2010) sequestering 16 Mt CO_2e/ year. Estimated certainty: 90%.
- In-situ storage of 15 million tonnes CO_2e/ year in standing timber through Carbon-management of existing and new woodland (Read *et al.*, 2009). Estimated certainty: 80%.
- About 47Mt of CO_2e per year sequestered in long lasting biomass products such as buildings and other wood products, and in engineered biomass silos. Estimated certainty varies between 40% and 80% (please see Table 7.7).

The use of biomass for energy and sequestration is discussed in Box 7.5.

The balance between the (reduced) positive emissions and the negative emissions is summarised in Table 7.7.

The scenario equivalent of Figure 7.3 is shown in Figure 7.9. Although livestock products still outweigh crop products in terms of emissions, their contributions are much reduced, and are counterbalanced by the expanded carbon-negative processes on the minus side of the carbon intensity scale

Fig. 7.9a Agricultural production, land intensity and greenhouse gas emissions in ZCB2030

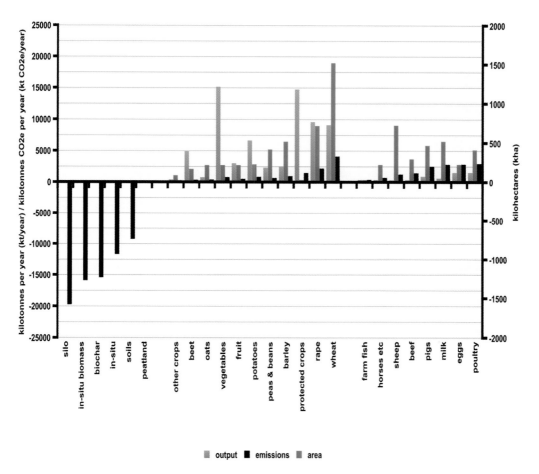

■ output ■ emissions ■ area

This Figure represents emissions, production, and land in the ZeroCarbonBritain2030 scenario for the same product classes as Figure 7.3a, with which it should be compared. A far smaller area of land is allocated to livestock products, and their contribution to food supply is substantially reduced, although their total emissions are still higher than those of the crop products. The proportion of output from non-grazing livestock is increased relative to grazing livestock. The total amount of nutritional vale is considerably increased. The remaining positive emissions from all agricultural products are counterbalanced by greatly increased sequestration processes on the negative side of the scale, and in fact there are 'excess' negative emissions available to help bring the rest of the economy to zero.

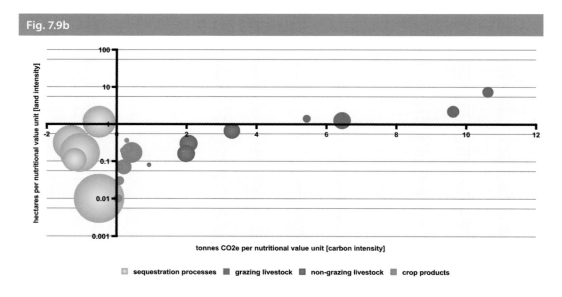

Fig. 7.9b

This shows the scenario equivalent of Figure 7.3b. The values on the horizontal scale show that the carbon intensities of all products have been reduced by various means. The absolute emissions of livestock products have also been reduced by switching to a greater output of crop-based products, although the bubble sizes show that livestock still make the largest contribution. The high carbon-intensity of protected crops has been very greatly reduced by the decarbonisation of the energy sector, and they make a very significant contribution to the food supply. The 'balancing' effect of sequestration processes can be clearly seen on the negative side of the horizontal axis. Carbon and land intensity values for net-negative processes depend on a variety of little-debated assumptions and their exact placing in this graph should be considered as provisional.

Conclusion

On the assumptions made, the agriculture, food and land use sector can reduce its emissions to one third, while maintaining – in fact increasing – output. It can offset these emissions through greatly expanded production of dedicated biomass crops. At the same time it can enhance biodiversity, deliver a generous stream of raw materials to industry, supply substantial quantities of dispatchable energy, and provide an abundant and healthy diet. Finally, it manages to sequester the residual emissions from the rest of the economy, to deliver a truly zero carbon Britain.

Table 7.5a Land use area for livestock in ZCB2030

Proposed grazing areas	Towns	Other arable	Arable for feed	Rotational	Lowland improved	Unimproved	Hill	Other upland	Peat moor	Existing woodland	Other farmland	Total for function
Totals available (1,000 hectares)	1000	3770	1100	1140	4492	920	1250	2040	1360	3225	505	
Beef	30	10	13	10	50	160	65	40				378.2
Sheep	20		12		10	40	300	430	200			1012.0
Pigs	10	5	418	3	4	4	5	2		10	3	464.0
Poultry	30	5	350	2	5	2	2	1		10	3	410.0
Dairy	50	10	75	120	150	55	10	3				473.3
Eggs	10	3	188	3	1	1	1	1			3	211.4
Horses etc.	8	2	15	2	2	2	2	1	1		2	37.0
Deer	3		5					12	10	20	2	52.0
Farmed fish			20								5	25.0
Total for grazing	161	35		140	222	264	385	13	211	40	18	1489.0

Area allocations (kilohectares) for categories of livestock land use within ZCB2030. Unshaded areas are those used indirectly for livestock production.

Table 7.5b Total land use area allocations in ZCB2030

Available (1,000 hectares)	1000	3700	1140	1100	4492	920	1250	2040	1360	3185
Animals	161	35	140		222	264	385	490	211	40
Feed crops				1097						
Direct crops	200	3500	50	C,F,S						
Energy silage			400	C,F	500					
Hemp		100	500	S,F						
Miscanthus				S,C	2800	50	200			
Short-rotation coppice					500	200	300	500		
Short-rotation forestry					200	200	200	500	50	
Wood	20	50	50		200	200	150	500	200	3000
Carbon									899	1370
Used	381	3685	1140	1097	4422	914	1235	1990	1360	4410

Area allocations (kilohectares) for principle categories of land use within ZCB2030.
Letters refer to by-products of the crop in that row that do not require an area allocation, as follows: "C" is for compost (organic matter for incorporation into soil); "F" is for animal feed of various kinds; and "S" is for straw bedding, biomass, biorefining, structural materials and so on.

Table 7.6 Use of biomass products in ZCB2030

Product	Quantity m odt	Use	Quantity m odt
Grass	10.45	Gas–AD	10.45
Miscanthus	51.39	Materials	10.49
		Biochar	1
		CHP	5
		Biogas	6
		Paper	2
		FT liquid fuels	16.45
		Heating	10
Willow	15.92	FT liquid fuels	13.1
		Buildings	2.32
		Paper	0.5
Hemp	6.17	Materials	6.17
Wood	9.48	Materials	9.48
Other forestry	14.02	CHP	9.60
		Biochar	1.52
		Biogas	2.90
Straw	4.50	Materials	4.5

The proposed use of biomass products in the ZCB2030 scenario.
This is simply one route of allocation. The categorisation between sources of "other forestry products" and "forestry waste" is blurred. Therefore to be prudent while we are using available "forestry waste" for biochar and biogas we have taken this resource from "other forestry". In practice it should be separate.
Biochar comes from a mixture of Miscanthus (1M odt), forestry residues, poultry, wood waste, paper and cardboard waste.

Table 7.7 Balance of positive and negative emissions in ZCB2030 land use scenario

Positive emissions		Sequestration (Negative emissions)	Calculated potential	Sequestration certainty	ZCB final figure
Livestock UK	13				
Crops UK	10				
Imports	4	Soil	-16	60%	-9
Sub total	27	In situ	-15	80%	-12
Less N$_2$O reduction	-8 19	Biochar	-16	90%	-14
Less 10% technical	17	Material exports	-11	40%	-5
		Material domestic	-7	70%	-5
		Engineered silo storage	-28	80%	-23
Total	17	Total	-93		-67
Net balance	-50				

Balance of positive and negative emissions in million tonnes of CO$_2$e (Mt CO$_2$e)
This shows the residual emissions and sequestration from land use in zerocarbonbritain2030. Material demand would mostly come from buildings. However by 2030 new uses for grown materials maybe more widely established. Soil includes peat sequestration. "In-situ" refers to the sequestration in growing forests.

References

ADAS Ltd (2009) "What is the potential to replace imported soya, maize and maize byproducts with other feeds in livestock diets?", paper for the Department for Food, Environment and Rural Affairs (Defra) feed import project. Available at http://www.defra.gov.uk/environment/quality/gm/crops/documents/foodmatters-otherfeeds-1308.pdf [Live: March 2010].

Atkinson, G. *et al.* (2004) "Framework for environmental accounts for agriculture", final report, submitted to Defra, the Department of Agriculture and Rural Development (Northern Ireland), the Scottish Executive, and the Welsh Assembly Government. Available at: https://statistics.defra.gov.uk/esg/reports/envacc/finalrep.pdf [Live: March 2010].

Audsley, E. *et al.* (2009) *How low can we go? An assessment of greenhouse gas emissions from the UK food system & the scope to reduce them by 2050*, study for WWF-UK and the Food Climate Research Network Godalming: WWF-UK.

Azeez, G. (2009) *Soil Carbon and Organic Farming: a review of the evidence on the relationship between agriculture and soil carbon sequestration, and how organic farming can contribute to climate change mitigation and adaptation*, November 2009, Bristol: Soil Association.

Banks, C. (2009) "Optimising Anaerobic digestion: Evaluating the Potential for Anaerobic Digestion to provide Energy & Soil amendment", presentation at the Evaluating the Potential for Anaerobic Digestion to provide Energy and Soil amendment, University of Reading, 25 March 2009. Available at: http://www.frcc.forestry.gov.uk/pdf/rrps_AD250309_optimising_anaerobic_digestion.pdf/$FILE/rrps_AD250309_optimising_anaerobic_digestion.pdf [Live: March 2010].

Barclay, C. (2008) "Fish Farming", House of Commons Library Standard Note SN/SC/924. Available at: http://www.parliament.uk/commons/lib/research/briefings/snsc-00924.pdf [Live: March 2010].

Bevan, R. & T. Woolley (2008) *Hemp lime construction. A guide to building with hemp lime composites*, London: BRE Press.

Biotechnology and Biological Sciences Research Council (BBSRC) (2009) "Bibliography", Global Food Security: Sustainable healthy food for all [online]. Available at: http://www.foodsecurity.ac.uk/resources/bibliography.html [Live: March 2010].

Borzêcka-Walker, M., A. Faber, & R. Borek (2008) "Evaluation of carbon sequestration in energetic crops (Miscanthus and coppice willow)", *International Agrophysics*, 22(3), pp. 185–190.

Brainard J, A. Lovett & I. Bateman (2003) *Social & Environmental Benefits of Forestry: Phase 2: Carbon Sequestration Benefits Of Woodland*, Report to Forestry Commission, Centre for Social and Economic Research on the Global Environment, School of Environmental Sciences, University of East Anglia. Available at: http://www.forestry.gov.uk/website/pdf.nsf/pdf/carbonseqrep0603.pdf/$FILE/carbonseqrep0603.pdf [Live: March 2010].

Brander, M. *et al.* (2008) "Consequential & Attributional Approaches to LCA: a Guide to Policy Makers with Specific Reference to Greenhouse Gas LCA of Biofuels", technical paper, April 2008. Available at: http://www.ecometrica.co.uk/wp-content/uploads/Consequential_and_attributional_approaches_to_LCA.pdf [Live: March 2010].

Broecker, W.S & R. Kunzig (2008) *Fixing Climate: What Past Climate Changes Reveal About the Current Threat – and How to Counter It*, New York: Hill & Wang.

Brown, L. & S. Jarvis (2001) "Estimation of Nitrous Oxide Emissions from UK Agriculture", IGER Innovations. Available at: http://www.aber.ac.uk/en/media/chapter_10.pdf [Live: March 2010].

Brown, L. *et al.* (2002) "Development and application of a mechanistic model to estimate emission of nitrous oxide from UK agriculture", *Atmospheric Environment*, 36(6), pp. 917–928.

Crawley, H. (2007) "Nutritional Guidelines for Food Served in Public Institutions", report prepared for The Food Standards Agency by The Caroline Walker Trust. Available at: http://www.food.gov.uk/multimedia/pdfs/walkertrustreport.pdf [Live: March 2010].

Cunningham, M.D. *et al.* (2006) *The effects on flora and fauna of converting grassland to short rotation coppice*, Department of Trade and Industry (DTI) Technology Programme: New and Renewable Energy, URN 06/1094, London: DTI.

Dawson J.J.C. & P. Smith (2006) "Review of Carbon Loss from Soil and its Fate in the Environment", Final Technical Review Report for Defra project SP08010. Available at: http://randd.defra.gov.uk/Document.aspx?Document=SP08010_4200_FRP.doc [Live: March 2010].

Department of Energy and Climate Change (DECC) (2008) "UK Emissions Statistics". Available at: http://www.decc.gov.uk/en/content/cms/statistics/climate_change/climate_change.aspx [Live: March 2010].

DECC (2009) "Carbon Appraisal in UK Policy Appraisal: A

revised Approach: A brief guide to the new carbon values and their use in economic appraisal". Available at: http://www.decc.gov.uk/Media/viewfile.ashx?FilePath=What%20we%20do%5CA%20low%20carbon%20UK%5CCarbon%20Valuation%5C1_20090901160357_e_@@_carbonvaluesbriefguide.pdf&filetype=4 [Live: March 2010].

Department of Environment, Food and Rural Affairs (Defra) (2004) "UK Crop Areas and Livestock Numbers" [spreadsheet]. Available at: http://www.statistics.gov.uk/STATBASE/Expodata/Spreadsheets/D3792.xls [Live: March 2010].

Defra (2006) "Food Security and the UK: An Evidence and Analysis Paper", Food Chain Analysis Group, December 2006. Available at: https://statistics.defra.gov.uk/esg/reports/foodsecurity/ [Live: March 2010].

Defra (2007) *Fisheries 2027: a long-term vision for sustainable fisheries*, London: Defra.

Defra et al. (2008a) *Agriculture in the United Kingdom 2008*, London: Defra.

Defra (2008b) "Ensuring the UK's food security in a changing world", Defra discussion paper, July 2008. Available at: http://www.defra.gov.uk/foodfarm/food/pdf/Ensuring-UK-Food-Security-in-a-changing-world-170708.pdf [Live: March 2010].

Defra (2010) "Observatory monitoring framework – indicator data sheet, Environmental impact: Climate change, Indicator DD1: Methane emissions", Defra [online]. Available at: http://www.defra.gov.uk/evidence/statistics/foodfarm/enviro/observatory/indicators/d/dd1_data.htm [Live: March 2010].

Evans, A. (2009) *The Feeding of the Nine Billion: Global Food Security for the 21st Century*, a Chatham House report, London: Royal Institute of International Affairs.

Fawcett, T., A. Hurst, & B. Boardman (2002) *Carbon UK*, ECI research report 25, Oxford: Environmental Change Institute, University of Oxford.

Food and Agriculture Organisation of the United Nations (FAO) (2010) *Global Forest Resources Assessment 2010: key findings*, Rome: FAO.

Friel, S et al. (2009) "Public health benefits of strategies to reduce greenhouse-gas emissions: food and agriculture", *The Lancet*, 374(9706), pp. 2016–2025.

Fox, T. (2009) *Climate Change: Have we lost the battle?*, November 2009, London: Institution of Mechanical Engineers.

Game and Wildlife Conservation Trust (2009a) "Short rotation coppice", Game and Wildlife Conservation Trust [online]. Available at: http://www.gwct.org.uk/research__surveys/biodiversity__ecosystems/woodland_biodiversity/322.asp [Live: March 2010].

Game and Wildlife Conservation Trust (2009b) "Birds in Miscanthus Grass Grown for Biomass", Game and Wildlife Conservation Trust [online]. Available at: http://www.gwct.org.uk/research__surveys/biodiversity__ecosystems/woodland_biodiversity/1570.asp [Live: March 2010].

Garnett, T. (1996) *Growing Food in Cities: a report to highlight and promote the benefits of urban agriculture in the UK*, London: National Food Alliance & SAFE Alliance.

Garnett, T. (2007a) "Meat and Dairy Production & Consumption: Exploring the livestock sector's contribution to the UK's greenhouse gas emissions and assessing what less greenhouse gas intensive systems of production and consumption might look like", November 2007, Food Climate Research Network, Centre for Environmental Strategy, University of Surrey. Available at: http://www.fcrn.org.uk/fcrnPublications/publications/PDFs/Livestock_paper_2006.pdf [Live: March 2010].

Garnett, T. (2007b) "Animal feed, livestock & greenhouse gas emissions: What are the issues?", paper presented to the Society of Animal Feed Technologists, Coventry, 25 January 2007. Available: http://www.fcrn.org.uk/fcrnPublications/publications/PDFs/Animal_feed_paper.pdf [Live: March 2010].

Garnett T (2008) "Cooking up a storm: Food, greenhouse gas emissions and our changing climate", Food Climate Research Network, Centre for Environmental Strategy, University of Surrey. Available at: http://www.fcrn.org.uk/fcrnPublications/publications/PDFs/CuaS_web.pdf [Live: March 2010].

Giddens, A. (2009) *The Politics of Climate Change*, New York: Polity Press.

Gifford, A. (1998) "Working Horses in Forestry", in Zeuner, D. (ed.) (1998), *The Working Horse Manual*, Tonbridge: Farming Press, p. 145–150.

Gordon A.M & S.M. Newman (eds) (1997) Temperate Agroforestry Systems, Wallingford: CAB International.

Groh, T. & S. McFadden (1997) *Farms of Tomorrow Revisited: Community Supported Farms – Farm Supported Communities*, Vermont: Chelsea Green.

Hahn, J. (2002) "Legal and financial possibilities for the promotion of phosphorus recycling", paper presented at the "Recovery of phosphorus in agriculture from liquid effluent and solid waste" symposium, Berlin, 7 February 2002, German Federal Environment Office. Available at: http://www.nhm.ac.uk/research-curation/research/projects/phosphate-recovery/UBApressrelease.doc [Live: March 2010].

Harper, P. (2007) "Sustainable Lifestyles of the Future", in Elliott, D. (ed.) *Sustainable Energy: Opportunities & Limitations*, Basingstoke: Palgrave.

Hartridge, O. & D. Pearce (2001) "Is UK Agriculture Sustainable? Environmentally Adjusted Economic Accounts for UK Agriculture", November 2001, CSERGE-Economics, University College London. Available at: http://www.ucl.ac.uk/cserge/AGNNP.FINALFINAL.pdf [Live: March 2010].

Haughton A.J. *et al*. (2009) "A novel, integrated approach to assessing social, economic and environmental implications of changing rural land use: a case study for perennial biomass crops", *Journal of Applied Ecology*, 46(2), pp. 315–322.

Hedenus, F. (2009) "Climate Taxes on Meat Consumption", presentation from Physical Resource Theory, Chalmers University of Technology, Gothenburg. Available at: http://www.se2009.eu/polopoly_fs/1.28869!menu/standard/file/14_dec_Climate_policy_and_land_scarcity-_finding_effective_responses_Fredrik_Hedenus.pdf [Live: March 2010].

Helm, D. & C. Hepburn (eds) (2009) *The Economics and Politics of Climate Change*, Oxford: Oxford University Press.

Hobbs, P. & D. Chadwick (2009) "Anaerobic digestion and its implications for agricultural greenhouse gas emissions", presentation from North Wyke Research. Available at: http://www.ppre.co.uk/pdf/events/Presentation%206%20-%20Hobbs.pdf [Live: March 2010].

Hole, D.G. *et al*. (2005) "Does Organic Farming Benefit Biodiversity?", Biological Conservation, 122(1), pp. 113–130.

Holliday, L. (2007) "Rye grass as an energy crop using biogas technology", Greenfinch Ltd report prepared for DTI New and Renewable Energy Programme. Available at: http://www.berr.gov.uk/files/file18131.pdf [Live: March 2010].

Jenkinson, D.S. (1988) "Soil organic matter and its dynamics", in Wild, A. (ed.) (1988) *Russell's Soil Conditions and Plant Growth*, 11th edition. London: Longman, pp. 564–607.

Jones, P. *et al*. (2003) "Return to traditional values? A case study of Slow Food", *British Food Journal*, 105(4/5), pp. 297–304.

Kadziuliene, Z., V. Tilvikiene, & Z. Dabkevicius (2009) "Biomass Of Tall Fescue As Raw Material For Biogas Production", International Potash Institute, Lithuanian Institute of Agriculture. Available at: http://www.ipipotash.org/udocs/Biomass_of_tall_fescue_as_raw_material_for_biogas_production_paper.pdf [Live: March 2010].

Klumpp, K. *et al*. (2009) "Grazing triggers soil carbon loss by altering plant roots and their control on soil microbial community", Journal of Ecology, 97(5), pp. 876–885.

Kramer, S.B. *et al*. (2006) "Reduced nitrate leaching and enhanced denitrifier activity and efficiency in organically fertilized soils", *Proceedings of the National Academy of Sciences of the United States of America*, 103(12), pp. 4522–4527.

Lackner, K., P. Grimes, & H.J. Ziock (2001) "Capturing Carbon Dioxide From Air". Proceedings from the First National Conference on Carbon Sequestration, 2001 (Session 7B. Capture V – Absorption Studies), National Energy Technology Laboratory. Available at: http://www.netl.doe.gov/publications/proceedings/01/carbon_seq/7b1.pdf [Live: March 2010].

Lehmann, J. & S. Joseph (eds) (2009) *Biochar for Environmental Management: Science and Technology*, London: Earthscan.

London Assembly (2006) *Cultivating the Capital: food growing and the planning system in London*, London: Greater London Authority.

Lovett A.A. *et al*. (2009) "Land Use Implications of Increased Biomass Production Identified by GIS-Based Suitability and Yield Mapping for Miscanthus in England", *Bioenergy Research*, 2(1–2), pp. 1939–1234.

MacMath, R. & P. Fisk (2000) "Carbon Dioxide intensity Ratios: A Method of Evaluating the Upstream Global Warming Impact of Long-Life Building Materials", Centre for Maximum Potential Building Systems, Austin, Texas. Available at: http://www.cmpbs.org/publications/T1.2–AD4.5-Up_Gbl_wrm.pdf [Live: March 2010].

Maillot, M. *et al*. (2007) "Nutrient-Dense Food Groups Have High Energy Costs: An Econometric Approach to Nutrient Profiling", *Journal of Nutrition*, 137(7), pp. 1815–1820.

Marine and Fisheries Agency (2008) *United Kingdom Sea Fisheries Statistics*, London: Defra.

Odum, E.P. (1959) *Fundamentals of Ecology*, second edition, Philadelphia: Saunders.

Pathak, H. (1999) Emissions of nitrous oxide from soil, *Current Science*, 77(3), pp. 360–369.

Rathje, W. & C. Murphy (2001) *Rubbish! The Archaeology of Garbage*, Tuscon: University of Arizona

Read D. J. *et al*. (eds) (2009) *Combating climate change – a role for UK forests: The synthesis report. An assessment of the potential of the UK's trees and woodlands to mitigate* and adapt to climate change. The synthesis report, Edinburgh: TSO.

Reijnders, L. & S. Soret (2003) "Quantification of the environmental impact of different dietary protein choices", American Journal of Clinical Nutrition, 78(3), pp. 664S–668S.

Rich T.J. et al. (2001) ARBRE monitoring – ecology of short rotation coppice plantations, interim report 2000, URN/01/768, London: DTI.

Richter G.M. et al. (2007) "Biomass supply for the UK energy market – modelling grass productivity", for the 3N – Bioenergy Farming Conference, Papenburg, Germany, 13–15 March 2007. Available at: http://www.tsec-biosys.ac.uk/index.php?p=9&t=4 [Live: March 2010].

Royal Society (2009) Geoengineering the Climate: Science Governance and Uncertainty, September 2009, RS Policy document 10/09, London: Royal Society.

Saggar, S. et al. (2004) "Modelling nitrous oxide emissions from dairy-grazed pastures", Nutrient Cycling in Agroecosystems, 68(3), pp. 243–255.

Searchinger, T. et al. (2008) "Use of U.S. Croplands for Biofuels Increases Greenhouse Gases Through Emissions from Land Use Change", Science, 319 (5867), pp. 1238–1240.

Semere, T. & F. Slater (2005) "The effects of energy grass plantations on biodiversity", second annual report, report for the DTI New and Renewable Energy Programme, URN 05/1307. Available at: http://www.bis.gov.uk/files/file15002.pdf [Live: March 2010].

Singh P.N, J. Sabaté, & G.E. Fraser (2003) "Does low meat consumption increase life expectancy in humans?", American Journal of Clinical Nutrition, 78(3), pp. 526S–532S.

Singh B.P. et al. (2010) "Influence of Biochars on Nitrous Oxide Emission and Nitrogen Leaching from two Contrasting Soils", published in Journal of Environmental Quality, 39, DOI:10.2134/jeq2009.0138.

Smith, P. (2004) "Carbon sequestration in croplands: the potential in Europe and the global context", European Journal of Agronomy, 20(3), pp. 229–236.

Smith, P. et al. (1997) "Potential for carbon sequestration in European soils: preliminary estimates for five scenarios using results from long-term experiments", Global Change Biology, 3(1), pp. 67–79.

Sohi, S. et al. (2009) "Biochar's roles in soil and climate change: a review of research needs", CSIRO Land & Water Science Report 05/09, February 2009. Available at: http://www.csiro.au/files/files/poei.pdf [Live: March 2010].

Sohi S. P. et al. (2010) "A review of biochar and its use & function in soil", Advances in Agronomy, 105, pp. 47–82.

Soussana, J.F. et al. (2007) "Full accounting of the greenhouse gas (CO_2, N_2O, CH_4) budget of nine European grassland sites", Agriculture Ecosystems & Environment, 121(1–2), pp. 121–134.

St. Clair, S., J. Hillier, P. Smith (2008) "Estimating the pre-harvest greenhouse gas costs of energy crop production", Biomass and Bioenergy, 32(5), pp. 442 –452.

Stehfest, E. et al. (2009) "Climate benefits of changing diet", IOP Conference Series: Earth and Environmental Science, 6(S26.09).

Steinfeld, H. et al. (2006) Livestock's Long Shadow: environmental issues and options, Rome: FAO.

Stern, N. (2007) Stern Review: the economics of climate change, Cambridge: Cambridge University Press.

Strand S.E. & G. Benford (2009) "Ocean sequestration of crop residue carbon: recycling fossil fuel carbon back to deep sediments", Environmental Science & Technology, 43(4), pp. 1000–1007.

Timber Research and Development Association (TRADA) (2005) "Wood: The UK Mass Balance and Efficiency of Use", report prepared for the Timber Industry Environment Trust, Biffaward Mass Balance Series, 2005. Available at: http://www.massbalance.org/downloads/projectfiles/2173-492.pdf [Live: March 2010].

Tudge, C. (2007) Feeding people is easy, Pari: Pari Publishing.

Tukker, A. et al. (2009) Environmental Impacts of Diet Changes in the EU, European Commission Joint Research Centre, EUR 23783 EN, Luxembourg: European Commission.

UK Energy Research Centre (UKERC) (2009) Making the transition to a secure low-carbon energy system, synthesis report, London: UKERC.

Urban Agriculture Programme (2003) "Annotated Bibliography on Urban and Periurban Agriculture", prepared for the Swedish International Development Agency (Sida). Available at: http://www.ruaf.org/sites/default/files/annotated_bibliography.pdf [Live: March 2010].

Walker, P. et al. (2005) "Public health implications of meat production and consumption", Public Health Nutrition, 8(4), pp. 348–356.

Wallage, Z. et al. (2006) "Drain Blocking: An effective treatment for reducing dissolved organic carbon loss and water discolouration in a drained peatland", Science of the

Total Environment, 367(2–3), pp. 811–821.

Weiske, A. (2007) "Potential for carbon sequestration in European agriculture", Impact of Environmental Agreements On The Cap, Specific Targeted Research Project no. SSPE-CT-2004-503604. Available at: http://www.ieep.eu/publications/pdfs/meacap/D10a_appendix_carbon_sequestration.pdf [Live: March 2010].

Whitfield, L. (1987) "City Farms: Livestock in Urban Communities", *Community Development Journal*, 22(3), pp. 242–245.

Willett, W.C. & P.J. Skerrett (2005) *Eat, Drink, and Be Healthy: The Harvard Medical School Guide to Healthy Eating*, New York: Free Press.

Williams A.G., E. Audsley, & D.L. Sandars (2006) *Determining the environmental burdens & resource use in the production of agricultural & horticultural commodities*, main report, August 2006, Defra Research Project IS0205, report from Natural Resource Management Institute, Cranfield University. Available at: http://randd.defra.gov.uk/Document.aspx?Document=IS0205_3959_FRP.doc [Live:March 2010].

Wirsenius, S. (2008) "The Biomass Metabolism of the Food System: A Model-Based Survey of the Global and Regional Turnover of Food Biomass", *Journal of Industrial Ecology*, 7(1), pp. 47–80.

Wolfe, M. (2004) "Ecological Cropping Systems – An Organic Target", Elm Farm Research Centre at Wakelyns Agroforestry, Suffolk. Available at: http://www.organicresearchcentre.com/manage/authincludes/article_uploads/art012.pdf [Live: March 2010].

Wolfe, M. (2009) The Organic Research Centre [personal communication], 8 September 2009.

Worrall, F. *et al*. (2003) "Carbon budget for a British upland peat catchment", *The Science of the Total Environment*, 312(1), pp. 133–146.

Ximenes F.A., W.D. Gardner, & A.L. Cowie (2008) "The decomposition of wood products in landfills in Sydney, Australia", *Waste Management*, 28(11), pp. 2344–2354.

Zeng, N. (2008) "Carbon sequestration via wood burial", *Carbon Balance and Management,* 3(1).

Figure sources

Copyright (2010) *zerocarbonbritain2030*. Current emissions data based on Williams A.G., E. Audsley, & D.L. Sandars (2006) *Determining the environmental burdens & resource use in the production of agricultural & horticultural commodities*, main report, August 2006, Defra Research Project IS0205, report from Natural Resource Management Institute, Cranfield University. Available at: http://randd.defra.gov.uk/Document.aspx?Document=IS0205_3959_FRP.doc.

Copyright (2010) *zerocarbonbritain2030*.

Copyright (2010) *zerocarbonbritain2030*. Based on numerical values from Williams A.G., E. Audsley, & D.L. Sandars (2006) *Determining the environmental burdens & resource use in the production of agricultural & horticultural commodities*, main report, August 2006, Defra Research Project IS0205, report from Natural Resource Management Institute, Cranfield University. Available at: http://randd.defra.gov.uk/Document.aspx?Document=IS0205_3959_FRP.doc. In each case the "product" is adjusted to allow for differences of nutritional quality, following the Nutritional Density Score index developed by Maillot *et al*. (2007) "Nutrient-Dense Food Groups Have High Energy Costs: An Econometric Approach to Nutrient Profiling", *Journal of Nutrition*, 137(7), pp. 1815–1820.

Copyright (2010) *zerocarbonbritain2030*.

Copyright a) University of Illinois, USA (2006) and b) Silvanus Nursery, Hungary (2008).

Copyright Carbon Gold (2010).

Copyright Rothamsted Research. Courtesy of Dr. G. Richter.

Burgess/Cranfield University.

Copyright (2010) *zerocarbonbritain2030*. Adapted from Willett, W.C. & P.J. Skerrett (2005) *Eat, Drink, and Be Healthy: The Harvard Medical School Guide to Healthy Eating*, New York: Free Press.

Copyright (2010) *zerocarbonbritain2030*. In each case the "product" is adjusted to allow for differences of nutritional quality, following the Nutritional Density Score index developed by Maillot *et al*. (2007) "Nutrient-Dense Food Groups Have High Energy Costs: An Econometric Approach to Nutrient Profiling", *Journal of Nutrition*, 137(7), pp. 1815–1820.

"" The answer, my friend,
is blowing in the wind ""

Bob Dylan

Chapter 8
Renewables

Introduction

This chapter makes the case for an energy scenario that produces all of Britain's heating and electricity needs from renewable sources. It proposes that the heating needs of our businesses and homes should be met by a combination of renewable heating technologies, such as those that run on biogas and biomass, and others that require electricity to run them, such as heat pumps, heat exchangers and immersion heaters.

Since *zerocarbonbritain: an alternative energy strategy* (Helweg-Larson & Bull, 2007) was published several others, including Jacobson and Delucchi (2009) and the European Energy Agency (EEA, 2009), have highlighted the potential of renewables. Jacobson and Delucchi (2009) claim that 100% of the world's energy needs can be met by renewable generation by 2030 and the European Energy Agency (2009) demonstrates that the economically competitive potential of wind generation in Europe is seven times the projected electrical demand for 2030.

In 2008 the UK used 1,815TWh of energy; 41% of that energy was used in heating and 21% in electricity (Department of Energy and Climate Change [DECC], 2009a). The preceding chapters within the PowerDown section have demonstrated that it is possible to cut our energy demands by over 55% through the energy-efficiency retrofitting of homes, offices and industrial premises to maintain more heat in buildings, and by improving transport systems through changes in technology and use.

Nonetheless, even with the above improvements implemented, significant energy demand will remain. In addition, the electrification of heating and vehicles, as envisaged in the PowerDown chapters, will only be carbon neutral if the extra electricity required is produced from renewable sources. This chapter demonstrates how Britain can create a carbon-free, electricity-based energy system by 2030, using renewable energy and biomass alone, and without recourse to nuclear power.

In the first part of this chapter the renewable technologies presently available are introduced and the various costs and benefits associated with each are analysed. This provides the rationale for the second part which offers a proposed overall energy mix for a zero carbon Britain in 2030. In the second part we also discuss how to overcome the technical difficulties associated with the rapid transition to renewables and how to manage the variable nature of the recommended renewable technologies.

The deployment of renewable electricity has already proven to be one of the fastest global technology switches in history. Until recently, the European Union has led the way in the development and application of renewable technology and Britain is in a strong position to take advantage of the expansion of offshore wind power in particular. The UK currently has the largest deployed offshore wind capacity in Europe and there are plans for significant further deployment.

However, Britain and Europe are beginning to lose their status as world leaders in renewable technologies. China and the United States have recently overtaken the rest of the world to install the largest renewable power capacities. At the end of 2008 the total installed renewables capacity of the top six countries were China (76GW), the United States (40GW), Germany (34GW), Spain (22GW), India (13GW), and Japan (8GW) (Renewable Energy Policy Network for the 21st Century [REN21], 2009). For comparison the UK had 6.8 GW (DECC, 2009a).

Nonetheless, Britain has the opportunity to become a net exporter of renewable electricity by 2030, as well as to export its expertise in renewable technologies across the globe. To do so, however, it is essential that we immediately begin implementing the policy structures and installing the infrastructure necessary to support the rapid expansion of enough renewable energy generation to support all of our requirements.

Exploring the options

THE CURRENT SITUATION AND BRITAIN'S ELECTRICITY REQUIREMENT

In the Energy security chapter, we briefly outlined Britain's increasing reliance on fossil fuels, specifically oil, gas and coal, to power both the heating and electricity sectors. While Britain has reserves of all three of these energy sources, UK production of them is declining, and since 2004 the UK has been a net importer of fuel (DECC, 2009a).

The total electricity generated in the United Kingdom in 2008 was 390TWh. Total supply was 401TWh (including net imports) (ibid.). Overall demand was 400TWh. Figure 8.1 demonstrates the relative quantities of different energy sources used for generating electricity, and the uses of the electricity produced.

As Figure 8.1 shows, the key fuels currently used for the generation of electricity in the UK are gas (40% of fuel used; 46% of gross supplied electricity) and coal (36% of fuel used; 32% of gross supplied electricity); with nuclear power (15% of fuel used; 13% of gross supplied electricity) the next largest.

In 2008, renewables were responsible for only 6% of energy used (7% of gross supplied electricity), with just 0.75% from wind, wave and solar sources (although this accounted for almost 2% of gross supplied electricity), the majority still being supplied by large hydro.

Fig. 8.1 UK electricity flow chart

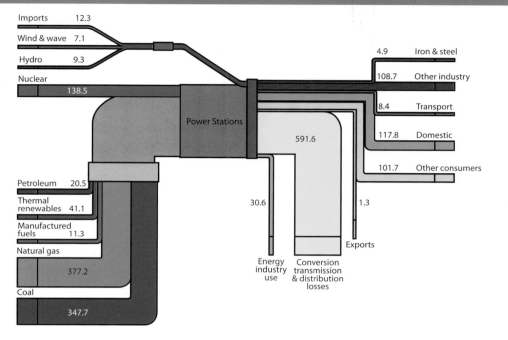

Electricity flow chart, 2008 (TWh) showing the supply sources of electricity losses and uses.
"Wind and wave" includes electricity produced from solar photovoltaics. Hydro includes generation from pumped storage, although this is essentially an energy storage device that makes a small net energy loss rather than being a net electricity generator.
Source: Adapted from DECC (2009).

Note that the conversion, transmission and distribution losses are dominated by conversion losses in thermal power stations.

In the ZCB2030 scenario, electricity generated from renewable energy sources will replace electricity generated from fossil fuels. Thus, while total energy use will be reduced by over 55%, Britain's current electricity demand will roughly double (see Box 8.1).

THE CHOICE OF ELECTRICITY GENERATION TYPE

There are three main possibilities available for decarbonising the electricity system using technology that is either currently available or close to maturity:
• Burning fossil fuels but using Carbon Capture & Storage (CCS) to prevent the release of the resulting CO_2;

Box 8.1 The energy density of Britain

The chart in Figure 8.2 plots the density of energy use by various countries against the density of their populations. Mackay (2009) claims that those countries consuming 0.1W/m² will find living off their own renewables very intrusive, because renewable power generation will have to be distributed over a large proportion of the national land area.

Those countries consuming more than 1.0 W/m² would have to give over a huge proportion of their land area for renewable technologies in order to power themselves at their present rate were they to use only nationally-produced renewable power (ibid.). This assumes that the space used for renewable power generation cannot be used for any other purpose, but this is not the case. For example, wind farms allow for plenty of other uses beneath them.

Fig. 8.2 Population density and power consumption per person

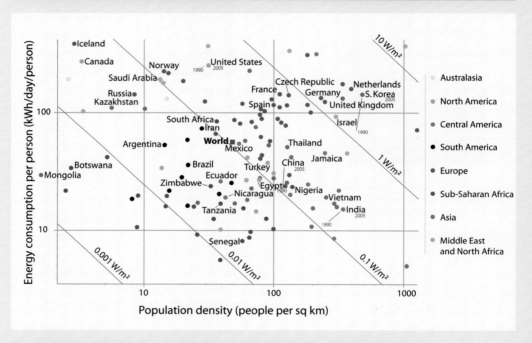

Population density (people per km²) and power consumption per person (kWh/day/person).
Scales are logarithmic and isoclines (in red) show lines of constant energy density. Countries which use a lot of energy per person are distributed towards the top of the graph; those which have dense populations are distributed on the right of the graph, and those that use a lot of power consumption per area of land are distributed towards the top right. The UK has a relatively high population density and high power consumption per person. As a result, the UK has one of the highest levels of power consumption per area of land.
Source: Adapted from Mackay (2009).

The United Kingdom is a high consumer of energy per person and has a moderately high population density. Overall UK consumption is just over 1W/m². There are some differences in our methods as discussed above. However, we will be able to avoid industrialising our countryside for three main reasons:

* The reduction of energy waste, especially in buildings and transport will reduce our total energy use (although the conversion of many services to running on electricity will increase electricity use).

• We do not insist that Britain be self-sufficient in electricity at all times, only that it is zero carbon on a net basis. Britain will exchange electricity with other countries, especially those with different renewable resources.

• We are able to utilise an area much larger than our land mass because of our exceptional offshore wind resource giving us an advantage over many other countries with less renewable energy potential.

• A mix of technologies will also reduce the risk of a power shortage. Zero carbon Britain will be far more robust if we maintain a spread of different renewables in case there should be a lack of any single one for any reason.

• Using nuclear fission, following the French model; or,

• Using renewable sources of energy such as wind, tidal, wave and hydropower, biomass, solar and geothermal.

It is possible to power Britain's electricity system using a combination of these three options, but not all mixes work equally well. A key concern relates to the ability for managers to turn the electricity produced by various power sources up and down. This is because power demand is far from static, varying significantly over the day and night.

With many renewable sources of power, such as wind, solar or wave, the energy supply at any one place and point in time is largely dependent on the weather, which can be accurately forecast over the short- to medium-term. However, as it is difficult to store large amounts of energy and because these energy sources are variable and therefore cannot easily "follow load", various technologies and policies need to be implemented to assist with balancing electricity supply to our varying demand.

Some renewable energy sources, such as large hydro and biomass, can be utilised to a lesser or greater extent for load following, depending on the level of demand. The key is the amount of "dispatchable generation" available, i.e. how much generation can be brought online quickly. Biogas (including bio-SNG) is ideal for this (see Box 8.2).

Some gas-fired power stations can be taken from zero to full output in under half an hour

Box 8.2 Biogas – gasification and anaerobic digestion

Biogas is gas made from biological origin via anaerobic digestion. Bio-SNG is gas made from biological origin via gasification.

Anaerobic digestion is a biological process by which organic matter can be turned into biogas. Organic matter is fed into a sealed digester where bacteria convert it into methane and carbon dioxide, leaving a nutrient-rich digestate which can be used as fertiliser. After the carbon dioxide and other trace gases are removed the remaining methane is known as biomethane and is virtually identical to natural gas.

Many types of biomass from waste or dedicated crops can be used for anaerobic digestion, including waste paper, grass, food waste and sewage. However woody biomass cannot currently be used because most microorganisms are unable to break down lignin – the tough fibre that gives wood its strength. Anaerobic digestion is particularly suited to wet organic material (McKendry, 2002).

In contrast, gasification is a thermo-chemical process that involves heating organic matter to high temperatures in the presence of a small amount of oxygen, but not enough to allow combustion to occur. This produces syngas which is a mixture of carbon monoxide and hydrogen. Syngas can be used in place of natural gas in some applications. It can also be turned into liquid fuels using the Fischer-Tropsch process.

In principle gasification can proceed from just about any organic material, including biomass and plastic waste, but the feedstock must have low moisture content and wet feedstock may need pre-drying.

Gasification can achieve higher efficiencies than anaerobic digestion (McKendry, 2002), but syngas is harder to integrate into natural gas infrastructure. Anaerobic digestion is a more mature technology than gasification, which is still developing (ibid.).

and can have their output adjusted almost simultaneously, while large hydro can be switched on in a matter of seconds. Geothermal and concentrated solar can also be used to balance loads being similarly dispatchable.

Fossil fuels and Carbon Capture & Storage (CCS)

The *zerocarbonbritain2030* scenario excludes the use of Carbon Capture & Storage (CCS) technology, other than with biomass, for two major reasons: deployment time and carbon footprint. CCS is currently only at the early demonstration stage and there is little chance of the technology being ready for deployment within the next ten years (McKinsey, 2008). It is imperative that we make the greatest possible carbon cuts before then.

Secondly, electricity produced using CCS technology still has a much higher carbon footprint than electricity produced from renewable sources as not all of the CO_2 emitted from the power station is captured. This is demonstrated in Figure 8.3.

Finally, a third reason based on cost can be given. McKinsey (2008) notes that "the total CCS

Fig. 8.3 Lifecycle emissions for electricity-generating technologies

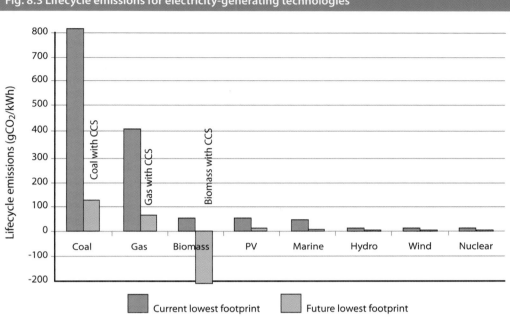

(UK, European, USA and Australian power plants)

Estimates of current and estimated future lifecycle emissions for 1kWh of electricity produced by each technology (gCO₂/kWh).

Carbon capture and storage is expected to produce significant reductions in lifecycle carbon emissions per unit of energy produced. However, this is still above that from current renewable technologies. For all technologies, future carbon reductions are possible if the construction phase (e.g. steel and concrete production) is fuelled by low or zero carbon electricity.

Additionally, reductions in the use of raw materials can contribute to further future reductions in life cycle emissions for solar PV and marine. Burning "carbon neutral" biomass and capturing emissions using CCS technologies would result in a net removal of CO_2 from the atmosphere.
Source: POST (2009).

expense would be at least 30% higher than that of new power plants (for the same scale plants), and possibly much more".

CCS installation will require active financing from governments if it is to be deployed on a large-scale (International Energy Agency [IEA], 2009a) as would the mass deployment of renewable technologies. However, CCS carries with it the risk of the accidental leakage of the stored CO_2 which would mean there were limited or no carbon savings, while still saddling the UK with the additional costs. CO_2 leaching would potentially degrade the quality of groundwater, damage mineral resources and have lethal effects on plants and sub-soil animals. If a leak were to cause a sudden release of captured CO_2 into the atmosphere, quite apart from the danger of the enormous extra emission itself, it would amount to a toxic hazard at a local level (Intergovernmental Panel on Climate Change [IPCC], 2005).

Despite these issues, we can still benefit from the development of CCS technology. CCS has a role as a transitional technology in those countries on a slightly shallower decarbonisation path and commercially as a potential "technology transfer" from the UK. The use of CCS to sequester emissions from biomass, albeit costly, is environmentally very attractive as it could be carbon negative. In addition, process-based CCS might, in the long run, help avert direct emissions from industrial processes should no better solutions be found. For these reasons the development of the technology should certainly continue.

Nuclear power

While the existing stock of nuclear power stations are presently needed and should be allowed to run their course until they are decommissioned, the *zerocarbonbritain2030* scenario excludes nuclear power from Britain's future energy mix for a number of reasons. The first is on the basis of human and environmental health. Nuclear power generation results in waste products which remain harmful for thousands of years. Similarly, whilst the likelihood of accidents involving nuclear power stations or waste is low, as Chernobyl has demonstrated, the economic, social and environmental costs of a nuclear accident can be catastrophic.

The second reason for excluding nuclear power is based upon concerns for international security. International co-operation will be vital in dealing with the impending peaks in fossil-fuel supplies. If the UK and other "developed" nations make new nuclear power a core component of their electricity supply, other countries with rapidly developing economies will want to follow suit.

Therefore, for short- and long-term safety, security, and financial reasons, nuclear is not included in *zerocarbonbritain2030*. Renewable energy technologies alone must meet our 2030 target.

The potential of renewable electricity

This section contains a brief summary of the potential of each of Britain's renewable energy resources: wind; hydro; biogas; biomass; landfill gas; solar; wave; and tidal.

The energy generation potential of each resource can be illustrated by two measures:

- Installed capacity, generally measured in MW (megawatts) or GW (gigawatts). This is the theoretical maximum amount of energy that can be generated at any one time.
- Total annual power generation, generally measured in GWh (gigawatt hours) or TWh (terawatt hours). This is the total amount of energy that can be generated per year.

No generation technology produces electricity at its maximum rated output all of the time and so "capacity factor" figures are also used. The capacity factor shows the average generation output actually achieved by a technology as a percentage of the theoretical maximum output (installed capacity). A reasonable capacity factor for wind turbines is in the region of 25–40% (DECC, 2009a), although recent installations have higher capacity factors, some over 40% (Jacobson, 2009). Photovoltaic solar panels have a capacity factor of nearer to 5% in the UK. As renewable sources of electricity don't have fuel costs the capacity factor is less relevant than for fossil fuels.

ONSHORE WIND

Onshore wind is an established renewable energy technology, and is already a rapidly expanding sector, having grown in the UK from 1.7TWh in 2004 to 5.8TWh in 2008 (DECC, 2009a). Whilst wind farms can spread over wide areas, numerous other uses of the land, including agriculture, can take place simultaneously.

Onshore wind farms are sometimes unpopular due to their alleged lack of aesthetic appeal and because of the inconvenience that may be caused to local communities by the extra traffic required to transport and install large turbines. The large lorries and cranes required to transport turbines can require local road-widening or entail traffic restrictions.

However, once windfarms are in place it is often found that communities are far less disturbed by them than they expected. An offer of part community ownership can also help gain local support.

As we will see, offshore wind suffers from fewer initial objections than onshore and also has much greater overall electricity-generation potential. Nonetheless, onshore wind will continue to have an important role to play in electricity production for **zero**carbon**britain**2030.

Based on a CO_2 price as low as $60 a tonne, onshore wind is cheaper per MWh than many other common sources of power, such as gas produced by combined cycle gas turbines (CCGT) and also cheaper than less common sources such as coal oxyfuel with CCS (IEA, 2009b).

In the **zero**carbon**britain**2030 scenario, there is 75TWh of onshore wind power, generated from 28.5GW of installed capacity.

Box 8.3 Wind turbine 'efficiency'

While many people quibble that wind turbines are only 25–40% efficient, while implying that they are ineffective, this is highly misleading and inaccurate. One cannot expect a higher output than 30% of a wind turbine's potential, as the wind is patently not going to blow at optimum speeds all of the time. It is important to remember that wind is a free resource so capacity factor is far less important than plant efficiency when one is paying for fuel, as in fossil-fuelled or nuclear power stations, where it is understandably crucial.

OFFSHORE WIND

Offshore wind represents one of the UK's most significant renewable resources. Firstly, because the potential site area for offshore wind generators is enormous, with around 40,000km² at depths of up to 25m and a further 80,000km² at a depth of between 25 and 50m (Figure 8.4). Secondly, because offshore wind turbines tend to have higher capacity factors than onshore wind turbines. This is because, at turbine height, wind speeds tend to be higher and steadier offshore, and power production from wind turbines is proportional to the cube of the wind speed.

Additionally, larger offshore wind turbines can be erected than onshore wind turbines as they can be more easily transported by sea than by road. The largest commonly used onshore turbines have capacities of 2 to 3MW each, whereas offshore turbines are currently up to 5MW each. Thus, large offshore wind turbine factories need to be positioned near large ports for transportation purposes.

If wind turbines were distributed across the total potential offshore area of Britain, and had a power per unit area of 3W/m², it could provide a total 360GW of capacity and 3154TWh of generation (Mackay, 2009). However, this figure takes no account of existing oil or gas rigs, shipping lanes, fishing areas, or any of the other uses that the sea is currently put to, so the area actually available for offshore wind development is smaller. Mackay estimates that

we can make use of 1051TWh of this potential.

In addition, significant improvements in the capacity of offshore wind turbines are expected in the next few years. Offshore wind is not yet a mature technology. The sea is a very different environment to a hilltop and yet until recently there have been problems with offshore turbines because they have been based upon onshore designs. Noise is less of an issue out to sea, and offshore turbines can be much larger so there is less need to sacrifice efficiency for the sake of creating more visually or acoustically pleasing designs. At present, both Clipper and Enova are developing 10MW offshore turbines so even larger turbines may well soon be available (Renewable Energy Focus, 2010).

However, the offshore environment is much harsher than the onshore one. Mechanical wear-and-tear and corrosion problems are amplified due to the harsh sea water environment and even simple maintenance and repair can be difficult. Once the salt water problems are dealt with, however, it is fair to expect offshore turbines' lifetimes to be longer than onshore ones as the wind offshore is more planar and therefore less turbulent. The energy industry is no stranger to dealing with the problems thrown up by the offshore environment so it can be hoped that the expertise gained from oil rigs will successfully be deployed to support offshore wind development. This may make offshore costs closer to onshore costs and potentially extend the construction season.

The total global installed offshore wind

Fig. 8.4 UK offshore wind power

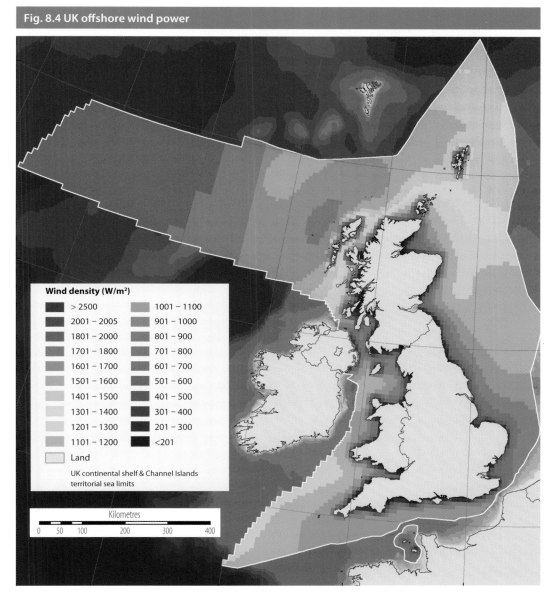

Wind density (W/m²)

> 2500	1001 – 1100
2001 – 2005	901 – 1000
1801 – 2000	801 – 900
1701 – 1800	701 – 800
1601 – 1700	601 – 700
1501 – 1600	501 – 600
1401 – 1500	401 – 500
1301 – 1400	301 – 400
1201 – 1300	201 – 300
1101 – 1200	<201

Land

UK continental shelf & Channel Islands
territorial sea limits

Kilometres

0   50   100   200   300   400

UK annual mean wind power density at 100m above sea level (W/m²).
Mean wind power is generally greatest with distance from the shore.
Source: BERR (2008).

capacity was 1.47GW at the end of 2008 (European Wind Energy Association [EWEA], 2009), with 39% of this located in the UK, making the UK a world leader in offshore wind installed capacity. However, this status is really due to slow implementation elsewhere in the world, with global offshore installed capacity currently only about 0.8% of the installed onshore capacity (Prats, 2009). Since 2000 however, the offshore market has grown very rapidly with developers already announcing plans to build a further 25GW of capacity in Round Three of the Government's offshore wind development plan (Crown Estate, 2010).

The energy required to make something is referred to as the "embodied" or "embedded" energy. This can then be compared to the amount of energy we get back from the renewable sources. This is known as the "energy return on energy invested" or EROEI. The EROEI for wind is higher than for other renewables. For example a 5MW turbine can give a return of 28:1 (see Lenzen & Munksgaard, 2002), whilst a high calculations of PV is 10:1, based on US weather (see U.S. Department of Energy [US DoE], 2004).

HYDROPOWER

The Department of Energy and Climate Change divide hydroelectric schemes according to their installed capacity, defining small hydro schemes as having a capacity of less than 5MW capacity, and large schemes having over 5MW (DECC, 2009a).

In 2008, the UK's small-scale hydro capacity of 173MW generated 568GWh of electricity (ibid.). There is a great deal of scope in the UK for the expansion of small-scale hydro schemes, with many potential sites at former water-powered mills, multiple low-head sites on rivers near towns and cities in the 10–100kW range, and plenty of potential for higher-head projects.

Recent studies indicate that the maximum untapped potential of hydroelectric generation extends to nearly 1.2GW across 12,040 sites in England and Wales (Environment Agency [EA], 2010) and almost 1.2GW across 7,043 sites in Scotland (Forrest & Wallace, 2010). The realistic potential will be significantly lower, since financial constraints need to be considered in the results from England and Wales. Environmental constraints will also limit the capacity predicted by these studies, although the English and Welsh study indicated that 4,190 sites, representing around 580MW of power, could provide environmental "win-win" situations (EA, 2010).

2008 also saw 1.5GW of large hydropower capacity installed (excluding pumped storage stations) in the UK, generating 4.6TWh (DECC, 2009a). The scope for expansion is extremely limited, with most of the accessible sites already in use. Large-scale hydropower can have very disruptive effects on natural habitats, and may actually increase greenhouse gas emissions through the release of methane in flooded areas (Fearnside, 2004). Potential sites for large hydro development in Britain lie either

in national parks or other highly-valued areas and landscapes making their development problematic at best.

BIOMASS

Biomass is the umbrella term used for any fuel that is derived from plants. It is considered carbon neutral because CO_2 is absorbed from the atmosphere through photosynthesis in order for the plant to grow. When the plant is burned the CO_2 is simply returned to the atmosphere rather than adding to it. This is why if CCS is used in a biomass power station then the process can be considered to be carbon negative.

Biomass can be grown, stored and used to provide power on demand. It can also be used to make liquid fuels for transport. Currently liquid transport fuels are generally made from only the sugary, starchy or oily fraction of crops but it is possible to make them from any biomass, including woody biomass or waste (see the Transport chapter for more details). Furthermore, if stored in a way that prevents it from rotting and releasing carbon into the atmosphere, biomass can also be used to sequester carbon, as occurs when it is utilised in construction, allowing a very positive case to be made for straw bale buildings.

As well as using co-products from forestry and timber processes, industrial-scale woody biomass can be grown in the form of many different plants. In the UK, miscanthus and short rotation coppice (SRC) willow offer the best possibilities.

The major problem associated with biomass is that growing it requires a lot of land. Between 1 and 16 oven-dried tonnes (odt) of miscanthus or SRC willow can be produced per hectare per year in the UK, depending on the quality of the land, with some possibility for increases in the future (Sims *et al.*, 2007). This is discussed further in the Land use and agriculture Technical appendix* 9. There are about 18GJ (5000 kWh) of energy in an odt of biomass (Woods & Bauen, 2003). The total area of Britain is 22 million hectares, 6 million of which is arable.

Hence it can be seen that a huge area of land would be required if an attempt to satisfy a high proportion of our heating or electricity demand from biomass was made. Based on the yield of 20 tonnes per hectare projected for biomass crops grown on good quality land in 2030 (Taylor, 2007; Woods *et al.*, 2009), and a generating plant efficiency of 40%, 38TWh of electricity could be produced from one million hectares of arable land. This is 11% of our predicted 2030 residual heating demand.

Although the role of biomass is necessarily limited, a zero carbon Britain will only be achieved with great innovation and the inclusion of many of the smaller technologies. Full details on the land allocation in the ***zero*carbon*britain*2030** scenario are discussed in the Land use and agriculture chapter.

Because of its large land requirements, overdevelopment of biomass has the potential to create destructive land use change. At present the UK generates around 2TWh of electricity per year from burning biomass. This is mostly in the form of co-firing with coal, but there are also a number of dedicated biomass electricity schemes in operation. In September 2009 a scheme in Port Talbot opened, generating 14MW, and using 160,000 tonnes of wood sourced from Welsh forests and timber by-products (Welsh Assembly Government [WAG], 2009). There is also a 350MW plant proposed for Port Talbot which will require 3 million tonnes of woodchip per annum (Burgermeister, 2008). This is expected to be supplied from Canada, the USA, Lithuania and Latvia, raising issues of fuel security (ibid.). While shipping is an efficient source of freight transport, emissions should also be considered in the carbon cost of electricity. Further details on shipping are available in the Transport chapter.

Careful selection of equipment is needed to minimise impacts on local air quality. The carbon impact of biomass depends on the type of fuel and distance between source and use. Typically, 4% of the energy produced in the combustion of wood is used in its harvesting, transportation and chipping.

BIOGAS

Biogas is usually made from wet biomass, such as animal dung, sewage, food waste or grass, using a process called anaerobic digestion. The feedstock is mixed with water to form slurry and fed into a digester, where microorganisms convert it into methane and carbon dioxide. The methane can then be used in place of natural gas.

A recent assessment by the National Grid (2009) shows a large potential for biogas in the UK (see Table 8.1). It is estimated that around half (48%) of the current residential gas demand could be met from biogas. This could be extremely useful for urban heating and cooking which biomass cannot sensibly help with as not enough of it could be grown locally. A breakdown of the estimated potential can be seen below. The "stretch" scenario is the calculated technical potential based on both all waste being sorted, and the maximum use of gasification and anaerobic digestion. This produces far higher outputs for the drier feed-stocks.

The National Grid also provided a "base case" scenario which they feel is more realistic. While there are several exceptions, this generally assumes 50% of available "waste" is sorted.

In a zero carbon Britain, processes will be more efficient, so the "waste" available for re-use will be lower. There will also be competition for the use of waste to make other products such as biochar. The role for biochar is explained in the Land use and agriculture chapter.

Food waste will not be available to be made into biomass or biogas since it will be used as animal feed and compost. The current legal and safety issues associated with this re-use can and should be addressed. Similarly, the

Table 8.1 The role for biogas in ZCB2030

Source	2020 Nat. Grid TWh (basecase)	2020 Nat. Grid TWh (stretch)	ZCB2030 scenario Biogas TWh
Sewage/waste water	2.45	5.67	5.67
Manure	2.31	4.58	0.27
Agricultural waste	2.10	8.71	4.36
Food waste	6.58	12.04	0.00
Biodegradable waste	9.41	75.20	15.34
Wood waste	11.30	24.36	6.66
Grass	0	0	22.30
Total waste	**34.15**	**130.57**	**32.29**
Dedicated energy crops: miscanthus	16.66	35.83	12.98
Total including energy crops	**50.81**	**166.40**	**68.97**

The potential biogas supply by original source type, under the National Grid 2020 scenarios, and the ZCB2030 scenario (TWh).
Source: National Grid scenario figures from National Grid (2009).

amount of available manure will be lower as the healthier ***zero**carbon**britain**2030* diet requires less livestock and, therefore, provides less waste. Some biodegradable and wood wastes may also be used to create biochar or wood pellets, which again will decrease their availability for use as biogas. Table 8.2 shows all feedstocks for biochar.

Making useful energy products from material currently classified as waste is beneficial in terms of reducing landfill and reducing the amount of new material being harvested and refined. In the case of biogas production from waste, the output is a dispatchable fuel which can be used as a core part in supply-side variability management.

LANDFILL/SEWAGE GAS

A technology related to biogas is that which simply taps and uses methane from landfill. At present, landfill gas and sewage gas are among the largest contributors to the UK renewable energy mix, generating 5.3TWh of electricity in 2008 (DECC, 2009a). However, limits to expansion are imposed by the amount of landfill and sewage actually available. It is also assumed that improved efficiencies will decrease waste.

It may also be possible to use this gas to supplement heating requirements instead of electricity generation. There is significant scope for further research into landfill flows, gases and degradation rates.

Table 8.2 The role for biogas in ZCB2030	
Biochar	**m odt**
Miscanthus (test)	1
Forestry waste	1.52
Poultry waste	1.09
Wood waste	2.26
Paper and cardboard	12.52

Biochar feedstock source quantities in the ZCB2030 scenario (million oven-dried tonnes).
There are a range of potential sources of material to make into biochar. The choice of feedstock is important as it impacts on its sustainability. As shown here the majority of feedstock derive from waste. There is a very small amount of grown miscanthus which can be used in a variety of different areas to test it's impact. This data will enable future analysis on the most sustainable form of biochar.

SOLAR POWER

The technological development of solar photovoltaic (PV) panels has been rapid and costs have been falling. A company based in America recently attained the industry goal of reducing manufacturing costs to less than one US dollar per watt of capacity (First Solar, 2009). However, the energy return on energy invested of PV is not nearly as strong as for wind (i.e. a good EROEI for PV is 10:1 in the US and a conservative EROEI for wind is 28:1). This is also linked to PV currently being less financially attractive.

Nonetheless, a key advantage of PV is that it can be installed at a domestic scale. If you assume the homeowner has no opportunity to own a wind farm through a community project, then a favourable price comparison can be made between domestic PV and the retail price of electricity. Largely because of this, the UK Photovoltaics Manufacturers' Association (2009)

are able to claim that PV will be cost competitive by 2013.

The Energy Technology Support Unit (ETSU, 2000, cited in Watson *et al.*, 2002) have estimated that if PV were to cover the surfaces of all available domestic and non-domestic buildings, the practicable resource could be 266TWh by 2025 (allowing for 10% non-suitable surfaces and 25% shading).

Unfortunately, to achieve this would be staggeringly expensive. Although solar PV is a key technology for countries located further south, in the UK sunlight has lower annual energy available per m² than southern European countries. Also, this energy is generated primarily in the summer, which clashes with our peak consumption which is highest on long, sunless winter nights. Therefore in the UK solar PV is mainly appropriate to those who are off grid and without a suitable wind or other resource. Based on cost figures from the European Commission (EC, 2008), installing PV is over twice the price

of offshore wind with maintenance costs being similar.

WAVE POWER

There are currently a range of competing technologies tackling the challenge of harvesting the energy from the waves. Over the years a wide variety of technologies have been developed and tested, from the Salters Duck in the 1970s to the Pelamis "sea snake" tested in Portugal in 2008.

The technical potential of wave power in the UK has been estimated by Langley (2009) at 20GW of capacity, providing 57TWh of electricity a year. Mackay (2009) estimates the theoretical potential as 87.6TWh, but suggests that, based on expanding the currently deployed technology; this would only provide an estimated 26.3TWh (see Figure 8.5).

For the *zerocarbonbritain2030* scenario, wave potential for Britain is based on realising 50% of the potential estimated by Langley (2009) by 2030, in other words, 28.5TWh per year based on 10GW of installed capacity.

TIDAL POWER

Tidal range technology adapts established hydro technology and comes in two types: barrages and lagoons. Barrages are built across rivers and estuaries and lagoons are built in shallow seas. These technologies have an advantage over most other renewable systems in that they provide predictable, dispatchable power.

Various power-generating barrages have been proposed for the Severn estuary. The proposed Cardiff-Weston barrage, commonly termed the Severn Barrage, would, if built, have an installed capacity of 8.64GW, and has been estimated as costing between £19.6 billion and £22.2 billion (DECC, 2009b). There are also several potential sites for tidal lagoons in the Severn estuary and in several other locations across Britain (Sustainable Development Commission [SDC], 2007).

Langley (2009) estimates the total UK tidal barrages and lagoon potential as 20GW of capacity and 60TWh of electricity a year (see Figure 8.6). In the *zerocarbonbritain2030* scenario, we use sixty percent of this figure: 12GW of installed capacity and 36TWh of electricity per year.

Additionally, tidal stream potential has been estimated at 22TWh per year (Langley, 2009) with 8GW installed. Within the *zerocarbonbritain2030* scenario, we use half this potential.

The costs of renewable electricity capacity

Table 8.3 from the European Commission (2008) shows estimated financial costs for various energy sources.

Wave and tidal technologies are not included in their analysis. Estimates of the initial cost of wave technology are £350–500 per MWh (Langley, 2009). This should be seen as a very

Fig. 8.5 UK wave power

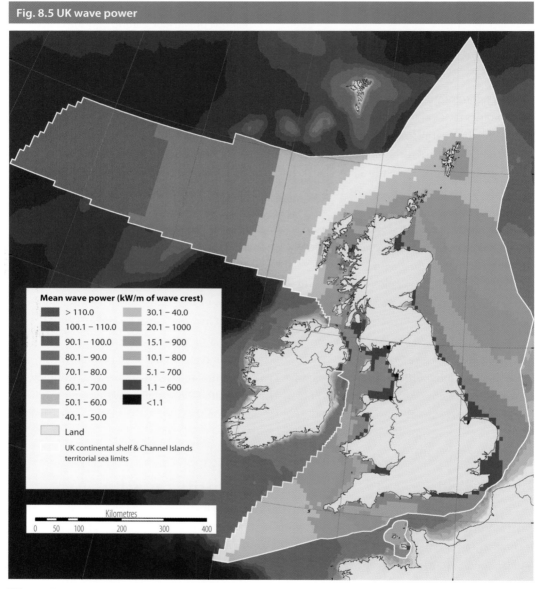

Mean wave power (kW/m of wave crest)

> 110.0	30.1 – 40.0
100.1 – 110.0	20.1 – 1000
90.1 – 100.0	15.1 – 900
80.1 – 90.0	10.1 – 800
70.1 – 80.0	5.1 – 700
60.1 – 70.0	1.1 – 600
50.1 – 60.0	<1.1
40.1 – 50.0	

Land

UK continental shelf & Channel Islands
territorial sea limits

Kilometres
0 50 100 200 300 400

UK annual mean wave power – full wave field (kW/m of wave crest).
Wave power is calculated for each horizontal metre of wave crest. Full wave field power is calculated using the total of wave power attributed to wind-wave and swell components.
Source: BERR (2008).

Fig. 8.6 UK tidal power

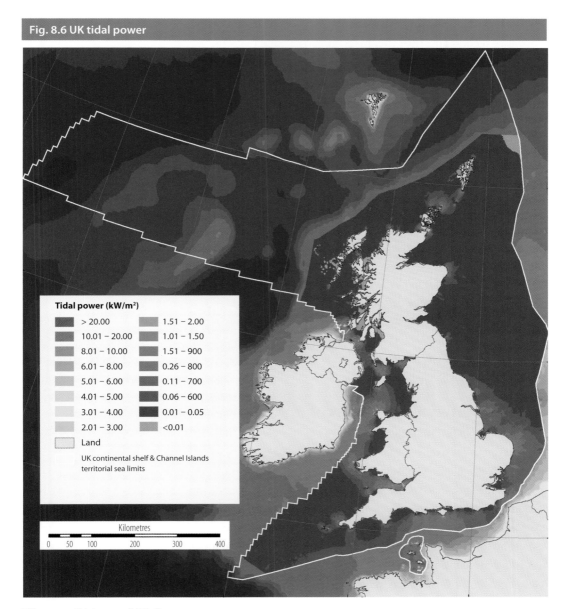

Tidal power (kW/m²)

> 20.00	1.51 – 2.00
10.01 – 20.00	1.01 – 1.50
8.01 – 10.00	1.51 – 900
6.01 – 8.00	0.26 – 800
5.01 – 6.00	0.11 – 700
4.01 – 5.00	0.06 – 600
3.01 – 4.00	0.01 – 0.05
2.01 – 3.00	<0.01
Land	

UK continental shelf & Channel Islands
territorial sea limits

Kilometres

0   50   100   200   300   400

UK average tidal power (kW/m²).
Tidal power is calculated in kW/m² of vertical water column. Tidal power is calculated at mid depth in the water column.
Source: BERR (2008).

approximate figure because it is a young innovative technology. Tidal stream technology is estimated as costing £300–400 per MWh, and tidal range is estimated as £200–300 per MWh for schemes under 50MW (ibid.), however, there are big economies of scale associated with this technology so larger installations would generate at a lower cost. All of these costs are expected to fall over time.

The above demonstrates that onshore wind has similar capital costs to coal but without the fuel requirements and that the price of coal with CCS is similar to that of offshore wind, but with substantial running costs. These calculations were made without adding in any carbon costs. The cost per kWh for customers will be dependent on a range of factors including the policy mechanisms in place, the ownership of the generation capacity, the capacity factors and future fuel costs.

Sharing renewable resources between countries

The amount of each renewable resource varies geographically. A renewable electricity system is therefore strengthened by the sharing of energy resources over large distances, consisting of areas with different key resources. This not only allows the supply of electricity to areas which lack sufficient renewable resources of their own; it also enables the best option to be utilised in each area and offsets problems of variability, as weather fluctuations become smoothed over larger distances. In addition, sharing energy resources enables the smoothing of demand fluctuations.

In **zero**carbon**britain**2030, we will import small amounts of electricity in order to manage variability. However, overall Britain will export more than it imports. As each country has unique renewable energy potential, the cost of decarbonising our electricity supply and managing variability could be reduced through increased energy trading with other countries.

This system can work on an international basis as well as within nations. Each country has its own demand profile and, as a result, its peak demand may not overlap with that of its neighbours. For example, in Norway the peak demand tends to occur in the morning on weekdays and in the evening at the weekend. Our peak demand occurs during the evening on weekdays. The intersection of the two demand profiles can be seen in Figure 8.7.

As electricity is deployed for transport and other areas' demand profiles are likely to change, the profile should become smoother especially with the increasing focus on grid balancing. At this point, access to other grids may become more beneficial in terms of being able to reach more widespread generation assets and therefore decrease the demand for backup generation.

The major renewable resources of Europe and North Africa are:

• Wind, wave and tidal resources around the western margins, including our own offshore wind resource.

Table 8.3 The cost of renewable electricity options				
Technology	**Captial costs £/kW**	**Operations and maintenance costs £/kW**	**Learning rate**	**Fuel £/MWh(e)**
Gas – OCGT (Open Cyle Gas Turbine)	140 –280	4 – 9	5	39
Gas – CCGT (Combined Cycle Gas Turbine)	330 – 510	13 – 18	5	26
Gas – CCGT & CCS Carbon Capture and Storage	690 – 900	25 – 30	2.2	30
Pulverised coal	690 – 1000	34 – 46	6 11	
Pulverised coal & CCS	1170 – 1860	52 – 70	2.1	15
Coal – IGCC (Integrated Gasification Combined Cycle)	970 – 1140	42 –48	11	12
Coal – IGCC & CCS	1170 – 1660	51 – 74	3	6
Nuclear fission	1360 – 2330	51 – 74	3	6
Onshore wind	690 – 950	23 – 29	8	0
Offshore wind	1200 – 1900	49 – 72	8	0
Hydro – large	620 – 3100	28 – 52	-0.5	0
Hydro – small	1380 – 4500	59 – 90	-1.2	0
Solar PV	2830 – 4750	50 – 79	23	0
Biomass	1400 – 3500	85 – 202	12.5	18–33
Biogas	2040 –4000	85– 202	12.5	51
Landfill gas	970 – 1380	137 – 145	11	0

Capital, operations and management costs, and learning rates of different power generation technologies.
Costs have been converted to sterling using an averaged 2005 exchange rate of £0.69/Euro (uktradeinfo, 2009).
Fuel prices have been converted from Euro/toe to £/MWh. The learning rate column represents the rate at which current prices are estimated to decrease as experience of the technology grows. For CCS systems the EU assumed that the first-of-a-kind systems will begin operation in 2015.
Source: EC (2008).

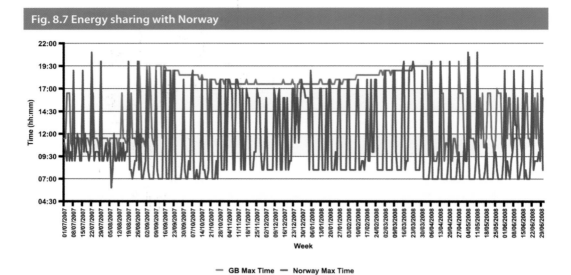

Fig. 8.7 Energy sharing with Norway

— GB Max Time — Norway Max Time

Peak demand time plot for Britain and Norway, using Greenwich Mean Time (01/07/2007–30/06/08).
Norway and Britain experience peak electricity demand at different times, therefore the ability to share electricity between the two states could help each meet peak demand. In Norway, peak demand occurs in the morning on weekdays and in the evening at the weekend. In Britain, peak demand occurs during the evening on weekdays.
Source: Based on data from National Grid (2008) and Stattnett (2007–8).

- Biomass resources from arboreal forests in the North.
- Solar resources in the South, harvested either with PV or concentrating solar thermal-electric power technology.
- Hydro resources in some mountainous areas.

Some electricity is inevitably lost in transmission over long distances. However, these losses can be minimised by using modern High Voltage Direct Current (HVDC) cables in place of traditional cables running alternating current (AC). Such cables can transport electricity over huge distances with low loss (under 10%), making long distance transfer of

electricity a viable option.

If a single electricity market is created for the whole of Europe, with a strong grid, able to transport substantial currents of electricity, this will encourage each country involved to specialise in and develop those generation technologies to which they are best suited.

In Spain, solar technologies are likely to generate two to four times the output of the same technologies installed in Britain. In other words, in Spain, capacity factors of about 20% for solar technologies are expected, while in the UK it is between 5–10%.

The economics are complicated and ultimately dependant on several factors

including regulation, how energy networks charge, and how fiscal incentives work for imported and exported electricity. However, if we assume these hurdles can be overcome, then importing solar electricity from Spain and exporting wind electricity from the UK would make the most sense.

This approach has to accommodate a slight loss of domestic control over electricity production, but it is likely to enable the development of renewable energy at a lower cost while also meeting the challenges of variability as all the countries involved would be working with a larger resource base. Utilising the UK offshore resources can in this way benefit both Europe and Britain.

CONCENTRATED SOLAR POWER (CSP)

As highlighted above, the best solar resources in Europe are found outside the UK in countries including Spain, where concentrated solar power (CSP) has been developed.

The German government has commissioned several studies into the feasibility and applications of CSP (see Trieb *et al.*, 2005, 2006, 2007). Researchers have projected that it has potential to become one of the cheapest forms of renewable electricity in the future. However, as discussed elsewhere in this chapter and report, the lowest generation cost does not mean the lowest market cost.

The benefits of CSP include the fact that many of its required components, such as generators and steam turbines, have already been developed for other purposes. This has helped minimise installation costs and enabled rapid construction due to a transfer of skills from other industries. The PS10 plant (11MWe) in Spain for instance was built in three years. As this is an emerging technology, experience is likely to speed up this process.

There are different types of CSP technology. One of the most popular incorporates a "parabolic trough" consisting of a semicircle of mirrors which reflects sunlight onto a heat transfer fluid. The collected energy can be applied in various systems but is generally used to power a steam turbine to generate electricity.

However, CSP is not suitable for development in the UK itself because it requires direct sunlight and Britain experiences far lower average levels of the direct solar irradiance required than countries nearer the equator. The EU could therefore benefit from CSP technology by deploying it in several suitable sites in the southern areas of Europe as well as in North Africa.

An interesting aspect of CSP development is that it is being developed fully as a commercial venture, as opposed to other technologies which have rarely been developed without government assistance. Funding CSP in suitable sites outside the UK may be a good use of the revenue from carbon import taxes, to account for the embodied energy of imports, in other words, the electricity demands caused by

Box 8.4 Desertec

In 2009, a consortium of European companies, under the name Desertec Industrial Initiative, declared plans to pool approximately €400 billion (£338 billion) in order to fund concentrated solar power projects in North Africa and elsewhere for electricity supply to Europe (Connolly, 2009). The generation potential of CSP in North Africa is not a key constraint even at this European level. Desertec claims to be able to meet all of the UK's electricity needs by using a "super grid". Losses in this grid will be kept below 10% if HVDC cables are used. Trieb *et al.* (2006) envisages that CSP in desert regions could meet 15% of Europe's electricity needs by 2050.

imported goods. Imported CSP electricity would add diversity to our current mix.

Within the *zerocarbonbritain2030* scenario, security of supply is important, and depending heavily on another region of the world therefore needs to be considered carefully in geopolitical, ethical and financial terms. CSP is not advisable in Britain and therefore does not form part of our generation mix. The scenario presented below enables Britain to be a net exporter of electricity without CSP. On a global scale, CSP is considered a valuable technology.

Energy in ZCB2030

INTRODUCING THE PROPOSED ELECTRICITY MIX

The potential of all the renewable resources above highlights that there are a whole range of ways to meet our electrical demand with renewable resources. For the purpose of this report we have identified one path which not only is decarbonised but also considers

sustainability more broadly, provides huge investment opportunities, provides domestic security of supply and meets the challenges of managing variability. *zerocarbonbritain2030* is a fully-integrated solution to climate change.

In a nutshell

The *zerocarbonbritain2030* scenario builds on the latest work conducted by the UK Energy Research Centre (UKERC, 2009) and the first *zerocarbonbritain* report (Hewleg-Larson & Bull, 2007). The UKERC recently published a series of scenarios based on an 80% decarbonisation of the UK. One of the scenarios consists of an energy base made up of renewables and gas.

The 2050 electricity capacity and generation mix which the UKERC envisages in this scenario is demonstrated in Figure 8.8.

As can be seen, the capacity mix is very different from the generation mix. Capacity refers to the amount of generation infrastructure installed, including power plants that may be used infrequently. The generation mix is the actual amount of electricity generated

Fig. 8.8 UKERC "renewables and gas" scenario

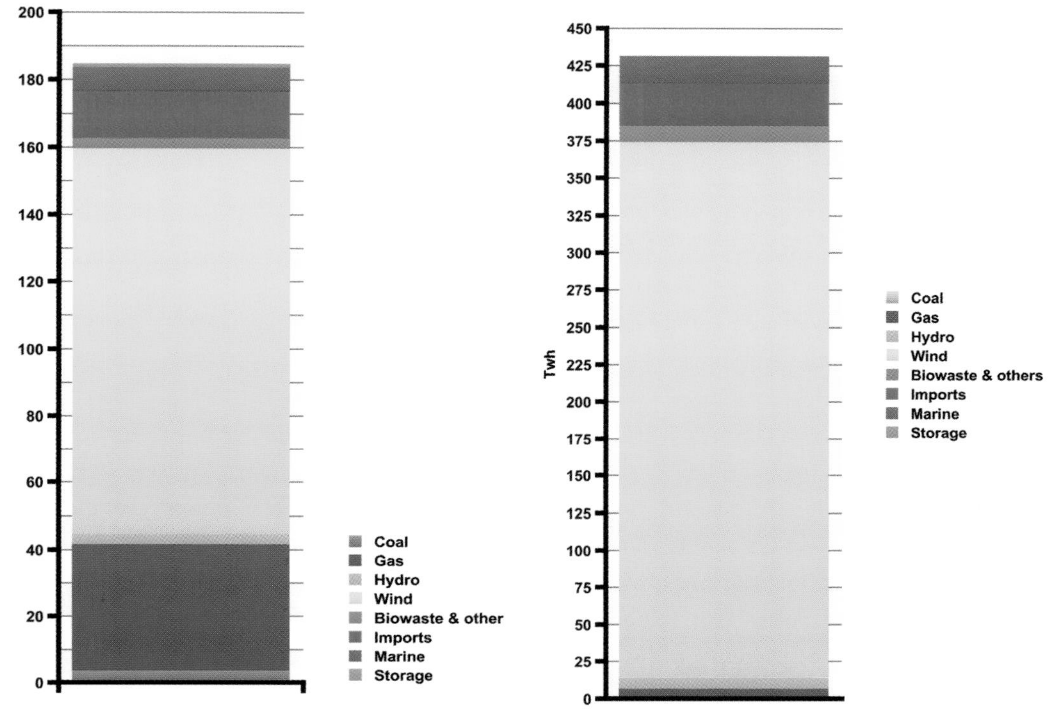
200
180
160
140
120
100
80
60
40
20
0
Coal
Gas
Hydro
Wind
Biowaste & other
Imports
Marine
Storage
450
425
400
375
350
325
300
275
250
225
200
175
150
125
100
75
50
25
0
Twh
Coal
Gas
Hydro
Wind
Biowaste & others
Imports
Marine
Storage

UKERC renewables and gas scenario showing a) electricity capacity (GW), and b) the electricity generation mix (TWh). Source: UKERC (2009).

by each technology over the year.

As shown, the bulk of the installed capacity in the UKERC scenario is wind (115GW), with significant amounts of gas (38GW) and small amounts of marine (7GW), biowaste (3GW), hydro (3GW) and imports (14GW). A far greater proportion of the actual generation comes from wind, which provides about 360TWh of a total of 430TWh (84%), and actual use of the gas plants is very small (5TWh per annum). Despite this, the gas plants are essential to the UKERC scenario as they provide backup generation for the occasional winter high-pressure events which occur over Western Europe and cause protracted periods of low (and possibly zero) wind. It also provides ongoing electricity grid-balancing services matching supply to demand.

The UKERC scenario requires modification to suit our urgent need to achieve a 100% cut in emissions. We need to produce more electricity:

around 842TWh (including exports) rather than 430TWh per year (including imports). Even after a decrease of energy demand of over 55% on current (2008) levels, electricity demand will roughly double compared to current demand because of partial electrification in the transport and heat sectors.

The first modification required, therefore, is the scaling up of renewable electricity production. As wind turbine deployment is increased, resilience and variability management become key concerns. These issues are discussed in detail later in this chapter.

The second modification required is the replacement of the natural gas element in the UKERC scenario. Although the quantity of natural gas burnt is small, the necessary exclusion of all fossil fuel use in *zerocarbonbritain2030* means that natural gas will be replaced with biogas. This biogas will mainly be used for producing electricity.

The gas technology which will be used for producing electricity from biogas will be Open Cycle Gas Turbines (OCGT). An OCGT operates by using gas mixed with air to fuel a gas turbine, which then spins a generator to make electricity. Combined Cycle Gas Turbines (CCGTs) are much more efficient because they use the heat from the turbine exhaust to heat a boiler which powers a steam turbine and a second generator. In the *zerocarbonbritain2030* scenario, gas is used to manage variability, therefore a large number of gas plants should be kept and possibly further plants installed even though

their usage will be fairly low. This will have a capital maintenance cost which we would prefer to minimise. One way is to use OCGT rather than CCGT. This is slightly less efficient but it would lower the capital cost and be more appropriate for balancing the grid.

ELECTRICITY IN *ZEROCARBONBRITAIN2030*

The final breakdown of electricity generation in the *zerocarbonbritain2030* scenario can be seen in Figure 8.9. Not all technologies are discussed in detail here. The focus is on the most significant elements of the energy scenario. Biochar is discussed in the technical appendix* of the Land use and agriculture chapter.

It is worth noting that the generation mix in this scenario will also result in significant improvements in air quality.

The *zerocarbonbritain2030* scenario can be seen in Figure 8.10, and the deployment rate of renewables to 2030 within the scenario is shown in Figure 8.11.

HEATING IN *ZEROCARBONBRITAIN2030*

The Renewable Heat Incentive (RHI) currently out for consultation aims to make Britain a world leader in renewable heat. This is projected to bring 78TWh of renewable heat online by 2020 saving 17Mt of CO_2 (NERA Economic Consulting & AEA, 2009).

Fig. 8.9 Electricity generation in ZCB2030

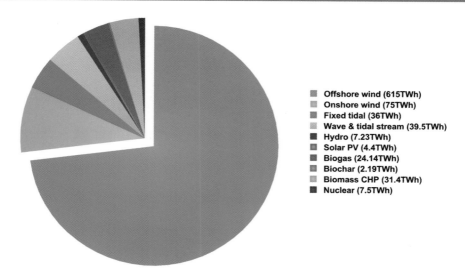

- Offshore wind (615TWh)
- Onshore wind (75TWh)
- Fixed tidal (36TWh)
- Wave & tidal stream (39.5TWh)
- Hydro (7.23TWh)
- Solar PV (4.4TWh)
- Biogas (24.14TWh)
- Biochar (2.19TWh)
- Biomass CHP (31.4TWh)
- Nuclear (7.5TWh)

Electricity generation by technology in the ZCB2030 scenario (TWh).
An array of sources of electricity energy can all contribute to meeting the needs of the nation. Offshore wind is a key resource for Britain.

The RHI works in a similar way to the feed-in tariff, discussed further later in this chapter, in that it pays a pre-set rate for the output of a generator's heat. However, unlike the feed-in tariff for electricity, this also allows potential for additional financial gains from enhanced energy efficiency. This is partly because with electricity if a generator provides more than is needed, the excess can usually be exported to the grid. However with heat this is not possible.

As part of the RHI work NERA Economic Consulting & AEA, (2009) examined three possible scenarios for renewable heat provision. In the stretch scenario it showed 232TWh being brought online by 2020 i.e. in 10 years, which includes heat pumps which use some electricity, but it excludes using electricity directly for heating.

Biomass heating

The AEA stretch scenario shows 121TWh of potential for biomass heating by 2020. Unlike their other scenarios, this assumes all limitations are overcome. As discussed above and in more detail in the Land use and agriculture chapter, there is a limit to the amount of biomass available in the UK. This fuel limit is a

Fig. 8.10 Electricity generation in ZCB2030

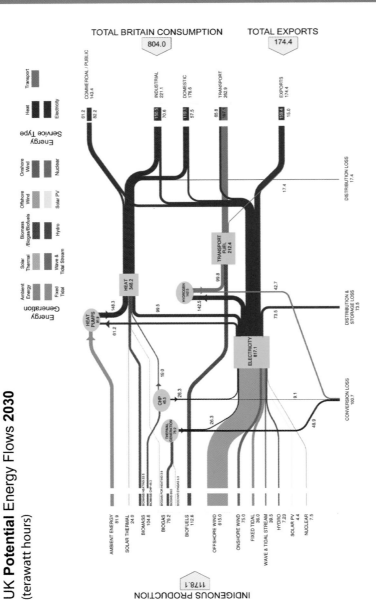

ZEROCARBONBRITAIN2030

UK **Potential** Energy Flows **2030**
(terawatt hours)

Proposed energy mix for ZCB2030.

This shows the flow of energy under the ZCB2030. The left-hand side shows the different sources of heat and electricity supplied. The right-hand side shows the energy delivered per sector. Lines coming off to the bottom show the losses from the system. The thickness of flows represents their size.

Fig. 8.11 The deployment of renewables in ZCB2030

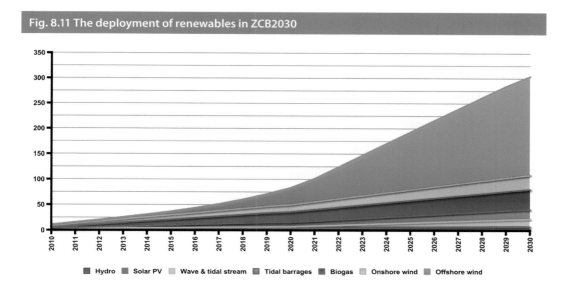

Hydro ■ **Solar PV** ■ **Wave & tidal stream** ■ **Tidal barrages** ■ **Biogas** ■ **Onshore wind** ■ **Offshore wind**

The deployment rate of renewables, 2010 to 2030, under the ZCB2030 scenario.

stricter limitation on capacity than the number of installations that can be built by 2030.

In **zero**carbon**britain**2030, Combined Heat & Power (CHP) provides 35TWh of heat, plus some biomass heating such as woodfuel which we envisage as a mixture of log stoves and wood boilers.

Heat pumps

A heat pump is a technology which uses "ambient heat" generally from the ground or from the air and moves (pumps) this to where it is needed for space heating.

Heat pumps can be used in both domestic and non-domestic settings. They can also be used in combination with heat stores, either using the heat pump to feed the store or using the store as the source for the heat pump. They can be used on an individual house basis or as part of district heating.

While in **zero**carbon**britain**2030 some heat pumps will have heat stores as their source, they are generally categorised as "ground source" or "air source" heat pumps. The ground source design could be used with heat stores.

Within the **zero**carbon**britain**2030 scenario, 54% of domestic demand and 40% of non-domestic demand is met by heat pumps. This corresponds with the limits of available appropriate sites from the AEA's report, and has deployment rates consistent with their stretch scenario.

The scenario

There are a variety of ways to meet the residual heating demand. Based on the biomass available, lack of suitable sites for heat pumps and other constraints, the mix shown in Figure 8.12 was chosen. Further research into this field is likely to find additional opportunities. This base heating scenario is consistent with the leading work in this area and tallies with the other sections of this report.

ENERGY PROVISION IN ZEROCARBONBRITAIN

Delivered energy provision for heat and electricity by power source within the **zero**carbon**britain**2030 scenario is shown in

Figure 8.13a. If we include the transport liquid fuels, we can get an even more inclusive picture of the energy source mix (see Figure 8.13b).

THE BUILD RATE, COSTS AND MATERIALS OF OFFSHORE WIND TURBINES

The costs of offshore wind were recently assessed by Ernst & Young (2009). Investment costs were found to have increased from £1.75 million per MW installed in 2003 to £3.2 million in 2009. The main reasons were the recent commodity price peak, the collapse of the pound and the limited number of wind turbine suppliers and cable delivery vessels.

There are currently only two viable offshore

Fig. 8.12 Heat generation in ZCB2030

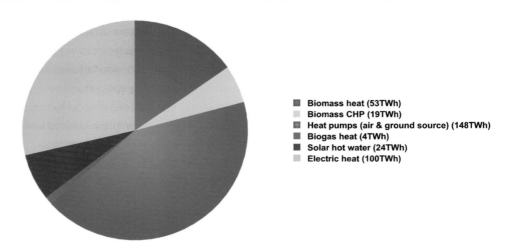

- Biomass heat (53TWh)
- Biomass CHP (19TWh)
- Heat pumps (air & ground source) (148TWh)
- Biogas heat (4TWh)
- Solar hot water (24TWh)
- Electric heat (100TWh)

Heat generation by technology in the ZCB2030 scenario (TWh).

Fig. 8.13 Delivered energy provision in ZCB2030

Fig 8.13a

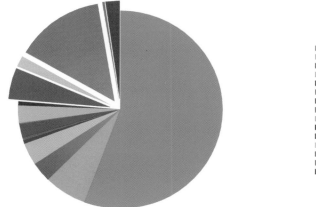

- Offshore wind
- Onshore wind
- Fixed tidal
- Wave & tidal stream
- Hydro
- Solar PV
- Biogas electric
- Biochar (gas)
- Biomass CHP
- Nuclear
- Biomass heat only
- Biomass CHP heat
- Heat pumps (air & ground source)
- Biogas heat
- Solar hot water

Fig 8.13b

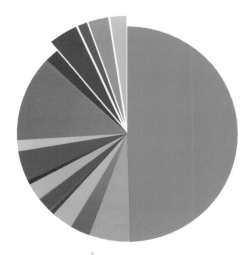

- Offshore wind
- Onshore wind
- Fixed tidal
- Wave & tidal stream
- Hydro
- Solar PV
- Biogas electric
- Biochar (gas)
- Biomass CHP
- Nuclear
- Biomass heat only
- Biomass CHP heat
- Heat pumps (air & ground source)
- Biogas heat
- Solar hot water
- Biodiesel
- Biopetrol
- Biokerosene
- Hydrogen (electrolysis)

Delivered energy provision, by source in ZCB2030, for a) electricity and heat sectors, and b) electricity, heat and transport fuel sectors.

Box 8.5 The area required for offshore wind

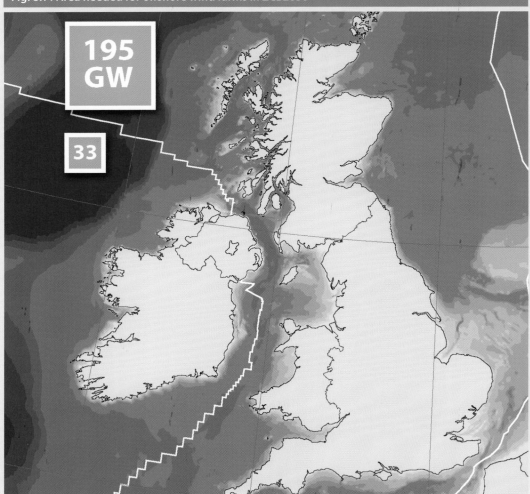

Fig. 8.14 Area needed for offshore wind farms in ZCB2030

195 GW

33

The total area needed to provide 195GW electricity (as envisaged in ZCB2030), and to provide 33GW (as planned by UK Government for 2020).

The estimates are based on an average wind farm energy density of 18.5 kWh/m². Technological improvements may allow this average energy density to improve; and the energy density can also vary significantly by location (see Figure 8.4). Nonetheless, the area necessary to provide 195GW is significant. It is viable given the large area available on the UK continental shelf. Source: Image of UK bathymetry from BERR (2008).

The area required for the creation of 195GW of offshore wind capacity can be calculated based on the power density of existing wind farms.

While wind turbines are set to increase in size, the energy-area ratio will remain roughly the same because the larger the turbine, the more space it requires in order not to interfere with the wind energy capture of neighbouring turbines. This is due to the turbulence they create for each other. Thus, generally the MW produced per km^2 evens out. Some efficiency improvements in the offshore wind turbines themselves are probable in the future, increasing the potential renewable electricity generated from the same area and some industry sources claim that $5W/m^2$ will be achieved in the future, rather than the $3W/m^2$ possible now. However our calculations will be based upon what is possible now.

North Hoyle was the first major UK offshore wind farm and started producing electricity in 2003. It consists of 30 Vestas V80 turbines spread across an area of approximately $10km^2$ and has a nominal capacity of 60MW (the nominal capacity is the amount of electricity generated when the turbines are operating at maximum output). The North Hoyle farm produced 184,737MWh of electricity between July 2006 and June 2007 (Department of Business, Enterprise and Regulatory Reform [BERR], 2007). This is equal to a constant power output of approximately 21MW. As the nominal maximum power output is 60MW, the capacity factor of the

farm was about 35%. Dividing the total electricity output by area gives us the energy density of the wind farm: $18.5kWh/m^2$ per annum. Therefore, to build 195GW of capacity would require an area covering about $32,400km^2$ (i.e. 180 x 180 km, or 112 x 112 miles).

The smaller square in Figure 8.14 is the area that would be taken up by 33GW of offshore wind capacity; the quantity planned in the Government's Round Three of offshore development (BVG Associates, 2009). The bigger square shows the area that would be used by offshore wind farms ($32,400km^2$) with a capacity of 195GW, the quantity envisaged by the **zero**carbon**britain**2030 scenario.

Table 8.4 illustrates how many turbines would be needed to provide our proposed offshore wind capacity. Using the 5MW wind turbines currently available would require a total of 39,000 turbines. However, we expect turbines to become larger over the next two decades, reducing this number as at present both Clipper and Enova are testing 10MW turbines. The current government target of 33GW of wind capacity by 2020 is also shown for comparison.

Table 8.4 Turbines needed for offshore wind farms in ZCB2030

Turbine capacity (MW)	5	10
Number of turbines required for the government's proposed capacity (33 GW)	6600	3300
Number of turbines required for our proposed capacity (195GW)	3900	19500

The total number of turbines needed to provide 195GW electricity (as envisaged in ZCB2030), and to provide 33GW (as planned by UK Government for 2020).
Estimates are based on current turbine capacity (5MW) and predicted near-future turbine capacity (10MW).

wind turbine suppliers and during 2007–8 only one of them was offering wind turbines for the offshore environment (British Wind Energy Association [BWEA], 2009). Because the UK has no domestic offshore wind turbine supply, developers are subject to exchange rate risks.

In order to decrease offshore wind costs, more suppliers are needed and it would be highly beneficial for the UK to strengthen the domestic supply chain. The potential for domestic production can be unleashed by systematic research and development investments and focused government support.

Table 8.5 illustrates how offshore wind capacity could be deployed over time and the estimated cost of offshore wind development. In order to meet the government target of 33GW by 2020, the running rate of capacity build-up will be around 9GW per year in 2020. By increasing the build-up speed to 17GW per year after that our offshore wind capacity target of 195GW could be met by 2030. The fastest build time would be from 2022 to 2029. Based on 5MW turbines, this would entail 3,400 turbines being deployed per year, or 9.55 per day. While this is clearly ambitious, it also seems the logical step after Round Three. As highlighted, there is plenty more area available for offshore wind, therefore development could continue after 2030.

Offshore wind is a central part, if not the core part, of building a green, sustainable economy in Britain. This transition and development of new industry requires investment. The peak

of £30 billion in 2022 represents only 2.2% of the UK's 2008 GDP and delivers an electricity generation system which has very low fuel costs. If we were instead to generate the proposed output of 599TWh in 2030 from 50% coal and 50% gas, it would incur a fuel cost of approximately £13.5 billion per annum at 2008 prices. In reality these fuel costs are likely to rise far higher by 2030 and would constitute an enormous unnecessary expense to the general public.

These cost figures are of the same order of magnitude as estimates from UKERC. UKERC estimates the cost of its scenarios relative to a base case under which electricity is produced almost exclusively from coal, calculated to be the cheapest form of production. It estimates that the price of creating any of its proposed low carbon electricity systems will be around £20 billion above the lowest-cost generation capacity, rising to £30 billion if a more ambitious cut of 90% is attempted rather than 80%. However, UKERC also calculates that the cost of the base case scenario itself is about £300–350 billion to 2050, and so decarbonisation only increases the cost of the electricity system by about 10%.

While this seems a great deal of money, if compared to what Britain has recently been prepared to spend on our banks and, historically, on the military, it looks a great deal more reasonable and ultimately necessary. In any case, the economic cost, amongst others, of not tackling climate change has been shown to

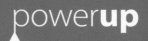

Year	Annual build up (GW)[1]	Total capacity (GW)[2]	Cost per MW of capacity (£ million)[3]	Investment (£ million)[4]	Cumulative investment (£ million)[5]
2009	0.4	1.0	3.2	1,376	1,376
2010	0.4	1.4	3.1	1,144	2,520
2011	0.5	1.9	2.9	1,501	4,021
2012	0.7	2.6	2.8	1,970	5,991
2013	1.0	3.6	2.7	2,586	8,578
2014	1.3	4.9	2.5	3,395	11,973
2015	1.8	6.7	2.4	4,456	16,429
2016	2.5	9.3	2.3	5,849	22,278
2017	3.5	12.7	2.2	7,677	29,955
2018	4.8	17.5	2.1	10,077	40,032
2019	6.5	24.0	2.0	13,227	53,259
2020	9.0	33.0	1.9	17,361	70,620
2021	12.3	45.3	1.8	22,788	93,408
2022	17.0	62.3	1.8	29,911	123,320
2023	17.0	79.3	1.7	28,570	151,890
2024	17.0	96.3	1.6	27,289	179,179
2025	17.0	113.2	1.5	26,066	205,245
2026	17.0	130.2	1.5	24,897	230,143
2027	17.0	147.2	1.4	23,781	253,924
2028	17.0	164.1	1.3	22,715	276,639
2029	17.0	181.1	1.3	21,697	298,335
2030	13.9	195.0	1.2	16,977	315,312

Table 8.5 Annual deployment of offshore wind capacity and estimated financial investment necessary for ZCB2030

Annual deployment of offshore wind capacity (GW) and estimated financial investment necessary (£ million) for the ZCB2030 scenario.

Model assumptions include that: 1) annual increases of capacity build-up of 37.4% occur until 2022, after which the annual increment stabilises at about 17GW; 2) total capacity increases to 33GW by 2020 (as planned by the Government under Rounds 1–3); 3) financial costs associated with offshore wind technology decrease 24% by 2015 (Garrad, 2009). A steady annual decrease of 4.7% is assumed to continue after that; 4) annual build-up times cost per capacity; 5) Inflation is not accounted for; all figures are in GBP 2009 values; 6) the cost of managing variability is not included.

be far higher (Stern, 2007).

The construction of wind turbines at the proposed rate would obviously require a considerable amount of materials. Mackay (2009) estimates 60 million tonnes of steel and concrete would be needed if we are to realise the theoretical potential from offshore wind. The capacity needed in **zero**carbon**britain**2030 is around 60% of his identified potential and therefore would require approximately 36 million tonnes of steel and concrete. Based on 45% being steel and 55% concrete that is 16.2 million tonnes of steel and 19.8 million tonnes of concrete used over twenty years. The embodied energy of steel and concrete for this total build would be 115TWh. The embodied energy in processing and maintenance would vary between turbine design, but in all current cases it would be a substantial contribution. However, this outline figure highlights the high energy return on energy invested for wind.

The UK currently uses 13.5 million tonnes of steel per annum (The Manufacturers' Organisation [EEF], 2009), therefore in 2013 offshore wind turbine installation would be using 0.6% of current annual UK steel, and in its peak year it would be 10.4% of current demand. This is an achievable quantity, especially given that the construction and the automotive industry are moving away from the use of steel.

At present 53% of steel in the UK goes to "stockholding merchants". If we exclude this and just look at final uses (pro rata), 23.4% goes to UK construction and 6.38% to the UK automotive industry. Both of these will be decreasing substantially through the new economics of carbon pricing, which will increase the market share of light-weight vehicles and biomass building materials such as wood.

The UK steel market specialises in high-quality steel, including steel designed for the manufacture of wind turbines. However, the largest UK steel producer, Corus, was forced to indefinitely mothball a number of UK production sites from January 2010 due to broken contracts, resulting in the loss of about 1,700 UK jobs (Corus, 2009).

The development of wind power in the UK has the potential to ease the decline of the UK steel industry in the medium-term and over the long-term it has the potential to contribute to its growth as we export our technology.

CHANGES TO THE GRID

In Britain the flow of electricity is currently from the north of the country to London and the south-east region. This is done via a High Voltage Alternating Current network that we know as the National Grid. This network is already in desperate need of strengthening and upgrading. The development of offshore wind offers the opportunity to develop a new High Voltage Direct Current network located in the sea to move electricity from the north of the country directly to the demand centre in the south-east, which would admirably complement our present system.

MANAGING VARIABILITY

The demand profile and the managment of the power supply

The National Grid is required to keep the electricity grid running (at 50 Hertz ± 0.5Hz). Maintaining this requires supply and demand to

be closely matched at all times. The current daily variability in demand for electricity in the UK from July 2007 to June 2008 is shown in Figure 8.15.

Currently, the variability between supply and demand is managed almost exclusively by changes on the supply side of the equation. A mixture of technologies including coal and gas provide a spinning reserve, ready to increase electricity generation required. We also have 1.37GW of hydropower and four pumped-storage systems that can be brought online.

Pumped-storage systems are a type of hydroelectric power battery used for load balancing. During periods of low energy demand, water is pumped from a low elevation reservoir

to a higher elevation reservoir. During periods of high electrical demand, the stored water is released through turbines to create electricity. Pumped-storage stations are net consumers of energy overall but they allow more electricity to be supplied during periods of peak demand when electricity prices are highest. Pumped-storage is the largest-capacity form of grid energy storage now available and is ideal for storing electricity produced by wind turbines overnight.

The UK's pumped-storage stations were built to complement the nuclear programme in the 1960s and have a total capacity of 2,730MW which can be relied on for a few hours. Management of the demand side of the equation is limited

Fig. 8.15 Electricity consumption variability

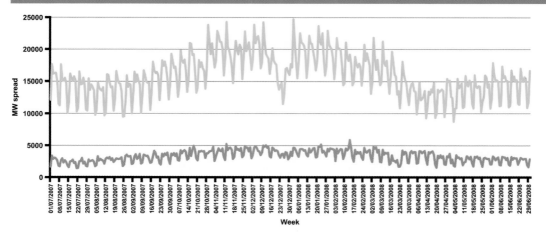

Variability (MW spread) in daily consumption (demand) for Britain and Norway (01/07/2007–30/06/08).
MW spread is calculated by the difference between peak demand and minimum demand. Variability in electricity demand is far greater in Britain than in Norway. Daily demand variability fluctuates seasonally in both Britain and Norway, being greater during the winter periods. In Britain, there was a significant drop in demand variability over the Christmas/New Year period.
  The mzaximum swing in demand, of 24,726MW, was on the 2nd of January 2008. Demand variability also fluctuates significantly over the week in both Britain and Norway, generally falling in the weekend. Marked dates are all Sundays.
Source: Based on data from National Grid (2008) and Stattnett (2007–8).

to the National Grid which offer "interruptible" contracts to heavy energy users, whereby users agree to be temporarily disconnected for short periods when necessary in return for cheaper tariffs.

In *zerocarbonbritain2030*, the bulk of generation will come from offshore wind, and the wind cannot be turned up and down at will like a gas-fired power station. Furthermore, there is inevitably some variability in the output of turbines, although the further apart wind farms are placed, the smoother the overall output. New offshore wind farms will be commissioned at dispersed locations around the country and the back-up generation, consisting of biogas, biomass, hydro and imports will help to manage the remaining variability.

However, all of this will need to be complemented by the highly increased efficiency of the management of electricity demand. Both the supply and demand sides of the equation are malleable and both will come under intensive management in the *zerocarbonbritain2030* scenario.

The *zerocarbonbritain2030* scenario has been successfully tested by the "Future Energy Scenario Assessment" (FESA) software. This combines weather and demand data to test several aspects including if there is enough dispatchable generation to manage the variable base supply of renewable electricity with the variable demand.

Demand-side management

Demand-side management is where energy-intensive but non-essential activities can be scheduled to take place when energy is most abundant (and therefore to the consumer, cheapest). This would work if certain appliances were connected to programmable smart meters that in turn would need controlling through fuzzy logic so that they did not all switch on and off simultaneously and cause power surges or cuts.

Appliances suited to demand-side management include electric storage radiators, heat pumps, electric vehicles, air conditioners, washing machines, fridges, freezers, dishwashers and tumble dryers. Smart meters or smart appliances would allow the owner to specify a time range during which they wanted their appliance or vehicle charged or in use.

If this time range coincides with periods of electricity surplus in the grid, the consumer benefits from lower prices. The benefit to the grid is that the surplus during such periods would be reduced, whilst demand would simultaneously be reduced during periods of high energy demand. In other words, the load on the grid is automatically managed. In order to facilitate this, such smart meters will need to be rolled out across the country. Smart meters that cannot recognise and implement actions based upon variable retail tariffs should not be introduced.

Using the night – transport and heating:
Because wind turbines continue to turn at
night when there is traditionally low demand
for electricity, a system based heavily on wind
will be most efficient if a significant variable
load can be demanded at night rather than
the day. Such an electricity system is therefore
excellently complemented by an electric
vehicle infrastructure in which vehicle batteries
would conveniently be charged overnight and
ready for use the next morning. Furthermore,
hydrogen for niche uses could also be produced
by electrolysis that takes place overnight.

In *zerocarbonbritain2030*, the majority of
space heating will be electric, including heat
pumps. Electric space heating can be combined
with a heat store so that it can be charged
overnight and store the heat until daytime
when it is required. There are energy losses
involved in such a system but the refurbishment
of buildings will decrease the impact of this.
In addition, the cost of using this night-time
generation will be lower.

In order to facilitate the development of this
technology, buildings could be fitted with larger
hot water cylinders containing smart meter-
controlled immersion heaters for heat storage.

Supply prediction and balancing services:
Substantial progress has been made in the
accurate prediction of wind speeds.

Further improvements in this, coupled
with government's legislating for obligatory
information sharing between companies, could
even facilitate the participation of wind farms
in following load. However, this should only
happen at peak power production times when
the excess power is unable to be used or stored.

Exports

There are over 150 TWh of exports. This builds in
substantial resilience into the ZCB2030 scenario.
At a price of 4p/kWh this159.34TWh is worth
£6.37bn. This annual income could really help
the UK balance of payments.

Policy issues and economics

The Policy and economics chapter discusses
the policies recommended for a zero carbon
Britain. This chapter looks in more detail at the
complexities of the different policy mechanisms
for incentivising renewable electricity
production.

EXISTING POLICY MECHANISMS

There are various different mechanisms in place
to reward people for producing renewable
electricity which include: Renewable Obligation
Certificates (ROCs), Levy Exemption Certificates
(LECs), the Climate Change Levy and feed-in
tariffs (FITs); as well as the Use of System (UoS)
charges for the electricity grid, the Transmission
(TNUoS) Distribution (DNUoS) and Balancing
Use of System (BSUoS) charges.

The most important policies on the electricity
side are the Renewable Obligation Certificates
and feed-in tariffs. Details of these two are

below. Ultimately, these try to provide benefits which make renewables more attractive in the long term. Levy Exemption Certificates are a way of integrating these policies with the Climate Change Levy.

Renewable Obligation Certificates (ROCs)

The primary existing policy mechanism for promoting renewable energy investment in the UK is the Renewable Obligation Certificate (ROC) system. It is intended to run until 2027, and is the descendent of the Non Fossil Fuel Obligation (NFFO) that was introduced in the early 1990s, largely to support the nuclear industry.

The ROC system requires electricity suppliers to obtain a certain number of ROCs or to pay a buyout price. They can obtain ROCs either by ensuring that a proportion of the electricity they sell comes from renewable energy sources, or by buying that quota of renewable electricity from other firms. The total required amount of renewable energy to be supplied is raised each year. It currently stands at 9.1%.

Initially, one certificate could be claimed for each 1MW of electricity produced regardless of the renewable energy system. This acted to prevent the development of offshore wind, which is more expensive to establish than onshore wind. Today however, the ROC system is "banded" so that different types of renewable energy receive different quantities of certificates. This has had a positive effect

on offshore wind development: offshore wind projects accredited up to March 2014 will receive 2 ROCs, and thereafter will receive 1.75 ROCs (Backwell, 2009).

However, banding has had the unfortunate consequence of increasing the risk of an oversupply of ROCs, leading to their fall in unit price (Department of Trade and Industry [DTI], 2007). The supply of ROCs is being increased without increasing the demand (the overall quantity of ROCs needed from all electricity suppliers). The simple solution to this would be to increase the number of ROCs required from electricity suppliers to avoid having to pay a buyout price. In this way, the price per individual ROC would not decrease.

The banding of ROCs is meant to reallocate ROC revenue to renewable energy suppliers, who incur higher costs. Therefore the price per ROC is less relevant than the average price for the generation. The average cost of renewable generation is likely to increase slightly as less immediately economically-attractive generation is supported through the banding.

To ensure this economic incentive also acts as a positive climate incentive, suppliers' demand for ROCs must be maintained at a similar level to the multiple supply of ROCs. To do this would require an estimation of the average multiple applied to generation on the supply side and then matching this to demand. As this cannot be quantified exactly, it is necessary to estimate a higher-than-actual demand to provide a small margin of error.

ROCs were introduced to help establish a renewable electricity-generating sector. However, it is not clear that this mechanism will be sufficient to support the enormous rapid structural changes necessary. While they offer some price support, the ROC system leaves the ultimate price per kWh up to the market, and so still leaves investors without a clear guaranteed return. The feed-in tariff used in Germany (which is a different system from the feed-in tariff which is expected to be implemented in the UK) offer a guaranteed price for any electricity produced from renewable sources. More wind power is installed in Germany every year than the UK has in total, which lends some support to the view that a guaranteed price generates strong investment in renewables. A second problem with the ROC system is that there is reason to believe it will break down as the number of ROCs increases as discussed above with banding.

A headroom mechanism

Another option would be the introduction of a headroom mechanism, whereby the demand is always maintained at a certain percentage above the amount available in the market. The implementation of this would require all the devolved governments of the UK to change their respective legislations and for the government to buy all unwanted electricity with the option of selling any excess to abroad.

The Climate Change Levy

A further existing policy mechanism that affects renewable energy is the Climate Change Levy. Introduced in April 2001, the levy is charged on taxable supplies of lighting, heating and power from non-renewable sources. It applies to many energy users, with the notable exceptions of those in the domestic and transport sectors. Business customers can agree by contract with their electricity suppliers to receive a set amount of renewable electricity thereby reducing the amount of climate change levy to pay. This is controlled through Levy Exemption Certificates (LECs).

TNUoS, DNUoS & BSUoS

As well as consumers, large electricity generators (who do not qualify for the feed-in tariff) must pay TNUoS (Transmission Network Use of System) charges. TNUoS charges at the moment represent the single biggest operating cost for renewable generators in several parts of Britain, especially in northern Scotland where demand lags behind generation (Strbac *et al.*, 2007). Generators must also pay the National Grid to balance the energy flowing through the grid via Balancing Services Use of System (BSUoS) charges. BSUoS charges are also applied uniformly, i.e. every generator pays the same per MWh. Compared to TNUoS, the BSUoS charges are relatively low.

To balance the grid more effectively, the Government should implement a form of locationally differentiated pricing for new generators within distribution networks to signal the best places to build new capacity, such as at the ends of constrained distribution networks (Strbac *et al.*, 2007). The zonal differentiation of Distribution Network Use of System (DNUoS) charges within distribution networks may be a reasonable initial step.

The disadvantage is that this will result in high charges for large renewable generators in Scotland where there is more potential for generation but less demand for energy. Nonetheless, this is advisable for an interim period, until the transmission network is reinforced to cater for greater generation from Scotland.

Feed-in tariffs (FITs)

A new policy mechanism has now been introduced. The government has recently decided to follow the German approach and introduce a feed-in tariff (FIT), with different rates for generators of under and over 5MW of capacity. The UK government's version of the FIT has banded payments to generators depending on the type and size of renewable energy system. In the case of Solar PV, the rate for retrofit will be different to new installations.

This FIT mechanism will pay for any electricity produced, even if it is used on site. An additional payment will be made for electricity which is exported to the grid. DECC believes that the FIT will lead to the production of 8TWh of electricity in 2020, adding 2% to the cost of electricity bills. This has not been a popular decision in all quarters as some have argued that it provides far less carbon saving than if this money been invested in large wind farms.

FUTURE POLICY MECHANISMS

Our future electricity system must do two things. First, it must continue to provide mechanisms that enable production and demand to be balanced in real time. Secondly, it must provide incentives to increase investment in the renewable generation capacity of Britain. To achieve the first will require the extension of variable electricity pricing to all electricity users via the incorporation of smart meters. This will enable the demand-side management systems described above. When there is an oversupply of electricity, prices will decrease, allowing appliances in homes and businesses to automatically switch on and take advantage of this lower rate.

To determine how best to incentivise investment in renewables, it is useful to examine the ways in which the economics of renewables differ from traditional power plants. In a power plant based on the combustion of fossil fuels, the majority of costs are ongoing (in particular the cost of fuel to power electricity generation) and dependent on the quantity of electricity produced. For renewables, the bulk of the cost is upfront and the operating costs are nearly constant regardless of power output. These differences create different levels of

risk to renewable and non-renewable energy generators.

For example, the managers of a gas-fired power plant may decline to operate the plant when the electricity price per unit of gas is deemed too low. However, the manager of a wind farm needs to recoup the major upfront cost of its manufacture and installation; and is therefore incentivised to sell power generated by the farm even when the price per unit of energy is very low. This locates their market risk exclusively in how much of the electricity they can sell and what they can receive for it in return, leaving them vulnerable to when the wind blows and the volatility of the market. Some of these differences are summarised in Table 8.6.

Upfront costs are slightly less attractive to investors than ongoing costs, particularly when subjected to the traditional tool for the assessment of large capital projects: discounted cash flow (DCF). DCF techniques discount future costs and revenues at various rates depending on the level of uncertainty about their values. When assessing a fossil fuel power station, both the revenues and ongoing costs are uncertain future values and are therefore discounted at the same rate. In the case of most renewable technologies, the majority of costs are incurred in the outlay for the project and are consequently certain. Therefore only the revenue is discounted. This can potentially make renewables appear less attractive. This promotes short-term gains which are not very congruent with strategic planning. However, once the upfront costs for renewable generation are paid there is no uncertainty about the future rising costs of fuel, which banks might well prefer, particularly as much of our fuel arrives from countries that in the past have not always proved to be the most stable business partners.

The feed-in tariff offers significant opportunity to decrease the economic risk associated with renewable electricity and promote strategic decision making. Investors must then be certain that they will be able to sell the electricity they produce at a good price.

As the penetration of offshore wind increases, it will become essential to look for a different funding mechanism. With increased experience,

Table 8.6 Investment and marginal costs of energy infrastructure		
	Investment cost per MW of installed capacity	**Marginal cost of electricity produced**
Wind farms	Higher	Nearly zero
Fossil fuels	Lower	Much higher and subject to market price of fuels

Investment and marginal costs of wind farm and fossil fuel generation infrastructure.

it should become possible to cost offshore wind farms more accurately and to estimate the total amount of electricity a farm will produce over its lifetime. This could help facilitate the replacement of the ROC system in favour of a system using a base price with a regulated profit margin.

Further work

There are details of our scenario that would need to be addressed in further work.

The key areas for further work and policy development are in the following areas:

- Developing new technologies.
- Creating market structures that will support a renewables-only energy policy, in terms of both integrating supply and demand and creating the right incentives for investment.
- Developing and supporting the domestic supply chain, particularly for wind turbines.
- Creating policies that prevent personal hardship as fuel prices increase.
- Addressing bottlenecks in the planning system.

With further research and development we will find more efficient means of creating and maintaining a successful renewable energy structure. However, this chapter demonstrates that it is already possible to rapidly decarbonise the UK's electricity system, rid it entirely of fossil fuels, and produce all the electricity needed for a zero carbon Britain.

References

Backwell, B. (2009), UK government extends ROC window for offshore projects, ReCharge: The global source for renewable energy news, 9 December 2009 [online]. Available at: http://www.rechargenews.com/regions/europe_russia/article201113.ece [Live: March 2010].

British Wind Energy Association (BWEA) (2009) *UK Offshore Wind: Charting the Right Course. Scenarios for offshore capital costs for the next five years*, London: BWEA.

Burgermeister, J. (2008) "Wales Spearheads European Biomass Push", Renewable Energy World, 22 January 2008 [online]. Available at: http://www.renewableenergyworld.com/rea/news/article/2008/01/wales-spearheads-european-biomass-push-51187 [Live: March 2010].

BVG Associates (2009) "Towards Round 3: Building the Offshore Wind Supply Chain", review for The Crown Estate on how to improve delivery of UK offshore wind. Available at: http://www.thecrownestate.co.uk/round3_supply_chain_gap_analysis.pdf [Live: March 2010].

Connolly, K. (2009) "German blue chip firms throw weight behind north African solar project", *The Guardian*, 16 June 2009.

Corus (2009) "Broken contract leads to mothball of Teesside plant", press release 04 December 2009. Available at: http://www.corusgroup.com/en/news/news/2009_tcp_mothball [Live: March 2010].

Crown Estate (2010) "The Crown Estate announces Round 3 offshore wind development partners: a quarter of UK electricity demand could be met from the programme", Crown Estate, press release, 8 January 2010 [online]. Available at http://www.thecrownestate.co.uk/newscontent/92-r3-developers.htm [Live: March 2010].

Department for Business, Enterprise and Regulatory Reform (BERR) (2007) "Offshore wind capital grants scheme: North Hoyle Offshore Wind Farm", Third Annual Report, July 2006 – June 2007, URN Number: 08/P47. Available at: http://www.berr.gov.uk/files/file47340.pdf [Live: March 2010].

Department of Energy and Climate Change (DECC) (2009a) *Digest of United Kingdom Energy Statistics 2009*, London: The Stationery Office (TSO).

DECC (2009b) *Severn Tidal Power: Phase One Consultation*, London: DECC.

Department of Trade and Industry (DTI) (2007) *Meeting the Energy Challenge A White Paper on Energy*, London: TSO.

Environment Agency (EA) (2010), "Mapping Hydropower

Opportunities and Sensitivities in England and Wales", Technical Report, February 2010, Bristol: EA.

Ernst and Young (2009) Cost of and financial support for offshore wind: A report for the Department of Energy and Climate Change, 27 April 2009, URN 09D/534. Available at: http://www.bis.gov.uk/files/file51142.pdf [Live: March 2010].

European Environment Agency (EEA) (2009) *Europe's onshore and offshore wind energy potential: An assessment of environmental and economic constraints*, Technical report 6/2009. Luxembourg: EC.

European Commission (EC) (2008) "Energy Sources, Production Costs and Performance of Technologies for Power Generation, Heating and Transport", Commission Staff Working Document accompanying the Communication From the Commission To the European Parliament, the Council, the European Economic and Social Committee and the Committee of the Regions, Commission of the European Communities. Available at: http://ec.europa.eu/energy/strategies/2008/doc/2008_11_ser2/strategic_energy_review_wd_cost_performance.pdf [Live: March 2010].

European Wind Energy Association (EWEA) (2009) "Seas of change: offshore wind energy", EWEA leaflet 2/2009. Available at: http://www.ewec2009.info/fileadmin/ewec2009_files/documents/Media_room/EWEA_FS_Offshore_FINAL_lr.pdf [Live: March 2010].

Fearnside, P.M. (2004) "Greenhouse Gas Emissions from Hydroelectric Dams: Controversies Provide a Springboard for Rethinking a Supposedly "Clean" Energy Source: An Editorial Comment", *Climatic Change*, 66(1–2), pp. 1–8.

First Solar (2009) "First Solar Passes $1 Per Watt Industry Milestone", press release, 24 February 2009. Available at: http://investor.firstsolar.com/phoenix.zhtml?c=201491&p=irol-newsArticle&ID=1259614&highlight [Live: March 2010].

Forrest, N & J. Wallace (2010) "The Employment Potential of Scotland's Hydro Resources", Nick Forrest Associates, September 2009. Available at: http://www.scotland.gov.uk/Resource/Doc/299322/0093327.pdf [Live: March 2010].

Garrad, A. (2009) "UK Offshore Wind: Near-Term Capital Costs and Delivery", presentation given at "BWEA Offshore Wind 09", London, 24 June 2009.

Helweg-Larson, T. & J. Bull (2007) *zerocarbonbritain: an alternative energy strategy*, Machynlleth: Centre for Alternative Technology.

International Energy Agency (IEA) (2009a) *Technology Roadmap: Carbon Capture and Storage*, Paris: Organisation for Economic Co-operation and Development (*OECD*)/IEA.

IEA (2009b) "Marginal Abatement Cost Curves in the Power Sector", Mitigation costs in the *World Energy Outlook 2009* 450 Scenario, IEA. Available at: http://www.worldenergyoutlook.org/docs/weo2009/Factors_influencing_mitigation_costs_in_power_generation.pdf [Live: March 2010].

Intergovernmental Panel on Climate Change (IPCC) (2005) *IPCC Special Report on Carbon Dioxide Capture and Storage: prepared by Working Group III of the Intergovernmental Panel on Climate Change*, Cambridge: Cambridge University Press.

Jacobson M.Z. (2009) "Review of solutions to global warming, air pollution, and energy security". Energy and Environmental Science, 2, pp. 148–173.

Jacobson, M.Z. & M.A. Delucchi (2009) "A Path to Sustainable Energy by 2030", *Scientific American,* November 2009.

Langley, B. (2009) "UK Marine Energy Potential – a utility project developer's perspective", presentation given to the ZeroCarbonBritain Renewable Energy seminar, 3 June 2009 [unpublished].

Lenzen, M. & J. Munksgaard (2002) "Energy and CO_2 life-cycle analyses of wind turbines—review and applications", *Renewable Energy*, 26(3), pp. 339–362.

Mackay, D. (2009) *Sustainable Energy – without the hot air*, Cambridge: UIT Cambridge Ltd.

Manufactuers' Organisation (EEF) (2009) "UK Steel: Key Statistics 2009, EEF. Available at: http://www.eef.org.uk/NR/rdonlyres/B1210239-A3C3-472D-B1E5-A48DBFBCF306/15206/UKSteelKeyStatistics2009.pdf [Live: March 2010].

McKendry, P. (2002) "Energy production from biomass (part 2): conversion technologies", *Bioresource Technology*, 83(1), pp. 47–54

McKinsey (2008) "Carbon Capture & Storage: Assessing the Economics", McKinsey Climate Change Initiative. Available at: http://www.mckinsey.com/clientservice/ccsi/pdf/ccs_assessing_the_economics.pdf [Live: March 2010].

National Grid (2009) "The potential for renewable gas in the UK", January 2009. Available at: http://www.nationalgrid.com/NR/rdonlyres/9122AEBA-5E50-43CA-81E5-8FD98C2CA4EC/32182/renewablegasWPfinal1.pdf [Live: March 2010].

NERA Economic Consulting & AEA (2009) "The UK Supply Curve for Renewable Heat", Study for the Department of Energy and Climate Change, July 2009, URN 09D/689. Available at: http://www.nera.com/image/PUB_Renewable_Heat_July2009.pdf [Live: March 2010].

Prats, J. (2009) "The European Wind Initiative (EWI)", presentation given at "EWEC 2009", Marseille, 17 March 2009.

Renewable Energy Focus (2010) "Sway to erect 10 MW offshore wind turbine", Renewable Energy Focus News, 12 February 2010 [online]. Available at: http://www.renewableenergyfocus.com/view/7279/sway-to-erect-10-mw-offshore-wind-turbine [Live: March 2010].

Renewable Energy Policy Network for the 21st Century (REN21) (2009) Renewables Global Status Report: 2009 Update, Paris: REN.

Sims, R.E.H. et al. (2007) "Energy supply", in IPCC (2007) Climate Change 2007: Mitigation. Contribution of Working Group III to the Fourth Assessment Report of the Intergovernmental Panel on Climate Change, Cambridge: Cambridge University Press.

Stern, N. (2007) Stern Review: the economics of climate change, Cambridge: Cambridge University Press.

Sustainable Development Commission (SDC) (2007) Turning the Tide: Tidal Power in the UK, London: SDC.

Strbac, G., C. Ramsay & D. Pudjianto (2007) "Integration of Distributed Generation into the UK Power System", Summary Report, DTI Centre for Distributed Generation and Sustainable Electrical Energy, March 2007. Available at: http://www.ofgem.gov.uk/Networks/Trans/ElecTransPolicy/TADG/Documents1/DGSEE_EWP_DG_Value_Paper_v3_0.pdf [Live: March 2010].

Taylor, G. (2007) "Improving trees for bioenergy production", presentation for the 15th European Biomass Conference, Berlin, 2008. Available at: http://www.tsec-biosys.ac.uk/index.php?p=9&t=4 [Live: March 2010].

Trieb, F. et al. (2005) "Concentrating solar power for the Mediterranean region", German Aerospace Center, Institute of Technical Thermodynamics, Section Systems Analysis and Technology Assessment. Available at: http://www.dlr.de/tt/en/Portaldata/41/Resources/dokumente/institut/system/projects/MED-CSP_Full_report_final.pdf [Live: March 2010].

Trieb, F. et al. (2006) "Trans-Mediterranean Interconnection for Concentrating Solar Power", German Aerospace Center, Institute of Technical Thermodynamics, Section Systems Analysis and Technology Assessment. Available at: http://www.dlr.de/tt/en/Portaldata/41/Resources/dokumente/institut/system/publications/TRANS-CSP_Full_Report_Final.pdf [Live: March 2010].

Trieb et al. (2007) "Concentrating solar power for seawater desalination", German Aerospace Center, Institute of Technical Thermodynamics, Section Systems Analysis and Technology Assessment. Available at: http://www.dlr.de/tt/en/Portaldata/41/Resources/dokumente/institut/system/publications/Trieb_AQUA-CSP-Full-Report-Final.pdf [Live: March 2010].

UK Energy Research Centre (UKERC) (2009) Making the transition to a secure low-carbon energy system, synthesis report, London: UKERC

UK Photovoltaic Manufacturers Association (UK-PV) (2009) "2020: A vision for UK PV: An up to date and accurate analysis on the investment case for solar photovoltaics (PV) in the UK". Available at: http://uk-pv.org/wp-content/uploads/2009/10/UK-PV-report-03-09.pdf [Live: March 2010].

uktradeinfo (2009) "Exchange rates" [online]. Available at: https://www.uktradeinfo.com/index.cfm?task=exchange&lastcountry=european%20community [Live: March 2010].

U.S. Department of Energy [US DoE] (2004) "What is the energy payback for PV?", PV FAQs, The National Renewable Energy Laboratory. Available at: http://www.nrel.gov/docs/fy04osti/35489.pdf [Live: March 2010].

Watson et al. (2002) "Renewable Energy and Combined Heat and Power Resources in the UK", Tyndall Centre for Climate Change Research, Working Paper 22, April 2002. Available at: http://www.tyndall.ac.uk/sites/default/files/wp22.pdf [Live: March 2010].

Welsh Assembly Government (WAG) (2009) "First Minister to officially open Wales' first commercial biomass plant", press release from the Office of the First Minister, Welsh Assembly Government [online]. Available at: http://wales.gov.uk/news/topic/officefirstminister/2009/090908biomass/?lang=en [Live: March 2010].

Woods, J. & A. Bauen (2003) "Technology Status Review and Carbon Abatement Potential of Renewable Transport Fuels in the UK", report for Department of Trade and Industry New & Renewable Energy Programme, URN 03/982. Available at: http://www.bis.gov.uk/files/file15003.pdf [Live: March 2010].

Woods, J., M. Black, & R. Murphy (2009) "Future feedstocks for biofuel systems" in Howarth R.W. & S. Bringezu (eds)

Biofuels: Environmental Consequences and Interactions with Changing Land Use, CreateSpace, pp. 215–232.

Figure sources:

Adapted from DECC (2009) *Digest of United Kingdom Energy Statistics: 2009*, London: The Stationery Office (Electricity flow chart 2008, p. 116). © *Crown Copyright 2009. All rights reserved.*

Adapted from Mackay (2009) "The future of energy", 29 August 2009 [blog]. Available at: http://withouthotair. blogspot.com/2009/08/future-of-energy.html. Image available at: http://www.inference.phy.cam. ac.uk/sustainable/book/data/powerd/ (download: PPPersonVsPDenL.eps).

Parliamentary Office of Science and Technology (POST) (2006) "Carbon Footprint of Electricity Generation", *Postnote*, 268, October 2006 (Fig. 4, p. 3). © Parliamentary copyright 2006. Note: errata in original image: gas power stations CCS are expected to have a carbon footprint of 63 gCO2/kWh (see http://www.parliament. uk/parliamentary_offices/post/pubs2006.cfm for errata notification).

Department for Business, Enterprise & Regulatory Reform (BERR) (2008) *Atlas of UK Marine Renewable Resources: Atlas Pages*, A Strategic Environmental Assessment Report, March 2008 (Annual Mean Wind Power Density at 100m, p. 15). © Crown Copyright. All rights reserved 2008. For further information on data, please see: http://www. renewables-atlas.info/index.asp.

BERR (2008) *Atlas of UK Marine Renewable Resources: Atlas Pages*, A Strategic Environmental Assessment Report, March 2008 (Annual Mean Wave Power – Full Wave Field, p. 11). © Crown Copyright. All rights reserved 2008. For further information on data, please see: http://www.renewables-atlas.info/index.asp.

BERR (2008) *Atlas of UK Marine Renewable Resources: Atlas Pages*, A Strategic Environmental Assessment Report, March 2008 (Average Tidal Power, p. 6). © Crown Copyright. All rights reserved 2008. For further information on data, please see: http://www.renewables-atlas.info/index.asp.

Copyright (2010) ***zero**carbon**britain**2030*. Based on data from the National Grid (2008) and Stattnett (2007–08). Data available from: http://www.nationalgrid.com/uk/ Electricity/Data/Demand+Data/ and http://www.statnett. no/en/The-power-system/Production-and-consumption/ Production-and-consumption-in-Norway.

UK Energy Research Centre (UKERC) (2009) *Making the transition to a secure low-carbon energy system, synthesis report*, London: UKERC (5.9a and b, p. 96).

Copyright (2010) ***zero**carbon**britain**2030*.

Copyright (2010) ***zero**carbon**britain**2030*.

Copyright (2010) ***zero**carbon**britain**2030*.

Copyright (2010) ***zero**carbon**britain**2030*.

Copyright (2010) ***zero**carbon**britain**2030*.

Image of UK bathymetry from BERR (2008) *Atlas of UK Marine Renewable Resources: Atlas Pages*, A Strategic Environmental Assessment Report, March 2008 (Bathymetry, p. 1). © Crown Copyright. All rights reserved 2008.

Copyright (2010) ***zero**carbon**britain**2030*. Based on data from the National Grid (2008) and Stattnett (2007–08). Data available from: http://www.nationalgrid.com/uk/ Electricity/Data/Demand+Data/ and http://www.statnett. no/en/The-power-system/Production-and-consumption/ Production-and-consumption-in-Norway.

Chapter 9
Distributed generation and microgrids

Introduction

In the Renewables chapter the potential of renewable technologies and how they can be integrated to create a resilient electricity system was identified. While the main focus of this report is on solutions that can be applied at a national level, it is clear there are some regions, local authorities and communities who wish to make changes faster. Although acting in isolation might be more expensive, such changes at a small-scale level can lead to improvements in the efficiency of larger-scale deployment.

The ideal mix of generation is not just about the individual merits of a technology, but also about the merits of technologies working in combination to supply different service needs. This chapter explores the potential and limitations of microgrids (operating at distribution voltage level) integrating distributed generators.

Distributed generation

A Distributed Generation (DG) strategy could be developed quickly to help meet renewable targets and addresses the potential energy supply shortfall in time. The universally accepted common attributes of a distributed generator are:

1 They do not require central planning by the power utility.
2 They are normally smaller than 50MW.
3 The generators are usually connected to the distribution system with typical voltages. 230V/415V up to 145 kV (Chowdhury et al., 2009).

Distributed generation can refer to power produced from both renewable and non-renewable sources (Institute of Engineering and Technology [IET], 2006). The chief advantage of distributed generation is that, because the energy source and the consumer tend to be located close together, little energy is lost in transmission and distribution lines (ibid.). Using regional projections of the location of DG across the UK for the placement of 10GW of capacity (as per the Government targets by 2010), initial analysis suggests that DG has the potential to reduce the requirements for transmission network capacity in the long term. The value of this benefit is estimated to be in order of £50–100 per kW installed DG capacity.

The total resource is 130TWh per year, with solar photovoltaics (PV) and biomass Combined Heat & Power (CHP) contributing over 100TWh to this target (Element Energy, 2009). Even though the majority of this

potential is not currently economically recoverable, it still represents a meaningful contribution to UK electricity supply. A tariff design that encourages uptake across a range of technologies and scales can deliver 10–15TWh per year of renewable electricity in 2020. With just PV and small wind, over 3TWh of electricity per year can be generated (ibid.). However this study examined only generating capacity up to 5MW. Considering distributed generators above 5MW and up to 10MW using microgrids, the potential generation capacity will be even higher.

Electricity networks are now in a major transition, from stable passive distribution networks with one way flows of electricity, to active distribution networks with bidirectional electricity transportation to accommodate distributed generation (Strbac *et al.*, 2007). The Office of Gas and Electricity markets (Ofgem, 2003) has titled this challenge of transition as *Rewiring Britain*. It requires a flexible and intelligent control with distributed intelligent systems. To harness clean energy from renewables, an active distribution network should also employ future network technologies, leading to smart grid or microgrid networks.

The UK-based Centre for Sustainable Electricity and Distributed Generation has demonstrated that the application of active network management can support more DG connections compared to the present "fit and forget" strategy of DG employment (Strbac *et*

al., 2007). If numerous micro-generators are connected directly, it will become increasingly difficult for Distribution Network Operators (DNOs) to manage and control the electricity flow (IET, 2006; Lasseter, 2007).

DNOs are companies licensed by Ofgem to distribute electricity in Great Britain from the transmission grid (managed by the National Grid) to homes and businesses. There are currently nine DNOs in the UK which distribute electricity in fourteen licensed areas based on the former Area Electricity Board boundaries.

Microgrids

A microgrid is a small-scale power supply network (with or without heat) designed to provide power for a small area such as a rural, academic or public community or an industrial, trading or commercial estate from a collection of decentralised energy technologies, and connected at a single point to the larger utility grid. It is essentially an active distribution network because it combines different forms of generation and loads at distribution voltage level (Chowdhury *et al.*, 2009). Microgrid managers are responsible for the control and management of several micro-generators, and they connect the energy generated from these multiple sources to the distribution network as if the energy had come from a single larger generator. Using microgrids therefore offers an advantage over DNOs, regarding the connection of individual micro-generators, in that there are fewer links to manage.

Microgrids also offer benefits to certain communities and organisations. Using the microgrid, a community can control and manage its own energy generation and distribution and connect to the utility grid as a single entity.

Microgrids can be used to increase security and reliability of energy supply at a local level as they are not dependent on national grid infrastructure. In this case they are also particularly useful for high energy users which desire an uninterrupted energy supply, such as public or academic institutions, as well as many commercial and industrial users (Lasseter, 2007). Transmission and distribution congestion in the utility grid is growing, with energy demand outpacing investment in new or improved transmission facilities. Power interruptions to high energy users in industry due to line overloading are increasing and many users currently rely on fossil fuel-based backup power systems to ensure an uninterrupted energy supply (Lasseter & Piagi, 2007). While one renewable asset might not provide the service desired, a microgrid may be able to provide a mix of generation assets suitable both as a backup and a contribution to daily demand, thereby allowing companies to decrease their carbon intensity while still providing the security of supply required. Microgrids can be designed to isolate themselves from the national electricity grid system i.e. work in "island mode" during a utility grid disturbance (Lasseter, 2007). A microgrid or distributed generation system can also decrease the power losses

in both the local network and the upstream network providing environmental benefits over conventional centralised generation. (Hatziargyriou et al., 2009).

ADDITIONAL BENEFITS OF MICROGRIDS

For greater security of supply at the national level, several microgrids could be interconnected together through the transmission and distribution network to form a larger power pool for meeting bulk power demands. It is possible to supply a large number of loads from several microgrids through this arrangement. This supports their potential use as aggregators in the power market (Chowdhury et al., 2009). By aggregating various distributed generators as a single power plant the microgrid can be used as a "virtual power plant" (VPP).

A microgrid is one way to deal with an energy shortage during peak demand because it can prioritise loads and selectively cut off power to certain loads (Lasseter, 2007). An interconnected microgrid would achieve greater stability and controllability with a distributed control structure. Connected microgrids could take advantage of short-term selling opportunities with a choice of spinning reserve. The spinning reserve is the extra generating capacity that is available by increasing the power output of generators that are already connected to the power system which is generating at lower than full power output.

Box 9.1 Example of minimising storage

The benefit of minimising storage demand can be illustrated by way of an example. A microgrid with online battery storage would incur losses from the batteries directly and through the inverters. Depending on the age of the storage and technology uses, these could be in the region of 15–25%. Compared to running from batteries with the grid, the transmission savings (6–7%) are going to be much smaller. However, if the onsite demand was largely (85%) met by onsite renewable or grid electricity, then the proportion of generation from storage would be low. This could make the losses lower (2.25 to 3.75%).

It is clear that there is a balance between storage losses and grid losses. We can calculate in what instances local storage is beneficial in efficiency terms. Assuming 18% local storage losses, a 5% saving of transmission losses and 1% (of all generation) network storage losses, then as long as less than 33% of demand comes from batteries, there will be both a resilience benefit and an efficiency improvement compared to grid electricity. However, there would also be an increase in embodied energy, cost and revenue (through selling at peak demand). There is clearly potential for detailed modelling in this area.

Taking into consideration the embodied energy from storage, it seems prudent to use it for less than 25% of demand. Storage brings resilience and potential, but also some costs and risks. In system design it should be remembered that operation always varies from design; less storage installed means lower cost and the less storage used the lower the losses. Well-designed local storage can improve overall electricity system efficiency.

Storage

In the *zerocarbonbritain2030* scenario, to manage variability and utilise all generation potential (i.e. curtailment of wind), a series of measures are used including hydrogen creation, electricity exports, storage and re-timing of loads. These are explained in the Renewables chapter.

One emerging technology is smart inverters which include a type of lithium ion batteries. These have two functions: firstly they can control the release of electricity from onsite generation to the grid; and secondly they have a dynamic demand control function which can delay the operation of certain appliances like fridges, washing machines, and dishwashers.

The controlled release of electricity via storage allows the grid to gain electricity when it is most needed and rewards the generator with a higher price per kWh for the electricity produced.

Storage is one of the required methods to manage the variability of the grid. Storage capacity always has financial costs and embodied energy implications. In addition, storage at any level will involve losses so avoiding the need for storage is the first priority. As seen in the Renewables chapter, this can be minimised by having backup generation, but some of the remaining storage needs could be met by capacity located in a microgrid. More generally, microgrids help to reduce the stress on transmission lines because they share the energy load locally. If a transmission line could be loaded uniformly over a 24-hour period the total energy transmitted can be doubled even after allowing for stability margins (Lasseter & Piagi, 2007). It requires energy storage systems across the country to capture energy whenever there is excess energy generated especially during night-time. Having a national network of storage systems connected through microgrids could provide both short-term operating reserve (STOR), backup capacity and black start facility. Black start is the procedure to recover from a total or partial shutdown of the national transmission system.

The range of established and emerging storage technologies include several types of established batteries, emerging flow batteries, hydrogen, pumped storage and compressed air. Well-designed local storage can improve overall electricity system efficiency. Costs and embodied energy must be taken into account in design decisions.

Technical and financial advantages of microgrids

1 Microgrids can offer a better match between energy supply and demand than the larger utility grid. The decentralisation of energy supply improves power quality and reliability. The electricity requirements of local demand can be met locally with a reliable and uninterruptible power supply (Chowdhury et al., 2009). The management of reactive power and voltage regulation at the microgrid can assist utility generators to generate energy at their optimum capacity and efficiency (ibid.).

2 Smooth voltage regulation locally reduces transmission (feeder) losses (Lasseter & Piagi, 2007). The transmission and distribution network losses currently are about 9% in UK. Local energy generation will reduce these losses to about 2–3% (Business Taskforce on Sustainable Consumption and Production, 2008). Cost savings are created by reducing the need to import power from the utility grid over long distances. Microgrids could reduce the maximum demand on the central generation system leading to large savings in operation and long term investments (Strbac et al., 2007). The reduction of transmission and distribution losses by 1% in the current UK electricity system would reduce emissions by 2 million tonnes of CO_2 per year (Pudjianto et al., 2005).

Advantages of decentralised generation, directly or through microgrids

1 Decentralised generation can be integrated into the current energy supply and distribution system. Microgrids do not require any re-design or re-engineering of the distribution system itself as they supply a single aggregated load to the grid (Lasseter, 2007). Microgrids have their own active management controls and must comply with grid rules and regulations, so the cost to DNOs is minimal.

2 The physical proximity of consumers to energy generation sources may help to increase their awareness of energy usage (Decentralised Energy Knowledge Base [DEKB], 2009).

TECHNICAL AND FINANCIAL CHALLENGES FOR MICROGRIDS

1 Presently the capital costs for distributed generation solutions and microgrids are high, with much of the technology still at the development stage.
2 There is a widespread lack of experience in controlling a large number of micro-resources. In particular, maintaining the power quality and balance, voltage control and system fault levels all pose challenges to operators (IET, 2006).
3 Further research is needed on the control, protection and management of the microgrid and standards addressing operation and protection issues need to be developed further. G59 is an Engineering Recommendation for embedded generation which details the protection requirements for generators when connected to a utility supply in UK. Standards like G59/1 should be reassessed and restructured for the successful implementation of microgrids (Chowdhury *et al.*, 2009).
4 Wider systems of support for microgrids still need to be developed. For example, specific telecommunication infrastructures and communication protocols need to be developed to encourage better communication between distributed generator controllers and the main controller, as well as between various microgrids. Research is going on into the implementation and roll-out of IEC 61850, a standard for the design of electrical substation automation, as well as into active distribution networks.
5 Additional distributed generators will increase the fault current level in the distribution network. A system to measure the fault level accurately and reliably to support distributed generation has been developed through a collaboration including the Electricity Networks Strategy Group (ENSG), the Department of Trade and Industry (DTI) and various UK power distributors. The future infrastructure network systems include "fault current limiter" technologies such as Resistive Superconducting Fault Current Limiter (RSFCL) and Pre-saturated Core Fault Current Limiter (PCFCL).

Financial costs of microgrids

The cost of a microgrid depends on the balance of a number of factors. The following are some examples of microgrid/decentralised energy networks with costs:

1 A 30kW microgrid established at the Centre for Alternative Technology integrating wind,

hydro and PV with 30kW battery store cost about £60,000. This excludes the cost of generators and grid connection.

2 A feasibility study to develop a microgrid at Ashton Hayes village near Chester (with approximately 1,000 inhabitants) estimated total costs of between £350,000 and £400,000. This included the cost of micro-generators appropriate to the demands of the village: two 20kW wind turbines, a biodiesel CHP and seasonal heat store and 27kW photovoltaic array. It was also expected to provide an income for the community (Gillie *et al.*, 2009).

3 The Southampton Decentralised Energy Scheme is the largest in the UK. It uses a 1MW gas CHP, 1.1MW woodchip boiler and 5.7MW geothermal power plant which provides 40,000MWh of heat, 26,000MWh of electricity to the city through private wire and 7,000MWh of cooling, mainly ice storage, with 11 kilometres of heating and cooling pipes. The system cost about £7 million (Utilicom, 2007).

Use of System charges (UoS) and supply licences

Within the current electricity pricing system, most consumers pay their supplier an all-inclusive price for the generation and supply of electricity. This includes tariffs for the use of the transmission and distribution networks (Energy Quote, 2008; National Grid, 2009). The Transmission Network Use of System charge

(TNUoS) is paid to the National Grid and costs a market average of 6% of the total electricity price paid by the consumer. The Distribution Network Use of System (DNUoS) charge is paid to the Distribution Network Operator and costs a market average of 20% of the total electricity price (ibid.).

TNUoS tariffs are zonal in nature; in other words, the country is divided up into different zones, each with a different tariff for generation and consumption. In general, tariffs are higher for generators in the north and consumers in the south. This is due to the fact that there is currently a north-to-south flow of electricity so the tariffs are designed to encourage generation to be built nearer the demand centres.

The system could be made less discriminatory if the tariff system were altered so that use of system charges more accurately reflected the actual cost of system use (European Distributed Energy Partnership [EU-DEEP], 2009). This would make electricity produced by decentralised generators much more cost competitive, and would act as an incentive for DNOs to support the connection of microgrids to the distribution network (ibid.).

Similarly, at present, Use of Service charges (UoS) for both the transmission and distribution networks are based on MW capacity. If the charging system were changed to one based on MWh, it would lower the overall charge payable by intermittent generators such as wind turbines and would therefore act as a further incentive for renewable generation (National Grid, 2009).

Within current energy pricing structures, distributed energy generators or microgrid managers have the option to become licensed suppliers and limited DNO licence holders. At present it is not possible to hold a distributor and supplier licence simultaneously. However, any generator producing under 100MW of power for own use and 50MW for third party use is exempt from licence. In the case of distribution, those distributing less than 1MW through private wires and 2.5MW through public wires are exempted from licence. Suppliers providing electricity generated from a distributed generator or microgrid can therefore reduce costs by avoiding certain UoS costs. Ofgem has worked to make supplier licence conditions for small-scale generators less onerous and more proportionate to their size and impact (Ofgem, 2009). Ofgem has now introduced two further incentive mechanisms in addition to the Distributed Generation incentive:

- the Innovation Funding Incentive (IFI) and
- Registered Power Zones (RPZ).

The primary aim of these two new incentives is to encourage Distribution Network Operators to apply technical innovation in the way they pursue investment in and the operation of their networks which will encourage microgrids.

In Woking, a cost-effective microgrid has been established through the use of the energy service company (ESCO) model, with the establishment in 1999 of Thameswey (Jones, 2004). A private wire distributes electricity to buildings within the microgrid and allows anyone connected to this to add small generation power, e.g. from a domestic solar panel, to this private wire network (ibid.). Therefore anybody generating energy and connected to the wire sells it directly to another customer within the microgrid, rather than selling power through the utility grid. Grid charges are therefore avoided, allowing consumers to benefit from the savings and these avoided charges act as incentives for investment in the local generation and distribution system. The Thameswey microgrid is connected to the larger grid at a single point at a central CHP station (ibid.). This model could be extended to other parts of the country to create a stable UK grid system. In summary, Thameswey got around the problem of a lack of DNO support by using the ESCO business model.

Microgrids and policy

The microgrids debate can be seen as part of two wider debates: one on the roles of distributed generation and another on the role of "smart grids". Both of these offer clear potential benefits, but they also have costs.

Sustainable distributed generation is a great asset to help us nationally decarbonise and it provides additional generation capacity, potentially a faster connection grid network, as well as the opportunity to help power our society and economy. It is generally not the most economically attractive in terms of direct capital costs. It does have social benefits which result in decreased energy demand by occupants of buildings after DG is installed. Plus, as DG is generally organised by individuals and communities, the feed-in tariff (FIT) has provided considerable economic support. There are several reasons for providing this economic support which go beyond carbon emission reductions. These include the expected increased energy efficiency and decrease in energy demand from those involved in the scheme, plus the movement of money from goods to capital. Moving money from goods to capital or simply saving more, rather than spending, is central to creating a sustainable economy.

There are always opportunity costs. If the government convinces people to spend money on renewables rather than on perishables then they are strengthening the economy directly through having renewable assets which can pay back their costs. They also decrease energy waste and demand, which is essential in the transition. Finally, they are decreasing consumption of (probably imported) perishables. However, there will also be a rebound effect which is also driven by the economics. For example, if PV becomes economic then this profit will be spent somewhere. This will impact the sustainability of PV.

Due to the current financial situation in the UK, there is a need to move money at an individual level away from imported

unproductive goods and into savings and investments (Roberts, 2010). This reversal of the current UK trend (Credit Action, 2010) should be applied at a national, local and individual level. Incentives such as the FIT could work to increase "savings and investment". They could also help ensure more UK ownership of renewable generation assets.

There is clearly a scale at which generation can be applied, at an individual, small community, city, regional or national level. At an individual level self-sufficiency can complement environmental objectives, though this is not always the case. However, at a national level self-sufficiency becomes comparable to energy security which involves significant political will. Renewable energy can meet carbon objectives. When invested in by UK capital, it can also meet economic objectives.

Conclusion

The appropriateness of any microgrid is site specific; where a mix of renewable sources is available in one area, a microgrid might work well. Distributed generation and microgrids can save on transmission losses and must be carefully designed to ensure that the use of storage and the losses associated are minimised. In particular, the storage losses must be lower than the national transmission and balancing losses.

Distributed renewable energy is part of the solution to decarbonise the UK energy infrastructure, society and economy. Smaller-

scale renewables are more expensive and have a higher embodied energy than large-scale renewables. However they increase the total potential of sustainable generation of the UK and help increase efficiency and decrease demand where they are deployed. Microgrids can be used in niche applications to assist distributed generation and help manage the variability of the transmission grid.

References

Business Taskforce on Sustainable Consumption and Production (2008) Decentralised Energy: Business Opportunity in Resource Efficiency and Carbon Management, Cambridge: SCP Taskforce.

Chowdhury, S., S.P. Chowdhury & P. Crossley (2009) Microgrids and Active Distribution Networks, Stevenage: The Institute of Engineering and Technology.

Credit Action (2010), Debt Statistics: Total UK personal debt, Credit Action: Better thinking about money [online]. Available at: http://www.creditaction.org.uk/debt-statistics.html [Live: March 2010].

Decentralised Energy Knowledge Base (DEKB) (2009) "What is Decentralised Energy?", DEKB [online]. Available at: http://www.dekb.co.uk/home/index.php?option=com_content&view=category&id=82&Itemid=93 *[Live: March 2010].*

Element Energy (2009) "Design of Feed-in Tariffs for Sub-5MW- Electricity in Great Britain: Quantitative analysis for DECC", final report, URN 09D/704. Available at: http://www.decc.gov.uk/en/content/cms/consultations/elec_financial/elec_financial.aspx (select "Quantitative Analysis of the Design of Feed-in Tariffs") [Live: March 2010].

Energy Quote (2008) "FAQs", Energy Quote [online]. Available at: http://www.energyquote.co.uk/faq/faq.html [Live: March 2010].

European Distributed Energy Partnership (EU-DEEP) (2009) "N1 : The current "Use of System" charge schemes cannot valorise DER that represents value for the system". Available at: http://www.eu-deep.com/index.php?id=429 [Live: March 2010].

Gillie, M., J. Carter & R. Alexander (2009) "A Community Microgrid for Ashton Hayes", EA Technology report 6456, prepared for Carbon Connections & Ashton Hayes Parish Council. Available from: http://www.goingcarbonneutral.co.uk/microgrid-study-informaton/ (select AH Microgrid report 2009.doc) [Live: March 2010].

Hatziargyriou N.D. *et al.* (2009) "Quantification of economic, environmental and operational benefits of Microgrids", *Power Tech, 2009 IEEE, Bucharest*, 28 June 2009 – 2 July 2009, pp. 1–8.

Institute of Engineering and Technology (IET) (2006) "Distributed Generation: A Factfile provided by the Institute of Engineering and Technology". Available at: www.theiet.org/factfiles/energy/distributed-generation.cfm?type=pdf [Live: March 2010].

Jones, A. (2004) "Woking: Local Sustainable Community Energy", Moreland Energy Foundation. Available at: http://www.mefl.com.au/documents/woking-1.pdf [Live: March 2010].

Lasseter, R.H. (2007) "Microgrids and Decentralised Generation", *Journal of Energy Engineering*, 133(3), pp. 144–149.

Lasseter, R. H. & P. Piagi (2007) "Extended Microgrid using (DER) Distributed Energy Resources", *Power Engineering Society General Meeting IEEE*, 24–28 June 2007, pp.1–5.

National Grid (2009) "The Statement of the Use of System Charging Methodology", Issue 5, Revision 1, April 2009. Available at: http://www.nationalgrid.com/NR/rdonlyres/252B0D45-0F60-4E6F-AE84-475997230E23/35221/UoSCMI5R1.pdf [Live: March 2010].

Office of Gas and Electricity Markets (Ofgem) (2003) "Rewiring Britain: Industry experts point the way forward", Ofgem, press release, 8 April 2003. Available at: http://www.ofgem.gov.uk/Media/PressRel/Archive/2975-ofgem32.pdf [Live: March 2010].

Office of Gas and Electricity Markets (Ofgem) (2009) "Distributed Energy – Final Proposals and Statutory Notice for Electricity Supply Licence Modification", Decision Document, Ref 08/09, 06 August 2009. Available at: http://www.ofgem.gov.uk/Sustainability/Environment/Policy/SmallrGens/DistEng/Documents1/DE_Final_Proposals.pdf [Live: March 2010].

Pudjianto, D., E. Zafiropoulos & L. Daoutis (2005) "Large Scale Integration of Micro-Generation to Low Voltage Grids: Methodology for Quantifying Economic and Environmental Benefits of MicroGrids", July 2005, The University of Manchester. Available at: http://www.microgrids.eu/micro2000/delivarables/Deliverable_DG4.pdf [Live: March 2010].

Roberts, S. (2010) "Stuff, stuff and long car trips: application of the 4see socio-economic-energy model to the UK and designing future scenarios", Arup Foresight Group, seminar to the Design Group, The Open University, Milton Keynes, 13 January 2010 [online]. Available at: http://design.open.ac.uk/the_department/SimonRobertsSeminar.htm [Live: March 2010]

Strbac, G., C. Ramsay & D. Pudjianto (2007) "Integration of Distributed Generation into the UK Power System", Summary Report, DTI Centre for Distributed Generation and Sustainable Electrical Energy, March 2007. Available at: http://www.ofgem.gov.uk/Networks/Trans/ElecTransPolicy/TADG/Documents1/DGSEE_EWP_DG_Value_Paper_v3_0.pdf [Live: March 2010].

Utilicom (2007) "Southampton Geothermal: The Company Delivering Sustainable Energy to Southampton", Utilicom. Available at: http://www.utilicom.co.uk/documents/SGHCBrochure211107.pdf [Live: March 2010]

"Governments underestimate what they can do in the long term and overestimate what they can do in the short term"

Geoff Mulgan

Former Director of the Strategy Unit and head of policy in the Prime Minister's Office; Founder and former Director of thinktank, Demos; Director of the Young Foundation.

framework ▶

Chapter 10
Policy and economics

Introduction

This chapter outlines the options for a new international and national policy framework which can support a rapid and deep decarbonisation process in the UK and in other countries across the globe.

A number of internationally-directed and managed carbon trading or tax schemes can be implemented which will make the decarbonisation effort truly global. However, it seems, in the short- to medium-term at least, that it is both more realistic and appropriate for individual nations or regional blocs to choose and implement their own decarbonisation strategies based on a strong international framework of binding national carbon budgets. Some countries may go a step further and join up into regions to achieve these binding targets.

National carbon budgets should provide some of the necessary impetus for the UK to adopt low or zero carbon technologies in historically carbon-heavy sectors, such as energy generation, transport, and housing, as has been discussed in the preceding chapters. However, there is further potential to implement various economy-wide policy interventions aimed at costing carbon. These include high-level cap schemes such as Cap and Share and Tradable Energy Quotas (TEQs) as well as carbon tax schemes.

Additional policy interventions should aim to change energy pricing structures and optimise or create incentive mechanisms for the use of renewable energy, be it heat or electricity. Finally, whilst the transition to zero carbon Britain will not be cost-free, a number of welfare policies and job creation strategies linked to the decarbonisation of the UK economy can be put in place to reduce the negative impact of change, and to create the seeds of green growth.

Before turning to the various policy proposals it is useful to revisit some of the assumptions that underpin this report. The first relates to the level of political acceptability of the interventions recommended here. This report examines what is physically and technically possible, and can therefore be achieved with significant political support.

Within the UK, whilst there is already broad cross-party consensus on the need for 80% cuts by 2050 under the Climate Change Act, support has been more muted for some of the more ambitious policies proposed in this report. However it is worth noting that politics is by its very nature dynamic; whole books can be written on what is, or is not, politically feasible, only to be made irrelevant by a certain event or shock such as 9/11, the 1980's oil shock, or the recent financial crisis. Less than two years ago, a commentator suggesting that three out of the four high street banks in the UK would be nationalised would have been laughed out of the room.

Peak oil could provide the necessary shock and it is clear that, whatever the exact timing of the peak, the supply of oil cannot keep up with rising demand and price rises will result. Increasing energy costs in the long run can provide a powerful economic incentive for reducing our reliance on oil and gas now, so as to avoid even higher costs in the future. Furthermore given the long time frames involved in changing infrastructure we need to start planning for peak oil decades before it hits to avoid a painful transition (Hirsch *et al.*, 2006). A growing number of calculations indicate that it is likely to occur somewhere between the present day and 2031 (Greene *et al.*, 2006) International Energy Agency [IEA], 2008 (Sorrell *et al.*, 2009). We need to have plans in place that can cover the whole range of predictions and be implemented immediately.

Moreover, we only have a finite amount of fossil fuel energy to underpin our transition to a zero carbon economy. Creating a low carbon economy has a significant embedded carbon cost, as it involves the manufacture of new infrastructure such as wind turbines, high voltage DC cables and electric car charging points. If fossil fuel resource depletion continues, energy supplies will become limited and may have to be rationed to assist a smooth transition away from fossil fuels; so that energy, rather than money, is the method by which society rations its quantity of goods. The sooner we make the transition, the easier it will be.

The transition to a zero carbon Britain must be our priority. The dangers of not taking action are immense and increase with every successive year of inaction. We have to act decisively and we have to act now.

International policy frameworks

Climate change is a global problem and as such it requires a global solution. An international agreement must be signed and ratified by all countries based on a cumulative budget aimed at keeping global temperature rise at below 2°C.

Achieving this is far from easy; it involves negotiations with large numbers of participants over matters that strike to the very core of a nation's economic and social policy and involve a high upfront cost, with the benefits only accruing later. Given the unbelievably complex web of interactions, between economics, development and the environment, as well as the sheer scale of the challenges we face, it is not surprising that no successful international agreement has yet been reached. Compromise will almost certainly reign supreme.

Yet it is crucially important to negotiate some form of binding international framework to overcome the freeriding incentive and the commensurate disincentive this creates for other nations. The intention to limit temperature rises to below 2°C was declared in Copenhagen.

Going further and setting a cumulative carbon budget should get all countries committed to the process over the long term and should draw countries together in a common purpose. It should provide certainty to the rest of the global economy that this is what needs to be done, and move the discussion onto exactly how such reductions can be achieved.

OPTIONS FOR ACHIEVING GLOBAL EMISSIONS REDUCTIONS

The depth of the framework at an international level will strongly affect the choices made at a national level. As a result, a distinction must be made between three contrasting road maps for an international agreement:

- The first road map involves the negotiation of an international agreement which aims for an internationally-harmonised carbon price across all countries which would largely negate the need for individual nations to price carbon individually. Nation states would still need to develop carbon reduction strategies but the pricing of carbon would be achieved at a global level.
- The second road map involves the negotiation of an international agreement which would provide the framework through which national carbon budgets were allocated, but allow individual nations

to develop their own policies for pricing carbon on an economy-wide level, as well as introducing the range of other carbon reduction policies needed.
- A third road map sees no global agreement but groups of likeminded countries coming together in regional blocs to set their own emission reduction targets and policies, supported by border tax adjustments to minimise carbon leakage.

We now discuss the alternative policy options available within the three international framework road maps in further detail.

Road map one: A global pricing mechanism

If a single carbon price could be implemented across the world, and the price was equal to the damage done by each tonne, then the fundamental economic problem caused by climate change would be solved. A single policy implemented universally across the world would be extremely powerful and solve the problem of leakage and freeriding incentives. However, this requires an extraordinary amount of cooperation between countries and a strong central authority, which can only be attained if governments are willing to cede some of their authority.

Within this framework, there would be little need for governments to devise schemes to price carbon in their own economies as this would already have been done on a global level. However governments would still need to design a range of policies to complement the global agreement, in particular, through developing support mechanisms for the vulnerable within their nations and through sector-specific interventions and infrastructural investment.

Whilst this still leaves nations with considerable scope for policymaking, it is unlikely that such a scheme will be implemented in the short-term as it is considered too inflexible (it is essentially a one-size-fits-all policy). There is also significant risk that the consequences of any policy design flaw would be amplified and felt globally.

Nonetheless, it is beneficial to understand the pros and cons relating to each of the key policy proposals applicable at the global level. Global carbon pricing systems can be distinguished as either upstream or downstream systems. Upstream systems are those in which a cap is enforced on a small number of fossil fuel extraction companies (fossil fuel suppliers), and sometimes other companies that produce large quantities of greenhouse gas emissions. Within upstream systems, a limited number of carbon permits are made available for these companies to buy every year.

Kyoto2 and Cap & Share (C&S) are examples of upstream systems which are considered in greater detail below. Kyoto2 is an example of an upstream auction scheme where the proceeds are channelled into an adaptation and mitigation fund. Other upstream auction schemes distribute proceeds directly to people

(Cap & Dividend) or to governments to use as either a supplement or substitute to taxes. Rather than through a central auction, the Cap & Share scheme involves permits being distributed directly to individuals who can then sell their permits to fossil fuel suppliers via banks and post offices.

Downstream systems are based on carbon rationing at the level of the consumer. Personal carbon trading schemes such as Personal Carbon Allowances (PCAs) and Tradable Energy Quotas (TEQs) fall into this category. They are unlikely to be effective at the global level due to the high levels of infrastructure and management required for their functioning. They are more viable at the national or regional levels. Carbon taxes are discussed briefly below. These can be levied upstream or downstream.

Kyoto2

Kyoto2 is a proposed framework for a new climate agreement intended to replace the Kyoto Protocol beyond 2012 (Tickell, 2008). It aims to place a limit on the amount of carbon that can be released into the atmosphere. This is achieved through a single annual global emissions quota or cap, which is then divided into permits. Organisations that extract fossil fuels (oil and gas companies), as well as businesses which produce significant carbon emissions such as cement refineries, are required to buy enough permits to cover their emissions. These permits would be sold in a global closed bid auction, subject to both a reserve price and a ceiling price.

The cap would mean that emissions reductions are almost guaranteed, and because only a relatively small number of organisations would need to buy permits, the cost of administration and enforcement would be quite low compared to other permit schemes. The cost associated with buying permits would usually incentivise companies to implement energy-saving measures.

Moreover, the closed bid auction process would produce substantial sums of money (estimated at approximately 1 trillion Euros per year)[1] for a Climate Change Fund which could be spent on adaptation and mitigation measures against climate change, including research and development into renewable energy production, energy-efficiency measures and sequestration projects (ibid.). Close regulation of the fund would be necessary to ensure that the billions invested in it were being spent appropriately.

Cap & Share

Like Kyoto2, the Cap & Share policy aims to place an annual cap on the amount of fossil carbon fuels that can be produced in the world which is brought down rapidly every year; but unlike Kyoto2, it aims to distribute most of the proceeds raised by the cap among the global adult population on an equal per capita basis. Within Cap & Share, each person would receive a certificate every year equivalent to their share of the CO_2 emissions allowance. These could

be sold to fossil fuel extraction companies, via financial intermediaries such as banks and post offices, which would then be allowed to produce that amount of CO_2 emissions (The Foundation for the Economics of Sustainability [Feasta], 2008).

Cap & Share insists a major share of the benefits go to individuals personally rather than to governments because as energy prices rise due to its increasing scarcity the price of goods will go up and people will need to be compensated directly for the increase in their cost of living (ibid.). Bypassing government also limits opportunities for major corruption at the national level (ibid.). Cap & Share provides greater autonomy to individuals than the equivalent upstream auction system, Cap & Dividend. Individuals can choose when (within a given period) to sell their permit, to achieve the best price. They can also choose not to sell their permit, with the result that the decarbonisation process will occur more rapidly.

However, a Cap & Share system need not share out all the money directly to individuals. The Global Atmosphere Trust overseeing the scheme, as well as retaining some funds to cover its own costs, could spend funds in three further ways. It could be used to offer guaranteed prices and other assistance to fossil fuel-producing nations to compensate the loss of income associated with decarbonisation. It could also support climate adaptation measures in countries which are particularly vulnerable to the effects of climate change. Finally, it could

[1] This was equivalent to £796,930 million, taking an average exchange rate for 2008.

also support sequestration efforts, through incentives for farmers and landowners to maintain and increase the carbon content of their soils and the biomass growing on them (ibid.).

At national levels, it would be possible to allocate portions of funds to community response schemes and children's funds, as well as to make allocations to communities such as tribes in place of individual allocations (ibid.).

This scheme has a number of attractive features. First and foremost, the cap ensures that emission reductions are almost guaranteed. Secondly, it can be implemented very quickly because a cap can be introduced effective immediately and the distribution of permits could feasibly take place over just a few months. Thirdly, the costs of enforcement and ensuring compliance are low because there are not many fossil fuel extractors to oversee. About 200 large companies dominate world fossil fuel production.

Finally, Cap & Share integrates an element of fairness in the scheme through the per capita downstream distribution mechanism. As the majority of people in the world use less than the average amount of energy used per person, most people would gain financially from Cap & Share (ibid.). In particular, permits have the potential to promote development in the poorest parts of the world where the sale of permits could provide a huge supplement to people's incomes and to the local economies, hopefully leading to improvements in the standard of living

(ibid.). Fairness would be further integrated if an adaptation and mitigation fund were adopted in the scheme.

However, at the global level, the scheme also has a number of significant disadvantages. As the scheme has never been tested on a large scale, the full macro and micro implications, of, in effect, giving every person on the planet a substantial sum of money, are not fully understood. Despite modelling, the impacts will remain inherently uncertain until implemented in practice.

There are also significant logistical difficulties in trying to provide every person on the planet with a permit, just as there are in trying to ensure that everyone gets a vote. The proposal provides a permit to each person but there are fears that in some areas the permits wouldn't reach their rightful owners. Those areas which lack the infrastructure to successfully deliver the permits are also those areas that could benefit most from the additional income.

Overcoming these infrastructural and logistical issues will play a key part in determining the value of this and similar proposals. There is some evidence from Mozambique to suggest that giving cheques directly to the rural poor is feasible, and can have positive development outcomes (Hanlon, 2004), but it would nonetheless be a significant and costly challenge to ensure that individuals could cash their permits at close to the global market price.

A Global Carbon Tax

Another policy option is the introduction of a globally-harmonised carbon tax. Taxes are a relatively simple, commonly-used method of reducing the demand for goods, and a global carbon tax could be implemented widely and easily. The impact of the tax on emissions is unknown, depending on the price elasticity of fossil fuels within different sectors. Nonetheless, we can assume that a high tax rate, such as £200/tonne, would incentivise decarbonisation sufficiently to lead to rapid emission reductions.

However, given global differentials in wealth, a global carbon tax is likely to be regressive as an increase in the price of fuel which is sufficient to change the behaviour of the wealthy will effectively price out the poor. An indemnity payment system would therefore have to be devised, which would both increase the complexity of the system and reduce the overall incentive to change.

Road map two: An international framework with national initiatives

An international framework aimed at limiting carbon emissions need not dictate the mode by which nations achieve this; instead it can simply decide how much each country is allowed to emit and then let individual countries decide which policies would work best. Such a framework should also be legally binding, backed up by a significant degree of sanction for those nations who exceed their budgets, to prevent freeriding.

Internationally-determined national carbon budgets would provide the impetus, and security from freeriding, for individual nations to cut emissions, and could therefore foster a "common purpose". Policy associated with implementing carbon emission reductions, including any policy aimed at the integration of the carbon cost into pricing mechanisms, would be retained firmly at the national or regional level. This could make policy more effective and efficient generally, as each nation would develop policies suitable to their own context.

The allocation of national carbon budgets

The stumbling block with such an international framework is determining how the cumulative carbon budget will be allocated between countries and across time. Contraction and Convergence (C&C) is one popular and well-known policy option which assumes that the only practical and equitable way of allocating carbon is on an equal per capita basis (Meyer, 2004).

The "contraction" element involves the determination of a "safe" level of greenhouse gas concentration in the atmosphere, which would be used to determine a year-on-year global carbon emissions budget. The annual carbon emissions budget would contract every year until the safe level of greenhouse gas concentration was reached. The "convergence" element involves the allocation of permits across nations, based on per capita emissions (ibid.).

Under this policy, some nations would be

required to cut their emissions more rapidly and more deeply than other nations. However, all countries would have to cut emissions, such that emissions from different countries would eventually converge at or under a set low level.

In general, poorer countries have far lower per capita emissions than richer nations. The policy therefore implies that emissions from rich, industrialised countries must fall immediately whilst emissions from some developing countries' would temporarily be allowed to rise. At a given point these emission levels would converge and then all countries would begin to contract their emissions at the same rate. An important point is therefore the convergence date – the date at which the developed and developing countries' per capita emissions meet, which is used to determine the year-on-year allocation.

Contraction & Covergence allows nations to choose their own policy path towards low emissions. This more flexible approach then creates the opportunity for lessons learnt to be adopted elsewhere and for policy efforts to be scaled up or down as appropriate. However once a system was established, a strong compliance mechanism would have to be in place to ensure that each country met their commitments.

Although Contraction & Covergence provides a viable framework for allocating allowances between countries, it can be argued that it does not sufficiently take into account global equity concerns, based on historic carbon emissions, or countries' current capacity to change, based on wealth (although current per capita emissions correlate fairly well with wealth).

It can also be argued that rich countries are allowed to overconsume until the convergence date without paying for this overconsumption, in contrast to a Cap & Share approach which implies an immediate convergence of equal per capita entitlements. Yet as imperfect as Contraction & Covergence is, a flexible international framework based loosely on it would ensure some level of global fairness and could provide Britain the opportunity to take a global lead on local action, international climate aid and technology transfer.

Once the carbon budget has been allocated between countries, governments can develop their own national policy framework, or band together with other countries to develop regional carbon cap or tax schemes.

Road map three: regional carbon pricing schemes

Another possible road map, and one that looks more likely after Copenhagen, is for countries who wish to decarbonise rapidly to forego a global framework – aimed either at an internationally-harmonised carbon pricing mechanism or at determining national carbon budgets – and rather to join together into blocs with other like-minded countries.

These blocs would then set a common cap, reduction targets and rules, and use border adjustment taxes and rebates to prevent unfair competition from countries with more lax carbon reduction targets. Powerful blocs could adopt a particular policy for determining carbon budgets or prices within the bloc, and could also include an international redistribution mechanism to benefit poorer nations. This could create a large trade bloc, incentivising other nations to join so as not to be excluded by the border adjustment tax (Douthwaite, 2009).

A potential downside of this approach is that the use of different systems for various regional blocs could lead to the double-counting of emission quotas. Additionally, it would not be feasible for countries to be members of more than one regional scheme. Regional carbon budgets should account for this, perhaps simply by allocating a lower regional emissions allowance.

Alternatively, like-minded oil importing and environmentally-aware countries could band together and enforce an immediate upstream tax on themselves to meet carbon targets and to reduce the impact very high oil prices may have on their economies in following years (Stretton, 2009). Stretton argues that if a tax rate of £200/tonne CO_2e was applied across the EU, and also levied on the carbon content of any imported goods, it would provide an incentive for countries exporting to the EU, most importantly China, to join such a scheme as they would want to retain such tax revenues for themselves rather than lose them to European governments.

The regional bloc approach is a practical response to the difficulties of international negotiations over the management of carbon. It attempts to limit the problem of leakage and may provide a viable way forward, avoiding the most procrastinated negotiations. However, such a piecemeal approach runs the risk of not achieving substantial enough reductions, allowing the world to overshoot its cumulative carbon budget.

ADDITIONAL INTERNATIONAL AGREEMENTS

Complementary policies are required at the global level that aim to reduce the level of carbon emissions, increase carbon sequestration capacities, and mitigate against the risks posed from climate change.[2] For example, deforestation must be stopped, and the current UN–REDD (the United Nations Collaborative Programme on Reducing Emissions from Deforestation and Forest Degradation in Developing Countries) proposals need to be replaced by a far more stringent protocol, backed up with greater funding. Similarly, more funding is required for investment in the research and development of low carbon technologies.

Alongside this, a global debate on intellectual property rights must take place so that essential new technology can be adopted across the world easily and cheaply, once it has been developed while promoting innovation. Finally, an adaptation fund needs to be put in place

---

[2] The Kyoto 2 proposal in particular already explicitly includes these features. Other major policy proposals could have these complementary proposals bolted on. However these are very important issues in their own right, and may therefore benefit from being treated separately.

almost immediately to start helping those already impacted by climate change. All of these policies require large amounts of money, the vast majority of which must be provided by rich nations. Some steps towards these goals were taken at Copenhagen but much more needs to be done.

FROM THEORY TO REALITY

Climate change is a global problem and as such it requires a global solution. The first step must be the signing and ratifying of a global agreement which determines a global cumulative carbon budget based on limiting global warming to 2°C. This is achievable; the G8 have already committed to an 80% reduction, and the accord signed at Copenhagen stated that temperature rises should not exceed 2°C. A cumulative carbon budget is the next key step.

Because of the difficulties of applying policies internationally, across nations which vary so greatly in wealth as well as social, economic and political structure, it will prove extremely challenging to develop a global carbon pricing mechanism which is effective yet fair.

It is therefore necessary that a more flexible international framework is adopted that can allow for the differences between countries, as well as be effective in limiting global carbon emissions. A more flexible international framework, probably based around Contraction & Convergence, should be able to achieve more,

faster. It will allow all countries to adopt national policy frameworks appropriate to their contexts, and it is to these that we now turn.

National policy frameworks

At the national level two types of scheme are discussed. Firstly there are schemes to price carbon on a national level – largely negated if an international scheme is in place. These include Cap & Share, Tradable Energy Quotas (TEQs) and carbon taxes. These schemes should cover the economy as widely as possible to ensure that carbon emissions are not simply transferred to other sectors or regions. Secondly, more targeted interventions by the government are required to ensure that the economy and businesses move to a more sustainable path.

Pricing carbon is critical to reducing emissions. However an over-reliance on the market to drive emission reductions could result in short-term profit and small efficiency gains being prioritised over more strategic, larger long-term carbon reductions. These larger, long-term reductions are achieved via large-scale investment in a low carbon infrastructure that is also vital for long-term economic prosperity.

In a similar way, the invisible elbow of the market can lock us into adopting technologies which in the long-run are far more carbon intensive (and possibly less cost-efficient) than other technologies which can be developed given support, either through government intervention or more strategic business investment. For instance, when a new technology develops it takes time for costs to fall as experience is gained. The Government has a key role to play in providing support for innovation to ensure that sufficient experience is gained in new sustainable technologies and unit costs fall. This is one of the main rationales behind government support of renewable technologies.

Similarly the market prioritises short-term gains by demanding high rates of return on capital in the present and discounting the prospects of future profits very heavily. Ensuring low interest rates and developing more appropriate discount rates will further help prioritise longer-term gains. The market is a key tool, however government intervention can bring forward innovation and help realise substantial strategic opportunities.

Therefore targeted interventions, focusing on particular sectors or groups of people must also be applied. This implies a greater role for the government in supporting innovation and being more actively involved in shaping the market. This role would include funding large-scale infrastructural investment schemes such as those implied within a Green New Deal scheme, as well as short- to medium-term subsidies to the renewable energy sector and investment in research and development. These interventions can stimulate the economy, providing win-wins in terms of jobs, security and environmental benefits. They should also break feedback loops, ensuring that we do not become locked in to inefficient and unsustainable paths.

National carbon pricing

A higher price for carbon should provide some of the necessary impetus for the UK to adopt low or zero carbon technologies in historically carbon-heavy sectors, such as energy-generation, transport, and housing, and for the UK public to alter consumption habits, as has been discussed in the preceding chapters.

National interventions which aim to increase the price of carbon in the economy work very similarly to the international schemes discussed in the previous chapter. Three types of schemes are analysed: cap schemes including Cap & Share and TEQs, carbon taxes and a hybrid of tax and cap schemes.

CAP SCHEMES

A variety of cap schemes have been promoted at the national and regional level with a number already in operation. For example, the European Union Emission Trading System (EU ETS) is the world's biggest Cap & Trade scheme and affects large power generators and other big industrial emitters within the European Union. These emitters are responsible for approximately 40% of the UK's emissions.

In the UK, the CRC Energy Efficiency Scheme, formerly known as the Carbon Reduction Commitment (CRC), came into force in April 2010. This is a Cap & Trade Scheme which aims to tackle emissions from big energy users not included in the EU ETS such as supermarkets which comprise a further 10% of the UK's emissions.

Cap schemes which affect large energy users should be complemented by action to tackle emissions from personal and small business users. Two proposed schemes appear to have particular potential as the basis of a UK personal carbon trading policy: the Cap & Share (C&S) scheme developed by Feasta, The Foundation for the Economics of Sustainability (see Feasta, 2008), and Tradable Energy Quotas (TEQs) developed by The Lean Economy Connection (see Fleming, 2007).[3] They differ primarily in the level of public participation built into each scheme, and therefore also in the administrative costs of the scheme.

Learning lessons from the EU ETS

The EU ETS is the largest carbon trading scheme in the world. A key problem has been that the caps for each country have not been stringent enough. This is because countries have an incentive to increase the cap and thus reduce the costs to their economy of cutting emissions.

Another issue is that permits have been given away on the basis of historic emissions. This effectively rewarded historic polluters while costing energy users and distorting economic incentives to cut emissions. This weakness has been acknowledged in the plans for phase 3 (2013–2020), with the plan to sell some of the permits (30% in 2013 rising to 100% in 2020 in the power sector, and from 20% in 2013 to 70% in 2020 for other sectors), but with lots of exceptions to this if the industry is exposed to global competition (DECC, 2009) to

(Department for Energy and Climate Change [DECC], 2009). The scheme so far has also been costly and ineffective resulting in almost no emission reductions. Any new system for the personal sector must learn lessons from its weakness.

Tradable Energy Quotas

Tradable Energy Quotas (TEQs) is an example of a Cap & Trade scheme, whereby a cap on greenhouse gas emission is set and individual parties receive permits to produce a set amount of emissions. Those with low emissions may sell unused permits, and those who wish to emit more must purchase these.

Under a TEQs scheme the Energy Policy Committee would produce annual carbon budgets based on the wider aim of limiting annual carbon emissions over 20 years. 40% of the annual issue would be distributed equally to every adult at no charge (Fleming, 2007). The remaining portion would be sold by tender, via banks and other outlets, to all other energy users, including the Government. All fuels would carry carbon ratings, and any purchaser would have to surrender carbon units to cover the rating of their purchase.

All carbon units would be tradeable and all transactions would be carried out electronically. Those who wished to emit more than their allowance would have to buy allowances from those who emited less than their allowance. Over time, the overall emissions cap (and therefore individual allocations) could be

---

[3] TEQ's are also known as Domestic Tradable Quotas (DTQs). A variety of other similar personal carbon trading policy schemes have been developed which cannot be considered here. For instance, Personal Carbon Allowances (PCAs), which differs only slightly in scope, allocation method and participation group from Tradable Energy Quotas (TEQs). Similarly, Cap & Dividend has many similarities to Cap & Share, the crucial difference being that permits are auctioned first and the money then distributed on a per capita basis.

reduced in line with international or national agreements.

TEQs offer the opportunity for high levels of public engagement in climate change politics and the public's active participation in the solution. Moreover, it offers a financial incentive: if an individual was prudent with their carbon, they would be able to benefit personally and earn money (ibid.). TEQs also make clear that higher consumption for one individual means less for everyone else. Proponents of the scheme believe this could lead to a sense of a common purpose which could in turn instigate radical behavioural change (ibid.). Certainly, TEQs would make the carbon content of fuels an important influence on spending decisions.

TEQs can also be switched from a system designed to restrict the amount of carbon

Fig. 10.1 The TEQ process

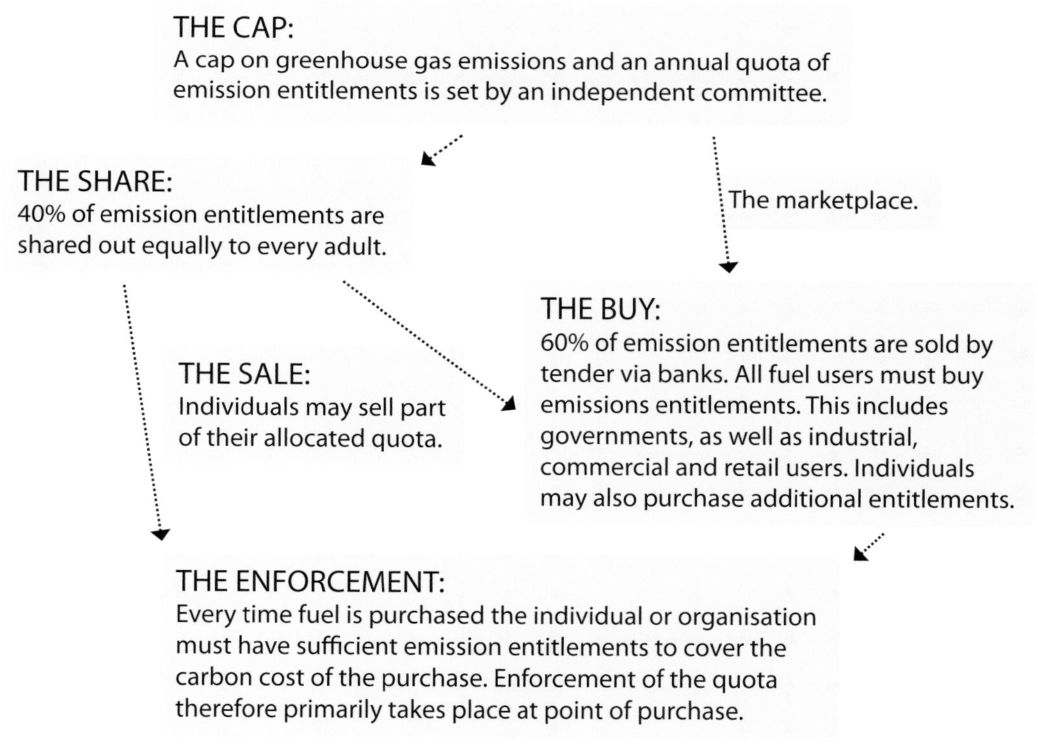

THE CAP:
A cap on greenhouse gas emissions and an annual quota of emission entitlements is set by an independent committee.

THE SHARE:
40% of emission entitlements are shared out equally to every adult.

The marketplace.

THE SALE:
Individuals may sell part of their allocated quota.

THE BUY:
60% of emission entitlements are sold by tender via banks. All fuel users must buy emissions entitlements. This includes governments, as well as industrial, commercial and retail users. Individuals may also purchase additional entitlements.

THE ENFORCEMENT:
Every time fuel is purchased the individual or organisation must have sufficient emission entitlements to cover the carbon cost of the purchase. Enforcement of the quota therefore primarily takes place at point of purchase.

How the TEQ policy would work as an annual process within one nation.

emitted to a system that can ration the amount of fossil fuels. This would involve changing the carbon cap to a fossil fuel cap and to allow everybody a certain amount of fossil fuel use. This is a potentially useful feature, especially if global oil supplies decline rapidly and supplies need to be rationed to prevent collapse.

However, the value of this feature is reduced as **zero**carbon**britain**2030 evisages around a 65% decrease in energy demand as part of the complete decarbonisation. The Energy security chapter highlights other measures needed to meet peak oil.

TEQs are designed to be responsive to market conditions. If there is a high level of inertia and people do not decrease their emissions, the price automatically increases to further increase the incentive for change.

TEQs also respond to the problem of "rebound". Sometimes energy efficiency investments result in maintained or even increased energy use rather than decreased energy demand. For example, following the installation of home insulation, an individual may choose to use the same amount of energy to heat the home as beforehand, with the result being a warmer home, rather than using less fuel to maintain the home at the same level of warmth. This means that potential carbon (and monetary) savings are not always realised.

Under a market-based mechanism, such as TEQs, this rebound will result in a higher carbon price, which will promote further improvements. This automatic price adjustment is not available in a carbon taxation scheme. A system based on a fixed carbon price is very inflexible and unresponsive. It would be possible to increase the fixed carbon price but this would take time and obviously involve significant bureaucracy.

On the other hand, responsiveness to market conditions may also lead to unwelcome price volatility, making it hard for individuals and organisations to make informed investment decisions. This could be minimised by having a minimum (floor) price and a maximum (ceiling) price.

The implementation of a TEQ scheme would require a comprehensive system to be established which could assign ownership of carbon allowances to participants, track allowance usage by participants across all relevant retail points (petrol stations, energy suppliers etc.) and reconcile usage against their account holdings. There are many systems we already have in place which have a similar level of technical requirements such as the Oyster card for travel in London or even retail loyalty cards, albeit on a smaller scale.

The Department for Environment, Food and Rural Affairs (Defra, 2008) has estimated that the set-up costs of such a scheme would likely range between £700 million and £2 billion, with the running cost being £1–2billion per annum. Though this estimate has been widely criticised (see for example, The Lean Economy Connection, 2008), there would be some additional set-up costs when working at a transaction level which which would make the scheme costly. It is also a difficult scheme to test in just one sector of the economy.

Cap & Share

Cap & Share works in much the same way at the national level as it would at the international one. If Cap & Share was not implemented at an international level, a dedicated national body would establish an upstream cap every year to reduce emissions in line with the Government's target. Carbon permits, up to the level of this cap, would then be issued and distributed equally to every adult citizen. Each adult could sell their permit to a bank or at a post office, receiving the market price on that day (Feasta, 2008) (Figure 10.2).

Businesses importing fossil fuels or producing them in the UK would have to buy sufficient permits from the banks to cover the carbon (CO_2e) that would be released downstream from the combustion of the fossil fuels they put on the market (ibid.). This upstream cap would provide a reliable environmental outcome with a low enforcement cost. If Cap & Share was in use internationally, of course, the national body's role would simply be to pass the permits it had received from the global agency handling the system on to each citizen.

The scheme aims to be equitable via the "polluter pays principle". Businesses are expected to raise the costs of their products in line with the increased cost of carbon. Therefore, those buying carbon-intensive goods would pay more; those who bought less carbon-intensive goods would save money (ibid.).

The artificial carbon-fuel scarcity created by a Cap & Share scheme would push energy prices up. The additional cost for fuel paid by consumers is known as a scarcity rent. The question is – who should get that rent? Within the EU ETS, the scarcity rent has traditionally been channelled back to large companies using fossil fuel, giving them a profits windfall, although in the future, with the sale of more permits, higher proportions are likely to go to the state.

With Cap & Share, though, the majority of the scarcity rent is distributed to the public. This is for several reasons. One is that with a rapid rate of decarbonisation, the scarcity rent would be high and the cost of living would go up steeply. Unless the rent was returned to people, many families would be plunged into fuel poverty.

Another reason is that certain energy-saving actions can only be carried out at the household level. Families will need to have the money to carry them out. If a family can rely on getting a fairly assured income each year from the sale of its permits, it can use that income to repay a loan taken out to make its house more energy efficient.

Not all energy efficiency measures can be carried out at the household level and it has been suggested that some of the permits people received should be cashable only by community organisations. People could choose which projects they give their permits to, and therefore local choice would determine which

Fig. 10.2 The Cap & Share process

THE CAP:	A cap on greenhouse gas emissions and an annual quota of emission entitlements is set based on scientific evidence.
THE SHARE:	Emission entitlements are shared equally to every citizen.
THE SALE:	Citizens sell their entitlements via post offices and banks.
THE BUY:	Primary oil, gas and coal companies buy entitlements to cover the emissions from their fuels.
THE ENFORCEMENT:	Inspectors match entitlements to emissions and enforce the cap by fining companies with too few entitlements.

How the Cap & Share policy would work as an annual process within one nation.

projects were given the go-ahead.

These features mean that the Cap & Share scheme has the potential to attract a strong political constituency as it provides a visible benefit to individuals and their communities. This should increase the robustness of the scheme.

The scheme aims to be equitable via the "Polluter Pays Principle". Businesses are expected to raise the costs of their products in line with the increased cost of carbon. Therefore, those buying carbon-intensive goods would pay more; those who bought less carbon-intensive

goods would save their money.

Despite these features it has been claimed that a disadvantage of Cap & Share is that public participation is limited. For example, the Environmental Audit Committee stated that a Cap and Share scheme would act like a tax on downstream users and not provide the public motivation incentives found in a TEQ-style scheme (EAC, 2008). Individuals would receive an income from the scheme, but there would be no direct link between reducing emissions and saving money. Those advocating Cap & Share do not accept this argument and point out that the higher prices for energy and energy-intensive goods would automatically encourage people to take a low emission path and, that Cap & Share would give them the income to do so. They also say that the public would be more engaged than under a tax scheme.

Another claim is that under Cap & Share, the price of the carbon permits would be volatile if, for example, there was a cold winter or a strong economic swing. This would be dangerous as a high carbon price is considered a key factor for getting investment in low carbon technologies. However, if a floor and ceiling price was introduced, this problem would be overcome.

The floor price could be maintained by the agency running the system, either by purchasing permits and witholding them from use, or by reducing the amount it issued. The ceiling price could be maintained by the agency providing permits from the ETS system and selling them to energy importers to use instead. Having floor and ceiling prices would reduce the scope for speculation, as would the use of time-limited permits distributed across the course of the year. Moreover, Cap & Share would tend to reduce total fuel price volatility because, if the world price of fuel rose, the amount that energy importers would be able to pay for the permits would fall.

In the purest form of the scheme the Government would receive no direct revenue. However, the Government would continue to charge VAT on fuel. As the cost of fuel would increase, the associated higher VAT revenue on each unit of fuel should more than offset the loss of tax revenue caused by the reduction in the amount of fuel sold. This extra tax revenue could be directed into a fund to mitigate or adapt against climate change, or used to support the fuel poor.

The Republic of Ireland has investigated introducing a Cap and Share scheme in the transport sector alone which could then, if successful, be scaled up to include other sectors. (AEA Energy and Environment & Cambridge Econometrics, 2008). This approach decreases the risk associated with introducing such a scheme.

A NATIONAL CARBON TAX SCHEME

A carbon tax is a tax on the fossil fuel content of any good, and could be used as a substitute or in addition to current taxation. The type of tax could vary from the incremental, for example, a few pence on a barrel of oil, to the radical, such as replacing VAT and/or income tax with a tax based purely on carbon. The focus here shall be on supplementary taxes.

An important policy choice would be deciding whether to levy the tax upstream or downstream. The reduced administrative burden and the fact that an upstream tax can reach all areas of the economy, suggests that an upstream tax would be preferable. Using static analysis, an upstream carbon tax which distributed the revenues on a per capita basis would be very similar to a cap and share scheme, except that under a tax scheme, the price of carbon would be the same for everybody; static and set by government.

A carbon tax has several advantages over a cap scheme. Firstly, taxes are a simple, proven method of reducing consumption in a good. Secondly, a tax is far less complex than a cap system and as such could be introduced immediately. Thirdly, it provides a stable, carbon price which incentivises investment in renewable technology and more energy-efficient processes. Finally, it could be made revenue-neutral. This would make it far more politically acceptable.

However, a key weakness in the scheme is determining a set tax level. While the cost of switching from one technology to another can be quantified, as can the carbon savings this will generate, the level of the rebound effect is unknown. This is part of a larger unknown such as the willingness for people to change their behaviour and what impact on that a change of price will have. A fixed price cannot handle these additional effects.

If emissions are elastic to price, in other words, if a small increase in price leads to a big decrease in emissions, then a tax could be very effective at limiting emissions. If emissions prove inelastic to price, then a tax should be very effective at raising revenue. If these revenues were then channelled into funding climate change mitigation and adaptation it could become even more effective as a climate policy.

Nonetheless, without a cap, the environmental outcome remains unknown. There is no guarantee that it would decrease carbon by enough to keep within a carbon budget. Achieving the optimal tax rate is likely to be a matter of trial and error, but that would create significant upheaval. The more often the tax rate is changed the easier it will be to keep the price escalating to reduce emissions and see how people respond. However, the more often the tax is changed, the less clear the signal is to business. Yet this is a key reason for the scheme. Unlike personal carbon trading schemes, taxes do not build a political constituency. A tax provides a stick to reduce emissions without the carrot of trading.

A tax on rising oil and gas prices is likely to prove very difficult politically. During the oil spike in 2008, the road lobby successfully lobbied to delay planned increases in fuel price duty. The result is that it is difficult to make any sort of long-term commitment to high tax rates as the incentive will always be there to reduce the tax. This contrasts with trading regimes that establish political constituencies which are then motivated to keep the scheme. It has been argued that it would be more effective to provide money to people so that they can invest in energy efficiency measures, rather than taking money away from them (Fleming, 2009).

CAP OR TAX?

On a static analysis, assuming perfect information, cap schemes and tax schemes should provide the same results. In practice they are quite different. Taxes are simple to design and implement, and should create a stable carbon price; but they tend to be unpopular and may lack long-term credibility. Cap schemes on the other hand are more complicated and may promote carbon price volatility; however they can create a political constituency, get the public actively participating and provide a limit on emissions. Both policies could also suffer from the problem of leakage unless there was a stringent international framework and/or border taxes relating to carbon content.

As to the choice of which cap scheme is better, TEQs should prove more effective at engaging people with the issue of energy consumption and have significant potential to motivate behavioural change. It is the only scheme discussed here which would actually actively reward those individuals who limit the greenhouse gas emissions they are responsible for. However, they imply a high administration cost, and offer little opportunity for pilot testing. While the simplicity of Cap and Share comes at the price of decreasing motivation, they are easier to implement and therefore may be tested more easily at a sector level before being implemented on a larger scale.

Given the urgency of the situation it seems clear that either would be better than none

and it is clear that any policy must be stringent if it is to be effective, i.e. through a tight cap or high tax rate. Having said that, taxes and cap schemes are not mutually exclusive and could be combined to accentuate the benefits of each and limit the uncertainty that each is associated with. In such a hybrid scheme the tax would provide the floor price in any cap scheme. This would provide the environmental certainty of a cap combined with relatively certain financial returns based on a tax.

However, it does increase the complexity of the scheme, and this would have financial implications. It could also be slightly regressive if those less able to understand the system were disadvantaged and in turn decrease motivation to participate in the system. Nonetheless, a hybrid policy probably provides the best national policy framework for the UK.

Targeted intervention

In addition to the national or international implementation of a scheme to price carbon, a range of targeted interventions in specific sectors are essential if we are to meet the ambitious carbon reduction targets. The market is a very powerful tool, but needs to be regulated and controlled to ensure a socially-just outcome. Targeted intervention can encourage more strategic action and ultimately lower emissions.

Government has an important role to play in disseminating information and promoting cross-sector initiatives, both public and private. After all, the economic assumption of perfect information in reality does not exist. Many organisations may have mutual needs or objectives. The Government can play a role in facilitating cooperation amongst these organisations. Government must also take a role in breaking the feedback loops which can often reinforce the continued use of unsustainable technologies and lock us into certain lifestyle packages.[4]

Whilst a call for such a hands-on approach from Government would have seemed radical even 18 months ago, the financial crisis and recapitalisation of the banks demonstrate the dangers of unfettered market forces, and reinforce the role of Government as a key shaper of our economy.

Both the Government's Low Carbon Transition Plan (DECC, 2009) and the recent report by the Committee on Climate Change (CCC, 2009) argue that the market alone will not be able to solve the problems facing the energy sector. The recent announcement made by Ed Miliband, Secretary of State for Energy and Climate Change, about the Government taking control over access to the National Grid from the Office of the Gas and Electricity Markets (Ofgem) (Macalister, 2009) highlights that when political leadership is needed it can happen.

FINANCING THE GREEN ECONOMY

The policy proposals within the Green New Deal report published in 2008 attempt to tackle the triple threat of climate chaos, peak oil and the financial crisis through a major Keynesian effort, reminiscent of the "New Deal" launched by President Roosevelt in the 1930's to pull America out of the Great Depression (Green New Deal Group, 2008).[5]

The programme would involve structural reform of the national and international financial regulation combined with major changes to taxation systems. For example, greater regulation of the domestic financial system would aim to ensure low interest rates which in turn should incentivise infrastructural investment which produces returns over the long-term. Merchant banking would be separated from corporate finance and securities dealing (ibid.).

However the programme is not limited to financial reform. It would also involve a sustained programme to invest in and deploy energy conservation and renewable energies as well as initiatives to manage energy demand, analogous to the *power up* and *power down* scenarios detailed in this report. This would entail an initial crash investment programme of £50 billion per year in energy efficiency measures and community-based renewable technologies, which would create jobs and massively decrease heat loss in buildings. The Government would therefore support investment in infrastructure and facilitate the roll-out of renewable and low carbon technologies, from smart meters in homes to the development of an offshore HVDC grid that would allow us to harness our offshore wind, tidal and marine resources.

---

[4] Although not discussed here, the renationalisation of industry is a further option for breaking such feedback loops.

[5] It could be argued that The Green New Deal is a macro scheme but this report regards it more as a combination of various micro-level interventions.

On the ground, teams could go street-by-street insulating and draught-proofing every house. Adopting an opt-out policy over an opt-in policy would greatly increase participation in the retrofitting scheme. Cost-savings would also be made by adopting this street-by-street approach and the overall size of the scheme would certainly allow substantial economies of scale. Ultimately, the environmental reconstruction programme could help shift the UK economy focus from financial services and retail to one powered by environmental transformation.

Financing the Green New Deal should involve both public and private money (ibid.). The programme aims to attract private investment by using public money as a guarantor. One such method would be Local Authority bonds such as the £600 million raised by Transport for London to fund the Crossrail train scheme. Birmingham Local Authority is currently examining the possibility of releasing bonds to fund large-scale energy efficiency improvements on approximately 10,000 Local Authority houses, with the bond paid back through the energy savings made.

One of the core parts of the Green New Deal is the belief that the future will be dominated by rising fuel costs which will allow ever greater profits to be made from increased energy efficiency and renewables (ibid.). It is the cost savings from moving out of intensive fossil fuel use that will repay the loans made under the Green New Deal.

The returns from sustainable technologies although modest at about 3% are fairly secure and are therefore well suited to be invested in by large pension funds and more risk-averse long-term institutional investors. The Government could encourage further small-scale private investment by promoting the sale of small-scale bonds such as "Grannie's Gone Green" bonds, the funds from which would be earmarked solely for investment in low carbon technologies, and by guaranteeing individual investments in the Green New Deal fund.

Finally there is still the potential for further quantitative easing to provide funds for such a deal. Whilst this may prove politically unpopular, quantitative easing was used to recapitalise the banks and the IMF recently gave its support for further rounds of easing (Elliott, 2009). Whether quantitative easing is used or not, adopting the Green New Deal will massively increase the level of government debt potentially undermining access to further credit.

The Green New Deal is both an environmental programme and an economic regeneration programme with a massive job creation element. At the same time, the programme would vastly improve UK energy security and improve our balance of payments deficit by reducing imports of oil and gas. Finally, given the potential for a double-dip recession to hit there is a drastic need to fundamentally restructure the economy away from an over-reliance on consumption and financial services towards a more balanced economy.

Box 10.1 What's the link between GDP and social progress?

In seeking to direct society onto a more sustainable path, there are issues other than carbon emissions that must also be addressed. Not least of these are the health and happiness of its population. Currently economic pressure tends to prioritise short-term financial gain over almost all other considerations. There is growing evidence that some of the personal and social costs of this emphasis include increases in stress-related disease, obesity, family breakdown and poor mental health.

At present, the almost universal yardstick for judging a society's success is the size of its gross domestic product (GDP), which is consequently used as a key criterion in policymaking. This is a crude indicator for economics which takes no account of other considerations such as environment or social factors.

Nor does GDP seem adequately to reflect the public's own aspirations and desires. Eurobarometer – a series of EU-wide polls conducted on behalf of the European Commission – asked in both 2004 and 2007 what criteria were important to people's assessment of their quality of life. The environment was the second most important aspect (Figure 10.3).

Fig. 10.3 Factors influencing quality of life

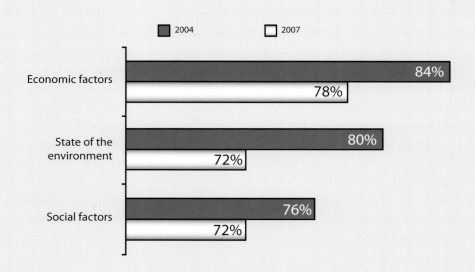

■ 2004 □ 2007

Economic factors — 84% (2004), 78% (2007)

State of the environment — 80% (2004), 72% (2007)

Social factors — 76% (2004), 72% (2007)

Responses as a percentage, in 2004, to the question "In your opinion, to what extent do the following factors influence your 'quality of life'?"
Source: Eurobarometer (2008).

In addition, it was concluded that "more than two thirds of EU citizens feel that social, environmental and economic indicators should be used equally to evaluate progress" (European Council [EC], 2009).

While it is relatively easy to quantify and measure economic factors, environmental and social factors are less straightforward. However, the European Commission is currently developing a range of alternative progress indicators and metrics. These include a comprehensive environmental index (not only carbon emissions), and measures of quality of life and well-being. The intention is to publish these indicators annually, in parallel with GDP:

"The aim is to provide indicators that do what people really want them to do, namely measure progress in delivering social, economic and environmental goals in a sustainable manner. Ultimately, national and EU policies will be judged on whether they are successful in delivering these goals and improving the well-being of Europeans." (EC, 2009).

In March 2009 the UK's All Party Parliamentary Group on Well-being Economics was established, with the same objective of identifying improved yardsticks for gauging societal progress.

The adoption of a broader range of indicators, including carbon content, as well as wider environmental and social impacts, has the potential to dramatically change the policy landscape. While some suggestions in this report may seem unusual compared to current practice, it should also be recognised that such innovation is already appearing within EU policy.

Supporting the vulnerable

Change is always an upheaval which usually impacts greatest on the vulnerable, even if the end-state is ultimately positive. Therefore, every effort must be made to financially support the vulnerable during the transformation into a zero carbon economy, through for example extra financing towards the Jobseeker's Allowance and the roll-out of "green skills" re-training schemes across the UK. The retrofit campaign will address one of the root causes of fuel poverty. Changes to energy pricing structures may also benefit the poor, for example, if the first energy units used are no longer the most expensive, or if it provides opportunities for individuals to save money by changing the times when they access energy.

Effort must also be made to increase the public's understanding of the process and their sense of control over it. Adult education schemes could be developed which teach people about carbon financing and the monetary value of efficiency measures, therefore empowering them to actively participate in the decarbonisation process. This would be particularly useful in facilitating the introduction of a personal carbon trading scheme. More generally, such training has the potential to decrease debt, increase saving rates, improve pension deficit, and reduce inequality. Encouraging peer-to-peer learning could be particularly effective and would provide a significant number of jobs in some of the most disadvantaged areas.

Motivated individuals are already voluntarily trying to significantly alter their own behaviour and make their communities more sustainable by acting within local action groups, through schemes such as Transitions Towns or Carbon Rationing Action Groups (CRAGs). Further support could be provided to promote and encourage such community-level action on these issues, without co-opting existing projects. Similarly, there is a lot of potential to make campaign alliances with non-environmental groups, whether they aim primarily for greater community cohesion or increased public health.

POWERING DOWN WITH NEW ENERGY PRICING STRUCTURES

The reduction of energy waste is essential if a zero carbon society is to be achieved. To combat inertia and promote efficient use of energy a range of measures can be taken. A key incentive is a new pricing structure.

Integrating the environmental cost of carbon emissions into the financial cost of goods and services reduces demand. In the same way, but at a more focused level, altering the pricing structures of energy can lead not only to lower total demand but also to a demand structure more in-tune with the generating capacity of energy from renewable sources, especially wind, which tend to be more intermittent.

A key step to allow variable pricing is smart meters. The Government has pledged that every

home will have a smart meter by 2020 and has just completed a consultation looking at the best way to achieve this goal. Smart meters are likely to have at least a 40-year lifetime and they must be fit for purpose. If deployed correctly, they should have a lasting impact and facilitate the reduction and management of demand from every household and business in the country.

Smart meters would allow the real-time price of electricity to be visible to the consumer, giving them the basic understanding and incentive necessary for them to voluntarily alter when they use energy based on the unit price at the time. Electricity is currently cheapest at night because there is reduced demand, but in the future, with more of our energy coming from offshore wind turbines, it is likely to be linked to periods of high wind.

There is also potential for the technological development of smart appliances which switch on and off automatically depending on the energy cost. This would save money to the consumer and would help the National Grid balance the supply and demand of electricity.

An alternative proposal involves a radical shift, away from treating energy as a commodity, and towards treating energy provision as a service. So for instance, instead of paying for electricity which is then used to generate light, individuals contract energy companies to provide a certain level of lighting. Similarly, a service provider could be contracted to provide a certain level of heating. As the energy supply company became an energy service company (ESCO), its incentives would be transformed. Rather than encouraging the heavy use of electricity in order to acquire greater profits, the company would have an incentive to produce the service as efficiently as possible.

This could involve the company installing energy efficient light bulbs or investing in cavity wall insulation, with the company benefiting from the energy savings in order to pay back the investment. The consumer would pay a similar price for the same service. The ESCO model or similar is also a key contender for financing (or part-financing) the large-scale refurbishment programme detailed in The built environment chapter. Such a model already exists for large industrial users and the challenge is now to make it work on a smaller scale.

POWERING UP WITH RENEWABLES

A range of incentives can be used to accelerate the development of sustainable forms of energy.

Developing a domestic supply chain for offshore wind turbines

As detailed in the Renewables chapter, the UK should develop its own supply chain for offshore wind turbines. The current high cost of wind power development is largely due to a lack of competition and supply capacity amongst suppliers as well as exchange rate variations. Developing a domestic supply industry would

go some way to resolving these constraints and ensuring that the vast wind resource is exploited more efficiently. The scheme would also provide jobs and help revitalise the manufacturing industry.

There are many ways of calculating the cost of building an offshore wind resource with key differences being based on different costs of installation and discount rates. Installing 195GW would therefore cost between £234 billion and £624 billion. The higher estimate is based on current costs rather than projected costs. Current costs are expected to be at a short-term spike due to demand temporarily outstripping supply. The lowest figure is from the range given by the European Commission's figures.

Supporting the roll-out of renewable electricity

Here we cover an overview of the renewable electricity incentive options; more technical detail is included in the Renewables chapter. At present, and although the situation is improving, renewable technologies are still not quite cost competitive with fossil fuel forms of power generation. If carbon was correctly accounted for they would be, but in the meantime enhanced policy support is necessary.

The current policy support mechanism for renewable energy is the Renewable Obligation (RO). This obligates suppliers of electricity to source a certain percentage from renewable sources. This obligation is increasing annually up to 15% in 2015. Suppliers must submit annual Renewable Obligation Certificates (ROC) to Ofgem showing that they have either generated this obligation themselves, or bought it from the market. However, if they have not succeeded in producing or buying sufficient renewable energy certificates/permits, they may make up the remaining shortfall by buying permits at a buy-out rate. The Renewable Obligation was changed in 2009 to include banding by technology so rather than every technology getting 1 ROC for every MWh produced each will receive a different rate of ROCs. For example, offshore wind projects accredited up to March 2014 will receive 2 ROCs, and thereafter will receive 1.75 ROCs (Backwell, 2009).

The Renewable Obligation has led to a rapid increase in renewable electricity production. Nonetheless, it has been criticised for a number of reasons. The idea was that firms would rather pay the government for buy-out permits even if this cost is slightly more than buying ROCs from their competitors. However, ROCs usually trade above the buyout price. The ROC price in July 2009 was just £52 (eROC, 2009); the whole buyout rate was £37.19 (Ofgem, 2009). It can therefore be argued that the buyout rate is too low and has not provided sufficient incentive for suppliers to meet their obligations.

Many commentators have suggested that the Renewble Obligation should be replaced with a feed-in tariff (FIT) scheme. A feed-in tariff is a guaranteed price support mechanism which stipulates the price at which suppliers must buy electricity from renewable sources. It could be banded according to technology and has been successful at incentivising investment in renewable technologies in other European countries such as Germany and Spain, although the price per kWh has been higher in those countries.

While the feed-in tariff has had higher prices historically (Kemp, 2008), if we assume the level of price support is the same then the difference between the two largely comes down to each scheme's complexity and the allocation of risk. The feed-in tariff is a simple and easy to understand scheme: under a feed-in tariff, if you produce x, you will receive y. Therefore, estimating returns and payback times is relatively easy. In contrast, under the Renewable Obligation, if you install x, you will probably get y, but it depends on the market price of the Renewable Obligation, which has many factors including the difference between the obligation and actual amount produced by industry.

Furthermore ROC prices are tied to market prices and these are again difficult to estimate. Estimating returns and payback times involves complex modelling exercises which increases the risk of any investment and indeed the cost of obtaining financing (Mendonca, 2007). In effect, under FITs the price risk of any investment is spread across the whole society while under the Renewable Obligation the developer takes this risk. This has made it difficult for smaller companies and individuals to invest in renewable energy and the Renewable Obligation may be less successful at promoting innovation than a FIT (Foxon *et al.*, 2005).

There is ample evidence to support the proposition that the feed-in tariff is more effective. On behalf of the International Energy Agency (IEA), de Jagger and Rathmann (2008) recently reviewed various renewable policy support efforts in numerous countries and concluded that FIT was the most effective. Ofgem has also stated that it does not want to continue to regulate the ever more complicated Renewable Obligation mechanism.

Both the Renewable Obligation and the feed-in tariff are incentives based around generation. The new infrastructure proposed in the Renewables chapter includes capacity specifically used to manage variability. This is vital for the grid to balance supply and demand for electricity but is not used very often. To avoid complicating the RO or FIT debate, it is recommended that this infrastructure is best handled outside of the core incentive mechanism based on generation capacity (see Box 10.2).

Whilst the Government recently decided against scrapping Renewable Obligation Certificates in favour of a feed-in tariff, apparently on the basis of large developers' objections of not wanting change (House of Lords, 2008), it is now introducing a feed-in tariff for projects under 5MW. It seems clear, that with the feed-in tariff being adopted across the board, the deployment of renewable generation would be accelerated. Therefore the feed-in tariff should replace the Renewable Obligation scheme.

Developing renewable heat incentives

Heat generation from renewable sources is in the early stages of development and the UK only produces 0.6% of its heat from renewable sources. However, it offers tremendous potential and therefore needs urgent attention. This needs to increase to at least 12% by 2020 to hit binding EU final energy targets (DECC, 2009). The latest modelling work by NERA and AEA (2009) for the Government suggests that to meet such a target would require growth rates that are at the maximum observed for individual technologies in other countries.

Policy support is required for heat technologies because the technologies are currently not cost competitive against the production of heat through fossil fuels or electricity. Many of the technologies are relatively new with much scope for learning, so flexibility will have to be at the heart of any successful policy support mechanism.

Heat from renewable sources can be provided through stand-alone technologies on a domestic or commercial basis, or through heat networks, which act much like gas networks, providing heat to a number of buildings. Successful large-scale heat networks already exist in Woking, Birmingham and Southampton which have saved many tonnes of CO_2 each year.[6] Policy

Box 10.2 Financing backup electricity generation

We have presented an overview of the measures needed to support the shift to a low carbon economy. The combination of proposals includes taxation, trading, direct incentives such as feed-in tariffs, strict legislation and compliance. There is however one piece of energy infrastructure that is unlikely to be developed within this framework.

In creating a secure renewable electricity supply, biogas-fuelled turbines form a small but crucial component, particularly to manage the variability of other renewables. But while biogas is needed for energy security, it is only likely to be required for a few weeks each year. The financial incentives for the construction of such facilities based on use are therefore likely to be inadequate. Even with the price security offered by feed-in tariffs, biogas generators are likely to produce insufficient energy to be economic, despite their importance to the overall mix.

Rather than changing the overall fiscal structure for one small exception, it may be better simply to handle it separately. One approach is for Government to offer a guaranteed return for the installation and maintenance of biogas generators, and put it out to developers for tender. Whether such long-term contracts between Government and developer are with the National Grid, or with other private companies, their role will be crucial in ensuring security of supply.

support for stand-alone technologies should run along the same lines as general support for other renewable electricity technologies. Emissions reductions through this technology would be incremental and involve the installation of a large number of units. The development and implementation of heat network schemes on the other hand is extremely complex and therefore requires a much more nuanced level of policy support.

Three policy options for supporting heat networks dominate: government grants, obligations on use or sourcing e.g. 30% of heat from renewable sources, and price support mechanisms such as the Renewable Obligation or feed-in tariff. Berg et al., (2008) have analysed the merits of the various options and conclude that government grants tend to inhibit the development of a heat industry, as policy support is determined by the level of political

funding.[7] When support is high, demand is high and vice versa. The boom-bust cycles that result, make it very difficult to efficiently plan production and investment by the heat industry.

Obligations on a percentage of use were also criticised because they make no distinction by technology. They also provide little scope for economic optimisation because they have no mechanism for ensuring a given level of efficiency.

Recognising that all technologies are not equal is the rationale behind the banding by technology in the Renewable Obligation or a feed-in tariff. If the rationale was short-term CO_2 savings the banding could be organised accordingly. However, the way these have been used so far is to encourage development and therefore the bandings are based on cost of deployment. This ensures that the market delivers longer-term technology innovation

[6] Woking has 13 CHP schemes including the first commercial scale fuel cell CHP, with a borough-wide emissions reduction of 21% on 1990 levels (Audit Commission, 2007). Birmingham uses a gas-fired CCHP to heat, cool and power the City Centre's most prestigious buildings saving 4000 tonnes CO_2/year (Birmingham City Council, 2009). Southampton uses geothermal energy, as well as a gas-fired CHP unit and in the future a biomass boiler, that saves 12,000 tonnes CO_2/year (Greenpeace, 2009).

[7] The paper focused on Germany but the same lessons apply.

rather than just nearest market. However, it can definitely be complimented by research and development investment.

Therefore, as with renewable electricity, a feed-in tariff scheme is recommended because it can precisely target support as with investment grants, being cost efficient because it is performance-based, and because it should help advance long-term infrastructural changes through banding. Investors should be attracted by the secure returns and reduced risk. A final benefit is that it could be funded by a tax on those companies that currently put fossil fuel heating fuels on the market, thus ensuring that the "Polluter Pays Principle" is satisfied.

A number of adaptations could be made to the standard feed-in tariff design. Firstly, it seems clear that tariffs should be banded by size and technology to take into account the different levels of development, costs and returns each involves. The Renewable Energy Association has also suggested a terraced tariff whereby the tariff is greatest for the first few units produced. This should remove perverse incentives for generators to stay below a certain capacity. The terraced feed-in tariff could also be configured to help support heat networks and would be more adaptable at delivering the beneficiaries the returns they need. However, it would be more complicated than a flat tariff and a record of cumulative production would be required.

Although a price support mechanism such as the feed-in tariff should help incentivise investment, a range of non-market barriers will also need to be tackled to allow the development of large-scale heat networks. A general non-market barrier to renewable heat development is the low level of information and knowledge about the heat sector and the range of options available. The Government has a clear role in tackling this, by disseminating information through bodies such as the Carbon Trust and the Energy Saving Trust. Training and education schemes for those in the heat industry could also play a key part in making the most of innovation as soon as possible.

There is a key role for the public sector in developing partnerships with the private sector and to provide an anchor heat load, long-term contracts and the physical building space required. Local authorities, mainly in urban areas, also have a role in energy mapping – identifying existing heat networks, areas of high heat demand and sources of waste heat to facilitate any development –, with the potential for heat mapping to be undertaken as part of their Local Development framework (Greater London Authority, 2007).

Conclusions

The challenges we face are unprecedented. We need strong decisive action now to fundamentally rewire our economy to ensure that the dual problems of climate change and peak oil can be tackled. A number of policy solutions are available at both the international and national level which address climate

Box 10.3 A Fair, green future

We have demonstrated how it is possible, through a wide range of policy interventions, to respond to climate change, peak oil and recession. However, the scale of the current challenges we face must make us consider whether a more radical reconfiguration of the economic system, something akin to a steady-state economy, might ultimately be more successful. Reinvigorating local economies would be a key first step as it has great potential to both reduce carbon emissions, largely through reduced transportation demands, and to make the overall national economy far more transparent and resilient.

Due to the fractional reserve method of banking, the vast proportion of our money supply is lent into the economy by banks. This money has to be returned in full with interest. On an economy-wide level, with a constant money supply, the only way this can be achieved is through economic growth. Resource constraints which limit such growth mean that the interest cannot be paid back and people begin defaulting. This can spread throughout the economy ultimately requiring government intervention to shore up the system. Developing a currency which is not lent, but instead spent into the economy, or is based on a finite resource, is an important area of future research.

change, energy security and our economy. These offer a better quality of life and employment for individuals plus opportunities for business and governments. A sustained political effort is required from national governments to work together and make the most of the opportunities available.

At the international level, the crucial first step is to sign a global agreement aimed at limiting atmospheric temperature rise to below 2°C, and setting a cumulative carbon budget that provides us with a high chance of meeting this goal. The exact policy mechanism could come later, but ensuring that all countries are on board with this overarching target is critical to changing the direction of the global economy. Copenhagen went some way to achieving this goal but a global cumulative carbon budget is needed.

A key decision then needs to be taken over which of the three international framework road maps should be taken. It seems that an international framework that allocates national carbon budgets over time and between countries, via Contraction and Convergence, currently offers the most feasible and effective solution.

Nationally, the UK must introduce a scheme aimed at reducing emissions in the domestic sector to complement the EU, ETS and CRC. Energy Efficiency Scheme aimed at reducing emissions in the domestic sector. Cap & Share, TEQs and carbon tax schemes all provide viable proposals and the answer may lie in combining a hard cap with tax schemes to provide the certain environmental outcome and a guaranteed floor price for investors. Over time such a scheme may develop and encapsulate the whole economy with the EU ETS merging with a personal carbon trading scheme. A clear, high carbon price will incentivise decarbonisation actions amongst all actors.

It is also clear that simply internalising the price

of carbon will not solve all our problems. We are locked into the present technologies and processes, and more targeted interventions are required to put the economy on a more sustainable trajectory. A Green New Deal is needed to provide the investment required in large-scale renewable energy technologies and energy efficiency improvements. Public money has to be used as a guarantor, and innovative financial arrangements have to be developed, in order to attract private finance for such an enormous investment programme.

Whilst the transition to a zero carbon Britain will not be cost-free, a number of welfare policies and job-creation strategies linked to the decarbonisation of the UK economy can be put in place to reduce the negative impact of change, and to create the seeds of green growth. Additional policy interventions should aim to change energy pricing structures and optimise or create incentive mechanisms for the use of renewable energy, be it heat or electricity.

References

AEA Energy and Environment & Cambridge Econometrics (2008) "Cap and Share: Phase 1; policy options for reducing greenhouse gas emissions", report produced for Comhar Sustainable Development Council, Ireland, ED43215, Issue No. 4. Available at: http://www.capandshare.org/download_files/C&S_AEA_report.pdf [Live: March 2010].

Audit Commission (2007) *Seeing the light: innovation in public policy – Woking: Cutting down the carbon footprint*, Local government case study 9, May 2007, London: The Audit Commission.

Backwell, B. (2009), UK government extends ROC window for offshore projects, ReCharge: The global source for renewable energy news, 9 December 2009 [online].

Available at: http://www.rechargenews.com/regions/europe_russia/article201113.ece [Live: March 2010].

Berg, H., A. Burger, & K. Thiele (2008) *Umweltschädliche Subventionen in Deutschland*, DessauRosslau: Umweltbundesamt. Available at: http://www.umweltdaten.de/publikationen/fpdf-l/3659.pdf [Live: March 2010].

Birmingham City Council (2009) "City Centre's First Combined Heat and Power Scheme" [online]. Available at: http://www.birmingham.gov.uk/cs/Satellite?c=Page&childpagename=Parks%2FPageLayout&cid=12230926 24459&packedargs=website%3D1&pagename=BCC%2 FCommon%2FWrapper%2FWrapper&rendermode=live [Accessed: 12 November 2009].

Committee on Climate Change (CCC) (2009) *Meeting carbon budgets: the need for a step change*, Progress report to Parliament Committee on Climate Change, October 2009, London: CCC.

Department for Energy and Climate Change (DECC) (2009) *The Low Carbon Transition Plan*, London: DECC.

Department for Environment, Food and Rural Affairs (Defra) (2008) *Synthesis report on the findings from Defra's pre-feasibility study into personal carbon trading*, April 2008, London: Defra.

de Jagger, D. & M. Rathmann (2008) *Policy instrument design to reduce financial costs in renewable Energy technology projects*, October 2008, IEA Implementing Agreement on Renewable Energy Technology Deployment (RETD), Utrecht, the Netherlands: Ecofys International. Available at: http://www.iea-retd.org/files/RETD_PID0810_Main.pdf [Live: March 2010].

Douthwaite, R. (2009) "Cap & Share", presentation given to the ZeroCarbonBritain Policy, Actions & Economics seminar, 30 September 2009 [unpublished].

Environmental Audit Commission (EAC – House of Commons) (2008) *Personal Carbon Trading, Fifth Report of Session 2007–08, Report, Together with Formal Minutes, Oral and Written Evidence*, HC 565, London: The Stationery Office.

Elliott, L. (2009) "IMF backing for Bank could signal more quantitative easing", *The Guardian*, 30 September 2009.

eROC (2009) "Average ROC prices", eROC: on-line ROC auction service [online]. Available at: http://www.e-roc.co.uk/trackrecord.htm [Live: March 2010].

European Commission (EC) (2009) "GDP & Beyond – Measuring Progress in a Changing World",

Communication from the Commission to the Council and the European Parliament. Available at: http://eur-lex.europa.eu/LexUriServ/LexUriServ.do?uri=COM:2009:0433:FIN:EN:PDF [Live: March 2010].

Foundation for the Economics of Sustainability (FEASTA) (2008) *Cap & Share: A Fair Way to Cut Greenhouse Gas Emissions*, Dublin: FEASTA.

Fleming, D. (2007) *Energy and the Common Purpose: Descending the Energy Staircase with Tradeable Energy Quotas (TEQs)*, Third Edition, London: The Lean Economy Connection.

Fleming, D. (2009) "Part 1: A Plan for All Seasons", in House of Commons All Party Parliamentary Group on Peak Oil (APPGOPO) & The Lean Economy Connection (2009) *Tradable Energy Quotas (TEQs): A Policy Framework For Peak Oil And Climate Change*, August 2009, London: APPGOPO, pp. 7–23. Available at: http://appgopo.org.uk/documents/APPGOPO_TEQs_2009.pdf [Live: March 2010].

Foxon, T. *et al.* (2005) "UK innovation systems for new and renewable energy technologies: drivers, barriers and systems failures", *Energy Policy*, 33(16), pp. 2123 – 2137.

Greater London Authority (GLA) (2009) *Powering ahead: Delivering low carbon energy for London*, October 2009, London: GLA.

Greene, D.L., J.L. Hopson & J. Li (2006) "Have we run out of oil yet? Oil peaking analysis from an optimist's perspective", *Energy Policy*, 34(5), pp. 515–531.

Green New Deal Group (2008) *A Green New Deal: Joined-up policies to solve the triple crunch of the credit crisis, climate change and high oil prices*, The first report of the Green New Deal Group, London: New Economics Foundation (nef). Available at: http://www.neweconomics.org/sites/neweconomics.org/files/A_Green_New_Deal_1.pdf [Accessed: 12 November 2009].

Greenpeace (2009) "Case Study: Southampton" [online]. Available at: http://www.greenpeace.org.uk/climate/case-study-southampton [Live: March 2010].

Hanlon, J. (2004) "It is Possible to Just Give Money to the Poor", *Development and Change*, 35(2), pp. 375–383.

Hirsch, R.L., R. Bezdek & R. Wendling (2006) *Peaking of World Oil Production: Impacts, Mitigation, And Risk Management*, New York: Nova Science Publishers.

House of Lords (2008) *The Economics of Renewable Energy, Volume I: Report*, Select Committee on Economic Affairs, 4th Report of Session 2007–08, London: The Stationery Office.

International Energy Agency (IEA) (2008) *World Energy Outlook 2008*, Paris: Organisation for Economic Development/IEA.

Kemp, M. (2008) "What are the implications for the evolving UK national policy framework of some new economic plans to dramatically cut Green House Gas emissions?", MSc dissertation, Machynlleth: Graduate School of the Environment (GSE), Centre for Alternative Technology (CAT).

Lean Economy Connection (2008) "DEFRA's pre-feasibility study into Personal Carbon Trading – A missed opportunity", 9th May 2008. Available at: http://www.teqs.net/DEFRAPFSresponse.pdf [Live: March 2010].

Macalister, T. (2009) "Labour orders green energy revolution: Miliband takes control of power grid and lays out plan for low-carbon UK", *The Guardian*, 15 July 2009.

Mendonca, M. (2007) "FIT for purpose: 21st century policy", *Renewable Energy Focus*, 8(4), pp. 60–62.

Meyer, A. (2004) "Briefing: Contraction and convergence", *Proceedings of the ICE - Engineering Sustainability*, 157(4), pp. 189–192.

NERA Economic Consulting & AEA (2009) "The UK Supply Curve for Renewable Heat", Study for the Department of Energy and Climate Change, July 2009, URN 09D/689. Available at: http://www.nera.com/image/PUB_Renewable_Heat_July2009.pdf [Live: March 2010].

Office of the Gas and Electricity Markets (Ofgem) (2009) "The Renewables Obligation Buy-Out Price and Mutualisation Ceiling 2009-10", 9 February 2009. Available at: http://www.ofgem.gov.uk/Sustainability/Environment/RenewablObl/Documents1/Press%20Release%20buy%20out.pdf [Accessed: 01 December 2009].

Stretton, S. (2009) *A Short Guide to a Secure Future* [e-book]. Available at: http://www.stephenstretton.org.uk/c/AShortGuide.pdf [Accessed: 30 November 2009].

Sorrell, S. *et al.* (2009) *Global Oil Depletion: An assessment of the evidence for a near-term peak in global oil production*, London: UK Energy Research Centre.

Tickell, O. (2008) *Kyoto 2: How to manage the Global Greenhouse*, London: Zed Books.

Figure sources

Copyright (2010) **zero**carbon**britain**2030.

Copyright (2010) **zero**carbon**britain**2030.

Eurobarometer (2008) "Attitudes of European citizens towards the environment: Summary", March 2008, Special Eurobarometer 295 (QF9, p. 10). Available at: http://ec.europa.eu/public_opinion/archives/ebs/ebs_295_sum_en.pdf.

Chapter 11
Employment
by the new economics foundation

> **The fiscal stimulus measures intended to pull the economy out of recession represent an invaluable opportunity to decisively transform the UK into a low carbon economy. A programme of investments in low carbon industries would help build a modern and sustainable economy, securing Britain's competitiveness and future prosperity in the new global economy that will emerge from this crisis.**

Environment Audit Committee, (2009)

Introduction

The country has been here before – an energy crisis with a recession trailing behind, rising unemployment, and the threat of savage cuts in public service spending. But the current economic crisis is different. It occurs when the imperative to decarbonise the economy has never been greater. There is now an urgent need for solutions that deal proactively with the long-term challenges of climate change and peak oil, while also offering a practical route out of the current recession.

All of these challenges, however, are symptoms of a much wider and systemic problem with the current neoliberal economic model. Instead of endless, stable growth and high and rising incomes equitably shared, we have had inequity, volatility and crises. These are not anomalies, but a natural and increasingly severe expression of the "normal" functioning of the system. As even Alan Greenspan, former Chair of the US Federal Bank, was forced to admit, there was "a flaw… in the model that defines how the world works" (Clark & Treanor, 2008).

Astonishingly however, this is precisely the path to which politicians are trying to return with their current economic stimulus packages. Governments around the world have passed stimulus plans that total US$3 trillion, but only a very small proportion of this has been used to promote the promised future low carbon economy. Instead, the recovery plans have been consumption-led – which, rather than taking the world away from a catastrophic climatic and ecological tipping point, will actually bring it closer.

For example, many of the measures that were hastily put in place at the start of the recession, such as VAT reductions and car "scrappage" schemes, were specifically designed to "kick-start" energy-intensive consumption. Because of such measures, aggregate consumption is now increasing again with the effect of pushing up the price of materials. At the same time, inflationary pressures are occurring again. There is increasing concern over the risk of a second crash in the coming months, and with it, the need for a second wave of stimulus packages.

There is now a strong international consensus in support of economic recovery packages that direct investment into the transformation of the economy to a low carbon state (see for example Green New Deal Group, 2008).

In addition to creating new jobs at a time of rising unemployment, the economic benefits of low carbon investments bring the additional benefit of avoided costs for fossil fuels and environmental damages.

The current chapter examines how the economic benefits of a transition to ZeroCarbonBritain can be realised. In particular, it explores the job creation potential of a transition to zero carbon, how this transition can be made to work, what policy framework is necessary in order to make it happen quickly, and the implications of the current recession. The focus is not simply on decarbonisation of the energy supply, but the decarbonisation of the entire economy – including energy (power and heat), food, transport and other goods and services.

It demonstrates that it is practically impossible to make a bad investment in proven and appropriate renewable energy. This is because of the multiple benefits of such investments, such as long-term mitigation against the causes of climate change, increasing energy security (future energy prices are likely to trigger future economic crises), and the employment intensity associated with energy efficiency improvements and renewable energy infrastructure. In addition, the chapter shows that:

• Shifting to a low carbon economy could provide significant economic benefits to the UK in terms of increased employment, and therefore increased tax revenues.

- Pound for pound, per unit energy, or per unit of investment, renewable energy and energy efficiency have the potential to create more employment opportunities than other more carbon-intensive industries. However, direct comparisons between studies are problematic due to different methodologies employed.

- The transition to a low carbon economy will inevitably undermine jobs in some areas, just as they grow in others. However, employment in carbon-intensive industries such as oil and gas, iron, steel, aluminium, cement and lime are already at risk from carbon pricing. An early spur to convert to a more sustainable industry is likely to safeguard more jobs in the long-term.

- The UK's oil and gas industry is also at risk from peak production in indigenous reserves, and the increased mechanisation of labour. Evidence, however, suggests that "green jobs" in energy, construction, transport and agriculture should more than compensate, even if they emerge in different geographical locations.

- Peak oil will have a huge impact throughout the economy. The decline in the availability of oil, gas and coal (in chronological order) means that the price of fossil fuels is likely to become increasingly high and volatile in the near future. This is likely to have a significant impact on employment across all sectors of the economy. Conversely, the economic impacts of peak oil and gas mean that investment into a low carbon economy will become increasingly attractive, with palpable increases in the potential for green employment.

Given the multiple benefits identified above, the feeble investments currently earmarked for low carbon economic conversion are puzzling. The transformation of the economy in a zero carbon Britain has the potential for numerous economic, social and ecological dividends that go beyond reducing greenhouse gases. However, these can only be realised if applied and delivered in the right way.

A socially-just transition to a zero carbon Britain is achievable, but the success of such a transformation and the speed at which it can occur depends on the magnitude of capital investment, the types of solutions employed, and the scale at which they are installed.

Carbon market failure

This chapter does not re-examine the economic debate over whether to deal with climate change now or in the future. This is partly because the science indicates that there is no choice but to act now and quickly. However, it is also because such arguments tend to fall to the paradox of environmental economics: namely, that without a meaningful cap on global emissions, all methods of pricing carbon create a market that fails to constrain pollution before a catastrophic tipping point is reached (Simms *et al.*, 2009).

For example, carbon markets have so far failed to create a nurturing environment for renewable energy. As French energy company

Box 11.1 We've been here before – job creation grants for home energy efficiency schemes in the 1970s

In the oil crises of the 1970s, job creation grants were used to fund initiatives benefitting both energy efficiency and local economic development.

For example, Friends of the Earth groups used these grants to support projects such as installing home insulation and providing energy advice. Successive job creation schemes enabled groups to take on unemployed people to do the work and also covered running costs.

In the North East, Durham Friends of the Earth used a job creation grant to create home insulation services for disadvantaged groups, such as pensioners (Lowe & Goyder, 1983). As the success of this and other similar projects were recognised, they gained support from local authorities and businesses and scaled out across the nation. The current government funding programmes to address issues of fuel poverty are the result of the institutionalisation of these initiatives (Owen, 1999).

EDF recently pointed out, the volatile price of carbon means that carbon markets are failing just like the market for sub-prime mortgages. For example, the recent fall in the price of carbon, currently €15/tonne (Point Carbon, 2009), has meant that some green energy schemes have stalled. The government could partly counteract the impact of low carbon prices by spending on renewable energy as part of the economic stimulus package.

A transition to a zero carbon Britain requires long-term structural change and extensive planning. But this will not have immediate effect and requires huge capital investment. The uncertainty related to the price of carbon also causes knock-on uncertainty regarding the speed of transition to a low carbon economy. This also means that the demand for "green skills" is difficult to predict.

The oil crises, industrial decline and rising unemployment during the 1970s provided an opportunity to demonstrate the multiple economic, social and ecological dividends from decentralised food and energy supplies. Many exemplary projects were developed at this time (Box 11.1). However, most failed to gain the traction necessary to displace carbon-intensive systems of provision in food, transport and energy.

This time however, there is no room for failure. In order to achieve the target, the transition must start now.

A MISSED OPPORTUNITY

Green spending in Europe is considerably smaller than in other regions such as Asia and the Americas. For example, South Korea's green recovery package was 30 times greater than the UK's.

Recent research by nef's climate change and energy programme investigated the

UK Government's green spending. New and additional spending included in the green stimulus package of the government's pre-budget report was astonishingly small compared with other recent spending commitments, at just 0.6% of the UK's £20 billion recovery plan. This key element makes up just 0.0083% of UK GDP, yet in the wake of the banking crisis, nearly 20% of UK GDP has been provided to support the financial sector. This is a stark contrast to recommendations made by consultancies Ecofys & Germanwatch that at least 50% of stimulus packages should be directed towards low carbon investments (Höhne *et al.*, 2009).

Given that a second wave of stimulus packages may be necessary, it is essential that this second opportunity is realised.

The great transition

As shown in earlier chapters, there are two key elements in the transition to a zero carbon Britain. First there needs to be dramatic reductions in levels of consumption of goods and services, and secondly a deployment of renewable generation. For example, it is much easier to:

• decarbonise an energy system when the demand is smaller and more stable.
• localise food production and create organic agricultural systems when there is less food waste and lower demand for livestock.
• manage waste when less is produced.
• decarbonise a transport system when good

planning practice and more localised supply chains reduce transport needs in the first place.

It is therefore significant that a growing body of research argues that higher levels of consumption are not related to higher levels of well-being (see Figure 11.1). Once people achieve material sufficiency and survive with reasonable comfort, higher levels of consumption do not tend to translate into higher levels of life satisfaction or well-being. Instead, people tend to adapt relatively quickly to improvements in their material standard of living and soon return to their prior level of life satisfaction (Abdallah *et al.*, 2006; 2009; Thompson *et al.*, 2007).

Known as the "hedonic treadmill", ever-higher levels of consumption are sought in the belief that they will lead to a better life. Simultaneously, changing expectations leave people having to run faster and consume more, merely to stand still. National trends in subjective life satisfaction (an important predictor of other hard, quantitative indicators such as health) stay stubbornly flat once a fairly low level of GDP per capita is reached (Easterlin, 1974). Significantly, only around 10% of the variation in subjective happiness observed in Western populations is attributable to differences in actual material circumstances, such as income and possessions (Lyubormirsky *et al.*, 2005).

It is also noteworthy that energy crises over the past forty years show that over short periods of time (weeks to months), with the

Fig. 11.1 Life satisfaction and consumption levels

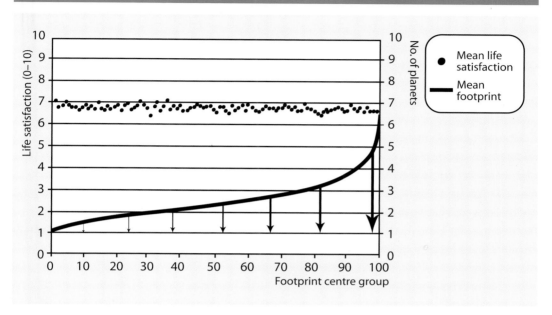

The results of an online survey of life satisfaction and consumption in Europe, gathered by nef.
The web-based survey contained questions about lifestyle – consumption patterns, diet, health, family history – as well as subjective life satisfaction. Using this data, estimates of footprint and life expectancy could be calculated. Over 35,000 people in Europe completed the survey.
Source: Thompson et al. (2007).

right information, individuals and households are very adaptable to energy shortages and are able to reduce consumption considerably and rapidly (International Energy Agency [IEA], 2005a; b). In particular, because the impacts of a crisis are often non-discriminatory, there is a temporary distortion of social norms. In other words, it becomes acceptable to do things differently for a while. This is politically important in the context of carbon rationing.

As the consumption of goods and services

decline rapidly, the second element – a dramatic decarbonisation of energy, food and transport systems – will also need to occur.

Outcomes that are just can also be good outcomes for individuals, for communities and for society.

Transition & social justice

While the nation goes through its transformation to a zero carbon Britain, social justice cannot be ignored. This is not only a moral imperative. As Richard Wilkinson and Kate Pickett (2009) demonstrate in *The Spirit Level*, less equal societies have poorer outcomes on nearly every social measure, and are less inclined toward positive environmental behaviour. This holds true for people across the income spectrum.

While those on low incomes obviously have a disproportionate share of poor outcomes, a middle-class person living in a country with high inequality will, for example, have a lower life expectancy than someone of the same socio-economic status in a more equal society. Furthermore, the capacity to adapt to climate change (or any exogenous shock for that matter) is inextricably linked to socio-economic circumstance. The most disadvantaged social groups are most likely to feel the impacts, and are less likely to be able to cope with and adapt to climate change (Johnson *et al.*, 2009).

Furthermore, education, poverty and employment opportunities are also tightly linked. Research has shown that children's attainment in school strongly reflects the socio-economic situation of their families. For example, children from low-income households, living in poor housing, disadvantaged neighbourhoods, with parents that have low qualifications, low-status jobs or are unemployed are less likely to gain good qualifications (Hirsch, 2007).

This has an overall impact of perpetuating existing socio-economic inequalities across generations. For example, the likelihood of being employed is higher for those with higher qualifications. Education is also central to explaining the inequality gaps between advantaged and disadvantaged groups in terms of health, living standards and social participation (e.g. voting) (Office of National Statistics [ONS], 2004). Education levels can therefore be viewed as a determinant of adaptive capacity.

Employability, skills, trades and professions will also all be affected by climate change. The transition to a low carbon economy is likely to displace jobs in unsustainable industries. To balance this displacement however, there will be an increase in employment in "green collar jobs".

For example, the Local Government Association (LGA, 2009) argues that for the UK government to meet its renewable energy targets, jobs in the renewable sector will have to increase from 16,000 to 133,000. However, the LGA also recognises that the economic opportunities to develop a low carbon economy and create new businesses and jobs will vary from place to place. To ensure that the transition is equitable, it will be essential to provide compensation such as training opportunities to boost the employment market in areas that have experienced significant job losses.

In the context of social justice, history is rife with examples of poorly-managed transitions. The transitions to industrialism, from industrialism to a service economy and the implementation of environmental policies have all had negative social and economic impacts. This is because no broader societal effort was made to limit the damage. Yet this is central for wider public support and acceptance.

For example, in the American Pacific Northwest, thousands of workers lost their jobs as a result of a conservation programme to protect the spotted owl. There was no public programme to support those left unemployed. Another example relates to the collapse and closure of the Northern Atlantic Cod Fishery. Over 20,000 workers in New England lost their jobs in this case. While there was a compensation scheme, there had been no plan for a transition programme, such as retraining to protect the workers affected by policies to manage the fishery. The social justice implications are obvious, however, failure to consider such impacts has been a key driver of tensions between the environmental and labour movements.

Moving 20 years forward, and the social justice context of transition again appears to have been marginalised, particularly in the UK. For example, despite all the rhetoric of a transition to a low carbon economy, the UK stimulus package in response to the recent economic crisis virtually ignores the issue of "green re-skilling" in comparison to the rest of the EU, while only France provided a fund for training (Hoffmann *et al.*, 2009).

Even in the 1970s there was evidence that the UK government embarked on a number of longer-term retraining schemes designed to relocate unemployed workers in new industries. Some car workers were offered training in forestry work, in addition to the provision of mobility grants to individuals to contribute to the cost of relocation (Elliot, 1976).

The job creation potential from renewable energy spans a wide range of occupational profiles, work skills, wage levels, worker representation and empowerment. Given this, a pure focus on the "green' aspect" of employment

---

Box 11.2 Manpower Service Commission

The Manpower Service Commission (MSC) was set up to co-ordinate training and employment services in the UK under Edward Heath's Conservative Government. Although housed within the Department of Employment, the Commission was created as a quasi-independent public body.

Compared with other countries such as Germany, Japan, Sweden and the US, the UK had a wholly inadequate industrial training provision. The creation of the MSC was a deliberate attempt to improve this position (Evans, 1992).

In the 1970s for example, Westminster designed and implemented a number of short-term "job creation" programmes through the MSC. The programmes included beach-clearing, tree-felling and similar activities, particularly to employ out-of-work youths. While here, the retraining component was small, there were also examples of longer-term schemes such as retraining car workers in forestry.

Box 11.3 A Green New Deal

Prompted by the emerging financial crises in August 2007, a group of leading policy entrepreneurs, predominantly from civil society associations, proposed a blueprint for a "sustainable economy" (Green New Deal Group, 2008). The Green New Deal based its name on President Roosevelt's 1930s New Deal to rescue the US from financial crisis. It was, perhaps, the first concrete policy proposal to link globalisation of financial markets to climate change, food and energy security, while redressing growing social inequalities within the UK and overseas.

The report outlines a vision for a low carbon energy system that includes "making every building a power station". Involving tens of millions of properties, their energy efficiency would be maximised, as would the use of renewables to generate electricity. This would require the creation and training of a "carbon army" of workers to provide the human resources for a vast environmental reconstruction programme. The authors argued that hundreds of thousands of these new high- and lower-skilled jobs could be created in the UK. This would be part of a wider shift from an economy narrowly focused on financial services and shopping to one that is an engine of environmental transformation.

An important component is to ensure more realistic fossil fuel prices. These must both include the cost to the environment, and be high enough to tackle climate change effectively, by creating the economic incentive to drive efficiency and bring alternative fuels to market. This would provide funding for the Green New Deal, via rapidly rising carbon taxes and revenue from carbon trading. It would also fund a safety net for those vulnerable to higher prices. The authors advocate establishing an Oil Legacy Fund, paid for by a windfall tax on the profits of oil and gas companies. The monies raised would help deal with the effects of climate change and smooth the transition to a low carbon economy.

It is also important to develop a wide-ranging package of other financial innovations and incentives to assemble the tens of billions of pounds that are required. The focus should be on smart investments that not only finance the development of new, efficient energy infrastructure, but also help reduce demand for energy, particularly among low-income groups, for example by improving home insulation. The science and technology needed to power an energy-and-transport revolution are already in place. But at present, the funds to propel the latest advances into full-scale development are not. The Green New Deal report was later followed by a similar report by the United Nations Environment Programme (UNEP) with the same name (UNEP *et al.*, 2008).

is therefore not sufficient. United Nations Environment Programme UNEP *et al.*, (2008) argue that green jobs should also be decent jobs:

"pairing concerns like efficiency and low emissions with traditional labour concerns including wages, career prospects, job security, occupational health and safety as well as other working conditions, and worker rights."

Green jobs & the transition to a zero carbon Britain

Stability of the labour market is central to a socially-just transition to a zero carbon Britain. The following section focuses on the job creation potential, first by identifying what is meant by a "green job", and second by exploring the employment potential in a number of sectors including energy, transport and agriculture.

WHAT IS A GREEN JOB?

Not all green jobs are equally green. The United Nations Environment Programme (UNEP) defines them as employment in agriculture, manufacturing, construction, installation and maintenance, as well as scientific and technical, administrative and service-related activities that contribute substantially to preserving or restoring environmental quality. They therefore include jobs that:

• help to protect and restore ecosystems and biodiversity,

• reduce energy, materials, and water consumption,

• decarbonise the economy and avoid generating waste and pollution (UNEP *et al.*, 2008).

In other words, green jobs need to be viewed in the broad context of employment policy, rather than on a sector-by-sector basis. However, there are a number of problems in defining a "green job". These include that:

• They must meet long-term demands and goals, with adequate wages and safe working conditions, otherwise their net benefits are not clear.

• Some of the calculations include other jobs that result from green spending, but that are not themselves necessarily "green" at all. This is because earnings from green jobs are spent in the wider economy, along with other induced expenditure (ibid.).

• There are different shades of green. UNEP's definition is based on the use of resources, but not on their origin. They count new jobs in the steel industry as "green" for example, if the steel produced is to supply the windpower industry (ibid.).

These questions may blur the issue. Indeed, some of the new jobs may not be a sign of progress at all. Nevertheless, as Box 11.4 shows, paying people to stay in employment, especially if what they do is a "green job" with long-term benefits that save on future costs has multiple benefits that are both social and environmental.

Box 11.4 The real cost of making someone unemployed

Research published by the Green New Deal Group examined the cost of making someone unemployed (Green New Deal Group, 2009). It showed that cutting a £25,000 job results in a public expenditure saving of less than £2,000 under conditions of less-than-full employment.

It is therefore clear that paying to keep people in work may be beneficial – particularly if what they do has long-term benefit that saves on future costs, such as the tasks proposed in the Green New Deal. Those cost savings – for instance from green efficiencies – need only be £2,000 for it to be worthwhile to keep that person in work. Furthermore, that is before considering the social benefits of being in employment, which are substantial in terms of *inter alia* reduced crime, improved educational outcome and increased well-being.

Box 11.5 Learning from the best – Germany's thriving renewable energy industry

Germany's renewable industries already employ more workers than the coal and nuclear sectors together and it is assumed that by 2020, a total of 500,000 people will be employed in this sector.

Germany's leadership is largely due to a strong political commitment and the introduction of a feed-in tariff, which was passed with the Renewable Energy Sources Act in 2000. This tariff consists of a fee on customers' utility bills that generates a revenue of €2.4 billion per year, costing on average just €3 per household. It guarantees renewable electricity producers a higher-than-market rate, and long-term stability with a very low risk level.

The tariff helped Germany meet its target early, of generating 12.5% of electricity from renewables by 2012. The target of 20% renewable energy by 2020 (set in a new Act in 2008) is also likely to be exceeded by 2011. By 2020, current forecasts expect renewables to contribute around 47% of the total energy mix[31].

In 2007, savings on imports of hard coal and natural gas totalled €1 billion, bringing the avoided external costs through an increased use of renewables to an estimated €5.8 billion.

WHAT MIGHT BE POSSIBLE?

Although it is difficult to offer a precise definition of a "green job", it is likely that the lion's share of them will come from the renewable energy and energy efficiency sectors. While transport and agriculture are also likely to contribute, these figures are much less certain. All estimates presented for jobs assume full-time employment for one year, unless otherwise stated.

According to the UK's renewable energy industry, it employs 8,000 people within the UK. This is set to increase dramatically, with estimates that 25,000 jobs will be created in the power sector alone by 2020 (British Wind Energy Association [BWEA], 2009). This represents a significant growth in employment for skilled workers. However, the UK has so far largely missed out on the boom in "green collar" jobs.

For example Germany, a world leader in renewable energy generation and manufacturing, has more than 31GW of installed renewable capacity, 250,000 people employed by the sector, an 18.5% reduction in greenhouse gas emissions (compared to 1990 levels) and a renewable energy manufacturing and generation sector turnover of more than €23 billion in 2007 (UNEP *et al.*, 2008).

Recent studies are almost unanimous that there is a huge potential for green jobs, and that non-fossil fuel industries offer greater "employment intensity" – which means more jobs per unit of energy, and more jobs for similar levels of investment. The findings include (Jungjohann & Jahnke, 2009):

• Wind and solar could alone create more than 8 million jobs worldwide over the next 20 years.

- Many more jobs could be created in the construction industry, if higher energy efficiency standards were applied.
- Current EU renewable energy policy has the potential to create a net total of 950,000 direct and indirect full-time jobs by 2010 and 1.4 million by 2020 in the EU-15. However, that figure could be as high as 2.5 million.
- Between 60 and 70% of these would be in the renewables industries (mainly biofuels, biomass and wind), with a significant proportion of the remainder in the agricultural sector.
- About one third of these jobs would be for skilled workers.

Renewable energy seems to generate more jobs per average megawatt of power manufactured and installed, per unit of energy produced, and per dollar of investment, in comparison with fossil fuel power plants. On the other hand, coal and natural gas-fired plants employ more workers in their operations and maintenance, where only solar PV systems still compare favourably (Kammen *et al.*, 2004). Expanding clean technology also offers considerable business opportunities for goods and services industries (Green New Deal Group, 2008).

Box 11.6 How a Spanish region became a world leader in renewable energy and saved its economy

Spain has witnessed considerable expansion of its renewable industry in recent years. Employment in this sector has been growing steadily since the 1990s, with recent estimates suggesting that 89,000 workers are now directly employed by renewable businesses (UNEP *et al.*, 2008).

In particular, Navarre, a region in Northern Spain, has become a European leader in renewable energy, and is enjoying a level of prosperity it could not have imagined 30 years ago.

In the 80s and 90s, the region suffered from an economic downturn, driven by high oil prices that affected competitiveness of the region's industry. As a result, unemployment was high, reaching 13% in 1993 (Hoffmann *et al.*, 2009).

Over the past 15 years, Navarre has undergone a radical energy transformation resulting in greater energy security, reduced unemployment (levels are now 4.76%) and wider economic benefits for the region. The figures are staggering: over 60% of Navarre's energy now comes from renewable sources and the region is among the wealthiest in Spain. Its 100 companies dedicated to renewable energy contributed to 5% of GDP and have created around 6,000 jobs.

Navarre is a mountainous area with a population of around 600,000. The Government of Navarre, autonomous from the central Spanish authorities, began the transition to renewable energy sources in 1995. It created the First Regional Energy Plan, placing significant emphasis on wind and solar PV sources. With wide public support, Government grants and the presence of a group of willing investors, the Plan was implemented with great success.

The workforce is characterised by its high level of skill and training, as well as being comparatively young. Forecasts suggest that investment in renewables will continue to increase, as will employment (Faulin *et al.*, 2006). Furthermore, to meet the demand for renewable energy specialists, Navarre launched the first graduate programme for electrical engineers in wind and solar electricity in 2006 (Fairless, 2007).

WIND

Wind is a vast energy source with an enormous job creation potential. The UK holds 40% of the EU's total wind resource, but only 4.2% of its total installed capacity (Lambert, 2008). Currently around 5,000 are employed in the UK wind industry (Boettcher *et al.*, 2008). By 2020 the government's Renewable Energy Strategy predicts an increase to 133,000 – more than a 25-fold increase from current levels.

However, this is a much higher estimate than other studies, and assumes 14GW additional capacity of both offshore and onshore wind (Department of Business, Enterprise and Regulatory Reform [BERR], 2008). At the other end of the scale, Greenpeace and the Global Wind Energy Council (2006) estimate between 5,000 and 34,000 in the same period, depending on whether there are one or three wind turbine manufacturers in the UK. This is based on a figure of 15 direct and indirect jobs per MW of installed capacity. Due to technological improvements, the employment intensity is expected to fall to 11 jobs per MW by 2030. Additionally, 0.33 maintenance jobs are created for every MW installed.

Another estimate by consultancy firm Bain & Company suggests that 4 direct jobs (FTE) are created in the UK for each MW installed onshore, and 5.3 jobs for each MW installed offshore (Boettcher *et al.*, 2008). However, there is no guarantee that these jobs would be in the UK, and the figure does not take into account jobs lost in other sectors. Thus, the net job creation potential is likely to be less, perhaps by more than 50%.

In terms of the social justice implications of the wind industry, research based on Spanish and German renewable industries suggests that wind has the potential to offer good job prospects, career paths and job security (UNEP *et al.*, 2008). Wind (particularly offshore) could act as an alternative career path for those currently working in the offshore oil and gas sector, automotive and aerospace industries. Furthermore, jobs are likely to be geographically dispersed, but also be created in areas that either suffer from high levels of unemployment, or are likely to, or already are suffering from industrial transition (Bird, 2009).

> **Wind: 15.33 jobs (direct and indirect) per MW**

SOLAR

Solar energy has the potential to provide both renewable heat and electricity. Given that just under 50% of the UK's final energy demand is related to heat and 47 % of the UK's CO_2 emissions, solar energy will play a significant role in *zerocarbonbritain2030* (Department of Energy and Climate Change [DECC], 2009).

The Solar Trade Association estimates that over 100,000 solar hot water systems are installed in the UK, and are growing at a rate of 50% per year (European Solar Thermal Industry

"The opportunities solar provides for the UK economy are massive with a huge potential for job creation – in excess of 100,000 people could be employed in the installation of solar across the country. Today, we are already witnessing these size industries in our European neighbours. Solar benefits both the homeowner and the economy."

David Matthews, Chief Executive of the Solar Trade Association[1]

Federation [ESTIF], 2009). While estimates for the job creation potential for solar thermal energy are limited, Solarexpo Research Centre, an Italian solar energy research institute, estimates that 1 job is created per 100m² (~70kW$_{th}$) of capacity installed, or 14 direct and indirect jobs per MW$_{th}$ (Battisti *et al.*, 2007). Another study suggests that solar thermal energy can create between 0.7 and 1.9 jobs per MW of installed capacity, but this estimate only includes direct jobs (Weiss and Biemayer, 2009)[2].

For solar photovoltaic (PV), Greenpeace puts that figure at between 50 and 53 jobs per MW of installed capacity (10 in manufacturing; 33 in installation; 3 to 4 in each of wholesaling and indirect supply; 1–2 in research) (Aubrey, 2007). This seems to be supported by the German experience of 7–11 direct jobs per MW of power (e.g. MWe) (UNEP *et al.*, 2008; Hoehner & Forst, 2006). Compared to wind (both offshore and onshore), solar energy, therefore, appears to be even more favourable in terms of the job creation potential per MW of installed capacity.

In the UK, total installed capacity for solar PV is currently about 6MW, which is a very small proportion of its overall potential – estimated to be approximately140TWh or 35% of total energy consumption[3].

Many jobs created by the use of solar PV and solar thermal water heaters are based at the point of installation (including installation, retail and service). This high level of localised employment holds the potential to create new jobs in many different regions. With expected greater automation, however, it is also assumed that over time, fewer jobs will be created in manufacturing and the ones remaining may not necessarily be located in the UK.

Solar thermal: 14 jobs (direct and indirect) per MW

Solar PV: 33–53 jobs (direct and indirect) per MW installed

[1] cited in Lambert (2008)

[2] The figure varies with scale. At 5.8 GW installed capacity, the employment intensity is equivalent to 1.9 jobs per MW installed. At 17.3 GW installed capacity, the employment intensity falls to 0.73 jobs per MW.

[3] This number is based on south-facing roofs & facades only. The figure roughly agrees with estimates of the maximum reasonably available on buildings by Mackay (2009) 4, of 111 TWh, & IEA 5 of 105 TWh, both based on south-facing roofs only. The absolute Resource Potential for solar PV in the UK is 460 TWh for building-mounted PV.

ENERGY EFFICIENCY

The estimates of jobs are particularly diverse in the energy efficiency sector, with estimates reaching up to 530,000 full-time jobs equivalent in the EU-25 (European Insulation Manufacturers Association [EURIMA], 2008). But what the literature does show is that investing in energy efficiency nearly always creates more jobs than any other low carbon investment, especially when it comes to retrofitting existing stock (EC, 2005). For example, retrofitting activities in the building sector adds positively to employment as they almost never substitute other activities and are highly localised

(Association for the Conservation of Energy [ACE], 2000; EC, 2005; UNEP et al., 2008).

When people save on their energy bills, the money saved tends to be re-spent in the surrounding area, also promoting employment, although the effect is hard to quantify (known as "induced employment") (UNEP et al., 2008). In particular, some of the estimates of total jobs from energy efficiency include:

- 10–30 jobs per £1m spent, rising to almost 60 if job creation and training are a priority (ACE, 2000).
- Another 70 jobs in induced employment per £1m spent (ibid.).
- 12–16 jobs for every $1m (US), compared to 4.1

Box 11.7 Warm Zones – an area-based initiative

Warm Zones is a subsidiary of National Energy Action, the national charity campaigning to end fuel poverty. There are now 13 Warm Zones in England, and two similar programmes in Wales called Warm Wales. New funding under the Community Energy Savings Programme (CESP) will develop these area-based initiatives further. Each Warm Zone has a range of local sponsors from the local authority to community bodies and a major energy utility.

Warm Zones bring funding into an area from a wide range of different sources, to deliver benefits such as energy efficiency, carbon savings, fuel poverty reductions, benefits advice, health improvements, fire and home security, employment skills and training. Warm Zones have been particularly effective in accessing the hard-to-reach and other vulnerable households who are at greatest risk. For example over a period of seven years, the Warm Zones programme in Sandwell in the West Midlands has led to the energy efficiency upgrade of over 37,000 homes, an investment of £23 million and a 90% increase in the thermal efficiency of the housing.

In 2008, a University of Durham study found a significant local economic multiplier effect from programmes such as the Energy Efficiency Commitment, Warm Front and Warm Zones. In 2005–2006, £13.72 million was invested through these programmes in energy efficiency measures in the North East of England, which resulted in the following economic impacts:

- £11.26 million of gross value added;

- 369 jobs created regionally (249 direct jobs, 120 additional jobs);

- a regional return of an additional 82 pence for every £1 invested.

---

⁴ Job years are defined as the number of full-time jobs per year times the number of years that the jobs are supported.

for an investment in a coal-fired power plant and 4.5 for a nuclear power plant (EC, 2005)[4].

• The German Council for Sustainable Development estimated that more than 2,000 jobs could be created for each million tonnes of oil equivalent (approximately 11.5TWh) that would be saved as a result of measures and/or investments specifically taken to improve energy efficiency as compared to investing in energy production (Rat für Nachhaltige Entwicklung, 2003).

Overall, retrofitting and new energy-efficient installations have a comparatively high labour-intensity, as they are carried out on-site. Indirect employment in supplying manufacturing industries are also often located close-by, and most firms are small- or medium-sized. For example, globally 90% of construction is performed by micro-firms. Induced employment is created through savings on energy that are re-spent within the community. This also enables a shift away from energy supply industries towards sectors that employ more workers per unit of currency received (UNEP *et al.*, 2008).

Energy efficiency: 173 jobs (direct and indirect) per TWh saved

COMBINED HEAT & POWER AND DISTRICT HEATING

Co-generation using Combined Heat and Power (CHP), although not always renewable, is one path to a decentralised, embedded or localised power system. One of the many benefits of production close to the point of use is that it enhances energy efficiency by minimising energy losses through transport and transmission. Small-scale co-generation plants, generally under 1MWe, can be used in multi-residential dwellings, leisure centres, hotels, greenhouses and hospitals. They are simple to install and are flexible. Individual households can use smaller units.

According to the Combined Heat and Power Association (CHPA, 2009), heat use – predominantly space and water heating – accounts for 47% of the UK's total CO_2 emissions. Approximately half of this is in the domestic sector. While district heating (including CHP) provides up to half of all heat in some European nations, the UK's CHP plants represent only 7% of the total supply (Allen *et al.*, 2008).

Despite the small contribution CHP and district heating make to the UK's energy mix, over 5,000 people are currently employed directly in this industry, with a further 25,000 associated with the supply chain for the industry (Delta Energy and Environment, 2009). There are limited figures on the employment intensity in this sector. However nef carried out a study on behalf of the CHPA that considered the employment impact of the wider development of CHP (Environmental Audit Committee, 1999).

The study concluded that up to 10,000 jobs in the UK economy could be stimulated by the wider use of CHP, based on a capacity of

Box 11.8 Case Study – Energy policy differences in Denmark, France and the UK

Denmark has shown that the potential for decentralised community-based energy is enormous. After the oil crises of the 1970s, three European countries – Britain, France and Denmark – responded to their increasing exposure to highly volatile energy markets in distinctly different ways. The UK brought its North Sea oil and gas reserves online, taking short-term advantage, in energy strategy terms, of these available fossil fuel reserves.

France aggressively developed nuclear power through the nationalised Electricité de France (EDF) (Hadjilambrinos, 2000). By contrast, Denmark pursued an extensive energy efficiency programme, and developed a decentralised energy system based on local CHP and district heating systems. The Danish solution particularly reflects the country's cooperative history and decentralised system of governance.

Since the 1970s, Denmark has improved its energy security by 150%, and is now a net exporter of energy due to its hundreds of small-scale "distributed" generators making use of wind, biomass and a range of fuels. By contrast, the UK lost its energy independence in 2004, and since this date has become increasingly reliant on imported energy.

At the time of the 1970s oil crises, Britain also explored the potential for a decentralised energy system, yet tragically failed to implement this visionary strategy (Dodd, 2008). The strategy, called the Marshall Heat Plan, recommended that energy decentralisation should begin with CHP and district heating development in the largest cities, with London, Birmingham, Manchester, Liverpool and Glasgow identified as the cities that would take the lead on implementation.

As a result of this failure, decentralised supply and micro-generation now represents only a very small proportion of the UK's energy mix. Had the UK pursued a similar programme to Denmark, fuel poverty could have been significantly reduced or completely eradicated. The UK could have been established as the world leader in wind and other renewable energy technologies, with energy insecurity a thing of the past.

However, the UK chose to exploit its North Sea oil and gas reserves, ignore alternative energy policies, and virtually abandon its short-lived energy conservation programme as soon as those reserves came online. Instead of addressing energy conservation through building regulations or retrofitting, which would have had a double dividend for climate change and fuel poverty, the Government chose to rely on free-market forces to increase energy efficiency.

This approach must now be judged to have failed in the light of the current climate change challenge, and increasing levels of fuel poverty. The UK cannot afford once more to miss the opportunity to significantly transform its energy sector to deliver sustainable social justice at the local level.

Nuclear-fuelled France has little to offer in terms of positive lessons on delivering an agenda of sustainable social justice through its energy sector. The toxic legacy of nuclear energy alone excludes it from consideration as a viable alternative, before even taking into account the prohibitively expensive cost of nuclear power stations, the length of time required to develop them, and the unacceptably high security risk they pose in terms of terrorism (Simms et al., 2005)

6GWe. Much of this would come through the development and operation of community heating, together with the re-spending effect of lower energy bills. A study for Friends of the Earth also estimates a potential of 30,000 jobs for a more substantial CHP target (ibid.).

Forum for the Future estimated that a 3,000 MW CHP programme covering 9 cities – including Sheffield, Newcastle, Leicester, Belfast and London – could create 140,000 job years over a 10–15 year period (where job years is the number of years one person would be employed in a full-time position). Accounting for the displacement of jobs lost through conventional generation, this scheme would produce a net gain of 7,875–12,535 jobs in manufacturing, installation and servicing (Hewett & Foley, 2000).

> ### CHP: 2.6 to 4.17 and indirect jobs per MW installed

AGRICULTURE

The agriculture sector is the second largest source of greenhouse gases in the UK (Baggot *et al.*, 2007). Intensive farming is also responsible for a range of harmful impacts on the natural environment, from hedgerow destruction to loss of wildlife. Beyond issues of sustainability, the evolution of modern and "efficient" farming practices has resulted in a huge loss of jobs. Estimates suggest that 37 farm workers leave the agriculture sector each day (Maynard and Green, 2008).

Within this context, the organic farming sector offers a window of hope. Organic farming presents a viable alternative to conventional practices, providing a range of positive outcomes including an increase in employment opportunities (Department for Environment and Rural Affairs [Defra], 2002). The organic sector is the fastest growing part of the agricultural industry. Moreover, organic agriculture requires higher levels of labour than conventional farming.

A recent Soil Association report identified that organic farms provide 32% more jobs than comparable non-organic farms (Maynard & Green, 2008). Projections suggest that a large-scale conversion to organic farming in England and Wales would result in a 73% increase of employment in the sector (Jones & Crane, 2009). Over 93,000 new jobs would be created, with great potential to attract new entrants to the agriculture sector (Maynard & Green, 2008). This could have positive impacts for rural communities, supporting local economies and engendering greater community cohesion (Jones & Crane, 2009).

TRANSPORT

The transport sector plays a central role in supporting the current economic system, and provides a wide range of jobs across freight, logistics and passenger transport. However, current transport policies have detrimental impacts on a range of outcomes from public health to climate change (Dora & Phillips, 2000). The sector is a major consumer of fossil fuels and thus a large contributor to greenhouse gases in the UK (Baggott *et al.*, 2007). In meeting the challenges of **zero**carbon**britain**2030, the transport sector can provide many opportunities for a significant growth in green jobs. While there is scope to deliver green

---

[5] For a discussion of aviation and employment see Johnson & Cottingham (2008) and Sewill (2009).

employment opportunities across the transport sector, this section will primarily focus on road and rail.[5]

Road transport

Road transport provides the majority of jobs and the greatest potential for reducing levels of carbon in the whole of the sector (Committee on Climate Change [CCC], 2008). In shifting towards a zero carbon economy, a range of measures would deliver an increase in green employment opportunities.

Moving towards sustainable forms of road transport would require better public transport and an increase in infrastructure for cycling and walking. Such investments would necessarily provide a range of employment opportunities from construction to bus driving. Public transport is already a large employer. In the EU for example, 1,200,000 people are directly employed by public transport operators.

There are also indicative figures for the number of indirect jobs created by this sector. For example, Germany estimates that 157,000 employment opportunities are indirectly created from the public transport system (International Association of Public Transport, 2009). With greater investment in and demand for public transport, the number of jobs in this sector would necessarily increase.

Schemes to increase walking and cycling would require new construction alongside improvements in existing infrastructure (Sustrans, n/d). A consequence of such measures would include the generation of jobs.

Technological developments, from the manufacture of electric or hybrid vehicles to increasing the fuel economy of new and old vehicles could provide opportunities for employment. Forecasts predict a rise in sales of electric and hybrid cars, with expectations that these types of vehicle will significantly penetrate the car market (CCC, 2009).

Such developments could give a new boost to the automotive industry, providing jobs in research, development and manufacturing. For example, the production of hybrid vehicles (those with an electric motor alongside a conventionally-fuelled engine) includes more components and processes than a conventional vehicle and thus requires greater human resource (UNEP et al., 2008).

Providing a boost to jobs in the UK car industry, Toyota has recently announced that it will start production of a hybrid car in an English plant (McCurry, 2009). Furthermore, Government investment in research and development in low carbon vehicles is providing many business and employment opportunities for UK manufacturing (HM Government, 2009).

Worldwide, the level of green job opportunities in the automobile industry varies considerably (UNEP et al., 2008). These opportunities may be positive in the context of wider shifts towards a low carbon economy. However, if the number of vehicles on the world's roads continues to escalate, the shade of green attributed to these jobs may be somewhat lighter.

Employment opportunities in the transport sector also include the repair and maintenance of vehicles, and the production of alternative modes of transport such as bicycles. The number of bicycles produced across the world has fluctuated since the 1980s, reaching an estimated 130 million in 2007. Since the 1970s, bicycle manufacture has risen more steeply than car production (Roney, 2008). The continuation of such trends would further increase the workforce.

Rail

Within the UK, there has been a year–on–year increase in rail passenger travel (Office of Rail Regulation [ORR], 2009). Rail freight has also grown by almost 50% in the past 10 years (Rail Freight Group, 2005). Similar trends can be observed in the railway industry across Europe. However, the privatisation of rail (both freight and passenger) has resulted in a severe reduction in jobs, both within Europe and beyond (UNEP *et al*., 2008). With market growth, industry representatives are optimistic that further employment opportunities will be created (European Monitoring Centre on Change [EMCC], 2004).

In order to deliver a net gain in green jobs, the transport sector will require major shifts in investment and alternative approaches to mass transit. Moving away from the heavy reliance on motor vehicles would inevitably result in a significant loss of jobs in the automobile

industry. However, the lighter weight vehicles of the future are more labour intensive to produce. A few studies have attempted to balance the overall employment impacts of sustainable transport, with predictions reporting an overall growth in jobs (ibid.).

Green energy transition costs

Most studies find it hard to put figures on the cost of transition to a zero carbon economy. The UNEP report describes it as "likely be in the hundreds of billions, and possibly trillions, of dollars", and recommended high-income OECD nations to spend at least 1% of GDP on low carbon investments over the next two years (UNEP *et al*., 2008). It is still not clear at this point however where such high volumes of investment capital will come from, or how it can be generated in a relatively short period of time.

The Institute for Public Policy Research (ippr) suggests that the UK should concentrate its attention on offshore wind, decentralised renewables like solar PV and better energy efficiency in buildings. It estimates that these costs would amount to £50–70 billion per year, or about two-thirds of the annual NHS budget (Lockwood *et al*., 2007).

There will also be a time lag between investment and economic return. This was estimated for Germany as increasing over the next decade up to a maximum of €5 billion in 2015 (Staiss *et al*., 2006). This lag should however go into reverse sometime in the decade after 2018. Until this happens, the German solution is to sell their engineering products abroad.

There would clearly also be costs later as a result of not making investments now. While GDP is not a meaningful indicator of progress, such estimates need to be seen in context. The Stern Review argues that climate change could reduce global GDP by at least 5%, although this might be as much as 20% by 2050.

Is it realistic?

On review it is hard to compare the various studies. Their methodologies are diverse, and are often unclear. They include different assumptions about knock-on job creation from green investments. The studies often fail to make clear where the huge sums involved might be raised from, and what kind of financial innovation – or government borrowing – might be required to achieve it. Work by the Green New Deal Group has, however, pointed to a wide range of potential sources of funding – public, private, mutual and personal – and takes account of current economic circumstances (Green New Deal Group, 2008).

Shifting to a zero carbon economy will definitely create jobs in the development of new technologies. There will be new industries that might preserve employment in existing firms that are committed to greening their operations. Others may demonstrate effective "conversion", such as aeronautical manufacturers serving the wind industry.

Calculations are however complicated by the fact that change does not only create winners.

As the non-renewable energy sectors become less important, people will also lose their jobs. Some employment will be directly substituted while still others will simply disappear. The studies are not always clear whether they are talking about gross employment or net employment. Nor will the new jobs always be in the same locations as the old ones.

The good news is that investment and employment in renewables is already growing fast around the world. Recently, the International Labour Organisation (ILO) and United Nations Environment Programme (UNEP) have released the findings of a study on the impact on labour of an emerging global green economy (UNEP et al., 2008). The report highlights that changing patterns of employment and investment resulting from efforts to reduce climate change and its effects are already generating new jobs in many sectors and economies.

About 2.3m people worldwide are employed in renewable energies (ibid.). In Germany for example, the renewable energy industries already employ more workers than the coal and nuclear sectors together, and by 2020, a total of 500,000 people will probably be employed in this sector.

An added problem for the UK is that it already lags behind Germany, Denmark, China the USA and Spain. It therefore has fewer opportunities to take a technological lead and to build new export markets.

The UK share of renewables in electricity

generation has already tripled within ten years to 4.5% in 2006 (excluding large-scale hydro), according to BERR (2008). However, total renewable generating capacity will have to increase seven to eight times from 2006 levels by 2020 if the UK is to meet its European renewable energy targets by 2020 (ibid.).

Even so, the CBI believes that the UK government's targets for 2050 are achievable at a manageable cost if early action is taken and government, business and consumers all work together (Confederation of British Industry [CBI], 2007). Whether the right investment happens in the UK depends on the following:

- A feed-in tariff that guarantees higher rates for renewable energy than the market provides, as in Germany.
- Emissions standards that cap the allowable greenhouse gases emitted for every unit of electricity generated, and tighter building standards similarly to drive the efficiency sector.
- Building a home-grown wind industry, perhaps by insisting on local content for turbine manufacture, as in Spain. Most jobs in the wind sector are assumed to be created in turbine manufacture and component supply, with only a small minority in operations and maintenance. Such jobs could easily move overseas.
- The political will to invest in energy efficiency on a major scale, along the lines of the German Alliance for Work and the Environment which aims to renovate 300,000 apartments, creating 200,000 jobs and reducing CO_2 emissions by 2m tonnes a year.
- The right incentives for private businesses, including an effective market price for carbon, along with tax reform to reward greener behaviour.
- New research and technology programmes in these fields, including education programmes for skilled workers. The CBI highlights a serious lack of technical specialists, designers, engineers, and electricians (UNEP *et al.*, 2008).
- Support from the labour movement for a major transition, even though it may mean job losses in some sectors.
- Phasing out subsidies for harmful industries, and shifting those funds to renewable energy, efficiency technologies, clean production methods and public transport.
- Fixing the current shortcomings in carbon trading and in Kyoto Protocol-related innovations like the Clean Development Mechanism, so that they can become reliable funding sources for green projects and employment.
- Eco-labels for all consumer products, to provide information to promote responsible purchasing and encourage manufacturers to design and market more eco-friendly products.

Research gaps

The most important gaps in the research relate to the impact on jobs in agriculture and transport. Both sectors are significant variables in *zerocarbon**britain**2030*. For example, any major shift in the approach to farming in response to rising fuel prices could lead to employment creation an order of magnitude greater than the figures quoted above.

However there is also a major problem with studies examining the economic benefits of low carbon infrastructure and investment, in that it is almost impossible to compare them. Some focus solely on direct jobs, therefore underestimating the full potential for job creation. Others use an input-output model that considers the direct, indirect and induced job creation potential. But many of the assumptions are not made clear.

As above, the European Commission study that predicts 12–16 job years for every $1m (US) spent on energy efficiency does compare this with spending on fossil fuel energy. It estimates 4.1 job years for investment in a coal-fired power plant and 4.5 job years for a nuclear power plant (EC, 2005). However there is a real need for more research to allow more direct comparisons to be made.

Effects of the recession

The banking crisis has led governments to make huge sums available for urgent rescue of their financial institutions. They have also experimented with novel ways of creating money, including "quantitative easing". So it is not clear that the recession will undermine support for this kind of green investment. There has been significant green investment included in the stimulus packages of many nations, although this has been minimal in the UK.

On the other hand, there is no doubt that the recession has enormously reduced the capital available for lending. It also appears to be ushering in a period when governments face increasing chasms in their budgets, and that this will make them less willing to invest, even though some argue that increased spending will, paradoxically, reduce debt by increasing tax receipts as a result of the stimulus. Once again, it comes down to political will, and a better understanding of the economic benefits of green investment. Other factors include:

- The outcome of efforts to reach an international climate agreement for the period after 2012, in which the UK is clearly involved.
- Obligations under the EU Climate and Energy package, published in January 2008, which sets out proposals to achieve a reduction in EU greenhouse gas emissions of 20% by 2020, increasing to up to 30% in the event of an international agreement on climate change (compared to 1990 levels).
- The Climate Change Act, which created a new legal framework for the UK to reduce its CO_2 emissions to at least 80% below 1990 levels by 2050, through domestic and international action. The Act requires the carbon budget for 2018–22 to be set at a level that is at least 34% below that of 1990.

Conclusions

- Shifting to a zero carbon Britain could provide significant economic benefits to the UK in increased employment, and therefore increased tax revenues.
- Pound for pound, per unit energy, or per unit of investment, renewable energy and energy efficiency have the potential to create more employment opportunities than carbon-intensive industries. However, comparisons between different studies are problematic due to the different methodologies employed.
- The transition to a low carbon economy will inevitably undermine jobs in other areas. Employment in carbon-intensive industries such as oil and gas, iron, steel, aluminium, cement and lime are already at risk from carbon pricing. Furthermore, the UK's oil and gas industry is also at risk from peak production in the UK's indigenous reserves, and the increased mechanisation of labour. However, evidence suggests that green jobs in energy, construction, transport and agriculture should more than compensate for this, although these may not emerge in the same geographical locations.
- Peak oil will have a huge impact throughout the economy. For example, long-distance transport, industrialised food systems, urban and suburban systems and many commodities from cars, plastics and chemicals to pesticides, air conditioning and refrigeration, are all dependent on abundant, cheap energy. The decline in the availability of oil, gas and coal (in chronological order) means that the price of fossil fuels is likely to become increasingly volatile in the near future. This is likely to have a significant impact on employment across all sectors of the economy. Conversely, the economic impacts of peak oil and gas mean that investment in a low carbon economy will become increasingly attractive, with palpable increases in the potential for green employment.

References

Abdallah, S. *et al*. (2006) The Happy Planet Index: An index of human well-being & environmental impact, London: New Economics Foundation (nef).

Abdallah, S. *et al*. (2009) The Happy Planet Index 2.0: Why good lives don't have to cost the Earth, London: nef.

Association for the Conservation of Energy (ACE) (2000) *Energy efficiency and jobs: UK issues and case studies*, report by the Association for the Conservation of Energy to the Energy Saving Trust, September 2000, London: Energy Saving Trust.

Aubrey, C. (ed.) (2007) *Solar Generation IV – 2007: Solar electricity for over one billion people and two million jobs by 2020*, Brussels/Amsterdam: EPIA & Greenpeace International.

Baggott, S. L. *et al*. (2007) "UK Greenhouse Gas Inventory, 1990 to 2005. Annual Report for submission under the Framework Convention on Climate Change", AEA Technology. Available from: http://www.airquality.co.uk/reports/cat07/0704261626_ukghgi-90-05_main_chapters_final.pdf [Live: March 2010].

Battisti, R. *et al*. (2007) "Solar Thermal Takes Off in Italy: First Statistical Survey & Market Study Year 2006", Solarexpo Research Centre. Available at: [Accessed: 19 March 2010].

Allen S, G. Hammond & M.C. McManus (2008) "Prospects for and barriers to domestic microgeneration: A United Kingdom perspective", *Applied Energy*, 85(6), pp. 528-544.

Department of Business, Enterprise & Regulatory Reform (BERR) (2008) *UK Renewable Energy Strategy: Consultation*, June 2008, London: BERR.

Bird, J. (2009) *Green jobs: Prospects for creating jobs from offshore wind in the UK*, London: Institute for Public Policy Research (ippr).

Boettcher M., N. Nielsen & K. Petrick (2008) "A closer look at the development of wind, wave & tidal energy in the UK: Employment opportunities and challenges in the context of rapid industry growth", independent study by Bain & Company. Available at: http://www.bwea.com/pdf/publications/Bain%20Brief_Wind%20Energy%202008_FINAL.pdf [Live: March 2010].

British Wind Energy Association (BWEA) *et al.* (2005) "The renewable energy manifesto: as proposed by the UK's renewable energy trade associations: An action plan to deliver 25% of the UK's energy from renewables by 2025", A statement by the renewable energy trade associations of the UK. Available at: http://www.bwea.com/pdf/Manifesto.pdf [Live: March 2010].

BWEA (2009) "UK wind energy statistics", BWEA [online]. Available at: http: www.bwea.com/statistics [Live: March 2010].

Confederation of British Industry (CBI) (2007) Climate change: everyone's business, London: CBI Climate Change Task Force.

Committee on Climate Change (CCC) (2008) Building a low carbon economy, The First Report of the Committee on Climate Change, December 2008 London: The Stationery Office (TSO).

CCC (2009) "Meeting Carbon Budgets – the need for a step change, October 2009, presented to Parliament pursuant to section 36(1) of the Climate Change Act 2008". Available at: http://hmccc.s3.amazonaws.com/21667%20CCC%20Report%20AW%20WEB.pdf [Live: March 2010].

Clark, A. & J. Treanor (2008) "Greenspan – I was wrong about the economy. Sort of", *The Guardian*, 24 October 2008.

Combined Heat and Power Association (CHPA) (2009) "Heat Strategy Fails to Lift Jobs Threat to Industry", press release, 12 February 2009. Available at: http://www.chpa.co.uk/news/press_releases/2009/Heat%20Strategy%20Fails%20to%20Lift%20Jobs%20Threat%20to%20Industry%20120209.pdf [Live: March 2010].

Delta Energy & Environment (2009) *CHP Employment Survey: Report of findings*, Edinburgh: Delta Energy & Environment.

Department for Environment, Food and Rural Affairs

(Defra) (2002) *Action Plan to Develop Organic Food & Farming in England*, London: Defra.

Department of Energy and Climate Change (DECC) (2009) *Digest of United Kingdom Energy Statistics 2009*, London: TSO.

Dodd, N. (2008) Community Energy: Urban Planning for a Low Carbon Future, report prepared for the Town and Country Planning Association (TCPA) & Combined Heat & Power Association (CHPA). Available at: http://www.chpa.co.uk/news/reports_pubs/Community%20Energy-%20Urban%20Planning%20For%20A%20Low%20Carbon%20Future.pdf [Live: March 2010].

Dora, C. & M. Phillips (2000) Transport, environment and health, WHO Regional Publications, European Series No. 89, Geneva: World Health Organisation (WHO).

Easterlin, R. (1974) "Does economic growth improve the human lot?", in David, P. & M. Reder (eds) (1974) *Nations & households in economic growth: essays in honour of Moses Abramovitz*, New York: Academic Press.

Elliot, D. (1976) "Job creation: how saving energy could save jobs", *Undercurrents*, 15, pp. 85–98.

Energy Saving Trust, Econnect & Element Energy (2005) "Potential for microgeneration: study and analysis", Final report, 14 November 2005. Available at: http://www.berr.gov.uk/files/file27558.pdf [Live: March 2010].

Environmental Audit Committee (EAC – House of Commons) (1999) "Seventh Report, Energy Efficiency, Volume 2, Minutes of Evidence, Supplementary Memorandum Submitted by the Combined Heat and Power Association, 23 February 1999", pp. 122–129. Available at: http://www.publications.parliament.uk/pa/cm199899/cmselect/cmenvaud/159/9022306.htm [Live: March 2010].

EAC (2009) Pre–Budget Report 2008: Green fiscal policy in a recession, Government Response to the Committee's Third Report of Session 2008–09, London: The Stationery Office.

European Solar Thermal Industry Federation (ESTIF) (2009) "Solar thermal markets in Europe: Trends & Market Statistics 2008", May 2009, Brussels: ESTIF. Available at: http://www.estif.org/fileadmin/estif/content/market_data/downloads/2008%20Solar_Thermal_Markets_in_Europe_2008.pdf [Live: March 2010].

European Insulation Manufacturers Association (EURIMA) (2008) "Buildings – a wasted opportunity to secure Europe's energy?", press release, 8 March 2008. Available

at: http://www.eurima.org/uploads/PressCorner/
documents/0308_PR_response_to_GP_on_energy_
security_of_supply.pdf [Live: March 2010].

European Commission (2005) *Doing more with less: Green paper on energy efficiency*, Brussels: EC.

European Monitoring Centre on Change (2004) *Trends and drivers of change in the European railway equipment sector*, Dublin: European Foundation for the Improvement of Living & Working Conditions.

Evans, B. (1992) The Politics of the Training Market: from Manpower to Training and Enterprise Councils, London: Routledge.

Fairless, D. (2007) "Energy-go-round: How did little Spanish province become one of the world's leading wind-energy giants?", *Nature*, 447, pp. 1046–1048.

Faulin, J. *et al.* (2006) "The outlook for renewable energy in Navarre: An economic profile", *Energy Policy*, 34(15), pp. 2201–2216.

Green New Deal Group (2008) A Green New Deal: Joined up policies to solve the triple crunch of the credit crisis, climate change & high oil prices, London: nef.

Green New Deal Group (2009) The cuts don't work: Why investing in the Green New Deal will reduce public debt, London: nef.

Global Wind Energy Council (GWEC) & Greenpeace (2006) *Global Wind Energy Outlook 2006*, September 2006, Brussels/ Amsterdam: GWEC/Greenpeace.

Hadjilambrinos, C. (2000) "Understanding technology choice in electricity industries: a comparative study of France & Denmark", *Energy Policy*, 28(15), pp. 1111–1126.

Hewett, C. & J. Foley (2000) "Employment creation & environmental policy: a literature review", report commissioned by the Trade Union Sustainable Development Advisory Committee (TUSDAC), report by Public Policy Research Associates Ltd. Available at: http://www.ippr.org.uk/members/download.asp?f=%2Fecomm%2Ffiles%2Femployment%5Fcreation%5Fand%5Fenviro nmental%5Fpolicy%2Epdf [Live: March 2010].

Hirsch, D. (2007) *Chicken & egg: child poverty & education inequalities*, CPAG policy briefing, September 2007, London: Child Poverty Action Group (CPAG).

HM Government (2009) "Ultra-Low Carbon Vehicles in the UK". Available at: http://www.dft.gov.uk/adobepdf/187604/ultralowcarbonvehicle.pdf [Live: March 2010].

Hoehner, M. & M. Forst (2006) Der Deutsche

Photovoltaikmarkt 2006/07—Vom Nachfrageüberhang zum Wettbewerb, Bonn: EUPD Research.

Höhne *et al.* (2009) "Economic/climate recovery scorecards: How climate friendly are the economic recovery packages?", April 2009, E3G/WWF. Available at: http://www.germanwatch.org/klima/score09.pdf [Live: March 2010].

Hoffmann, C., M. Duran Haro & O. Strietska-Ilina (2009) "Skills for the low carbon economy", paper prepared for the European Commission's workshop "Emerging stronger from the recession to tackle the challenges of social cohesion & sustainable development", 9 September 2009.

International Energy Agency (IEA) (2002), Paris: OECD/IEA.

IEA (2005a) *Saving oil in a hurry*, Paris: OECD/IEA.

IEA (2005b): *Saving electricity in a hurry: Dealing with Temporary Shortfalls in Electricity Supplies*, Paris: OECD/IEA.

International Association of Public Transport (2009) "Statistics", UITP [online]. Available at: http://www.uitp.org/knowledge/Statistics.cfm [Live: March 2010].

Johnson, V., S. Simms & C. Cochrane (2009) Tackling climate change reducing poverty: the first report of the Roundtable on Climate Change & Poverty in the UK, London: nef/Roundtable on climate change & poverty in the UK.

Jones, P. & R. Crane (2009) "England & Wales under organic agriculture: how much food could be produced?", CAS Report 18, Reading: Centre for Agricultural Strategy, University of Reading.

Johnson, V. & M. Cottingham (2008) Plane Truths: Do the economics arguments for aviation growth fly?, London: nef.

Jungjohann, A. & B. Jahnke (2009) *Europe: Creating new jobs with renewable energies*, 19 May 2009, Heinrich Böll Stiftung. Available at: http://www.boell.org/downloads/Creating_Green_New_Jobs_with_Renewable_Energies1.pdf [Live: March 2010].

Kammen, D., K. Kapadia & M. Fripp (2004) "Putting Renewables to Work: How Many Jobs Can the Clean Energy Industry Generate?", Report of the Renewable and Appropriate Energy Laboratory, 13 APRIL 2004, corrected 31 January 2006, University of California, Berkeley. Available at: http://rael.berkeley.edu/sites/default/files/very-old-site/renewables.jobs.2006.pdf [Live: March 2010].

Lambert, J. (2008) "Green work employment & skills – the climate change challenge". Available at: http://www.jeanlambertmep.org.uk/DocumentStore/GreenWork_report.pdf [Live: March 2010].

Local Government Association (LGA) (2009) *Creating green jobs: developing low-carbon economies*, London: LGA.

Lockwood, J., J. Bird & R. Alvarez (2007) *2050 Vision*, London: ippr.

Lowe, P. & J. Goyder (1983) *Environmental Groups in Politics*, London: Allen & Unwin.

Lyubormirsky, S., K. Sheldon & D. Schkade (2005) "Pursuing happiness: the architecture of sustainable change", *Review of General Psychology*, 9(2), pp. 111–131.

Mackay D. (2009) *Sustainable Energy – without the hot air*, Cambridge: UIT Cambridge Ltd.

Maynard, R. & M. Green (2008) Organic Works – providing more jobs through organic farming and local food supply, Bristol: Soil Association.

McCurry, J. (2009) "Toyota picks UK to make new Auris hybrid car", *The Guardian*, 17 July 2009.

Office of National Statistics (ONS) (2004) *Focus on Social Inequalities*, 2004 edition, London: TSO.

Office of Rail Regulation (ORR) (2009) *National Rail Trends: 2008–2009 Yearbook*, London: ORR.

Owen, G. (1999) Public purpose or private benefit? The politics of energy conservation, Manchester: Manchester University Press.

Point Carbon (2009) "Trading Analytics", Point Carbon [webpage]. Available at: http://www.pointcarbon.com/trading/ [Live: March 2010].

Rail Freight Group (2005) "Facts and Statistics", Rail Freight Group [online]. Available at: http://www.rfg.org.uk/aboutfreight/facts/ [Live: March 2010].

Rat für Nachhaltige Entwicklung (2003) *The Perspectives for Coal in a Sustainable Energy Industry: Guidelines for a Modern Coal Policy and the Promotion of Innovation, Berlin:* Rat für Nachhaltige Entwicklung. Available at: http://www.nachhaltigkeitsrat.de/uploads/media/Broschuere_Kohleempfehlung_02.pdf [Accessed: 18 March 2010].

Roney, M. (2008) "Bicycles pedaling into the spotlight", Earth Policy Institute, 12 May 2008 [online]. Available at: http://www.earthpolicy.org/index.php?/indicators/C48/ [Live: March 2010].

Sewill, B. (2009) *Airport jobs: false hopes, cruel hoax*, London: Aviation Environment Federation (AEF).

Simms, A., V. Johnson & S. Nissan (2009) *Green stimulus or stimulus?* London: Greenpeace/nef.

Simms, A., P. Kjell & D. Woodward (2005) Mirage and oasis: Energy choices in an age of global warming, London: nef.

Staiss, F. *et al.* (2006) Wirkungen des Ausbaus der erneuerbaren Energien auf den deutschen Arbeitsmarkt unter besonderer Berücksichtigung des Aussenhandels, Berlin: Bundesministeriums für Umwelt, Naturschutz und Reaktorsicherheit. Available at: http://www.buergerprojekt-photovoltaik.de/downloads/bmuarbeitsmarktee2006.pdf [Live: March 2010].

Sustrans (n/d) "Economic appraisal of local walking & cycling routes". Available at: http://www.sustrans.org.uk/assets/files/general/Economic%20appraisal%20of%20local%20walking%20and%20cycling%20routes%20-%20summary.pdf [Live: March 2010]

Thompson, S. *et al.* (2007) The European (un)Happy Planet Index: An index of carbon efficiency and well-being in the EU, London: nef.

UK Photovoltaic Manufacturers Association (UK-PV) (2009) "2020: A vision for UK PV: An up to date and accurate analysis on the investment case for solar photovoltaics (PV) in the UK". Available at: http://uk-pv.org/wp-content/uploads/2009/10/UK-PV-report-03-09.pdf [Live: March 2010].

United Nations Environment Programme (UNEP) *et al.* (2008) *Green Jobs: Towards Decent work in a Sustainable, Low-Carbon World*, Nairobi: UNEP.

Weiss, W. & P. Biemayer (2009) *Potential of Solar Thermal in Europe*, Brussels: European Solar Thermal Industry Federation (ESTIF).

Wilkinson, R. & K. Pickett (2009) The Spirit Level: Why More Equal Societies Almost Always Do Better, London: Allen Lane.

Figure sources

Thompson, S. *et al.* (2007) The European (un)Happy Planet Index: An index of carbon efficiency and well-being in the EU, London: nef (Fig. 7, p. 28).

conclusions

Residual emissions

Greenhouse gas emissions from the industrial, commercial and waste sectors currently constitute around 24% of total British emissions, excluding the emissions from the electricity that they use.

A brief exploration of how these may be reduced is given below. Some emissions in these sectors are very hard to reduce, hence there will be some residual emissions from these sectors left in the ***zero**carbon**britain**2030* scenario. Together with the residual emissions from other sectors, these residual emissions are offset with sequestration in the scenario, bringing the net emissions to zero.

Industrial and commercial combustion

In 2007 about 83 million tonnes of CO_2e, or 13% of British emissions arose from combustion carried out in industrial, commercial and manufacturing contexts (Jackson *et al.*, 2009).

In the ***zero**carbon**britain**2030* scenario these processes are supplied with electricity, hydrogen, heat pumps and biomass Combined Heat & Power (CHP). We have allowed sufficient renewable resources to replace the current energy used in industrial processes by these technologies, but further work would be required to flesh out the details of the best way to decarbonise each area and process.

Landfill

Methane emissions from landfill have declined significantly over the past decade as landfill gas recovery has improved. However, landfill sites were still responsible for emitting 19.5 million tonnes of CO_2e in 2007, about 3% of British greenhouse gas emissions (calculated from Jackson *et al.*, 2009, and MacCarthy *et al.*, 2010).

AEA Technologies (1998) have estimated that through a mixture of improved landfill gas recovery, improved capping of landfill and a reduction in biodegradable waste sent to landfill, emissions from landfill in the UK could be reduced by 2020 to 177,000 tonnes CH_4, or 4.4 million tonnes of CO_2e. Converting this UK figure to one for Great Britain gives 4.2 million tonnes which we will use for the ***zero**carbon**britain**2030* scenario.

The "super greenhouse gases": HFCs, PFCs and SF6

About 1.5% of UK greenhouse gas emissions are from the greenhouse gases hydrofluorocarbons (HFCs), perfluorocarbons (PFCs) and sulfur hexafluoride (SF6) (Jackson *et al.*, 2009; MacCathy *et al.*, 2010). Only tiny quantities of these chemicals are released but they are extremely potent with greenhouse gas potentials hundreds or thousands of times that of CO_2. They are used in many applications including refrigeration, air conditioning, aerosols, manufacture of foam, metals and semiconductors, electrical and thermal insulation, asthma inhalers and fire fighting.

Thankfully, with the exception of medical inhalers there are reasonably-priced mitigation options and substitutes available for nearly all applications. Lucas *et al.* (2007) suggested that a 90% reduction in CO_2e emissions from these gases could be achieved by 2050 at costs of less than $250 US/t$CO_2$e. Lucas *et al.* did not assess more rapid reductions, but as the technologies to reduce all of these gases to minimal quantities have been readily available for a long time (Heijnes *et al.*, 1999), the **zero***carbon***britain**2030 scenario assumes that by 2030 emissions from the super greenhouse gases will have been reduced to 10% of their current quantity.

Cement production

About 5.7 million tonnes of CO_2 equivalent, or 1% of British emissions were produced from the chemical processes involved in cement production in the UK in 2007 (Jackson *et al.*, 2009; MacCarthy *et al.*, 2010). The manufacture of cement involves turning limestone into calcium carbonate, and carbon dioxide is given off during the process.

It is possible to reduce greenhouse gases from cement by 80 or 90% by using geopolymer rather than ordinary Portland cement (Geopolymer Institute, 2010). In addition, in the **zero***carbon***britain**2030 scenario cement production is reduced due to the shift to more ecological building techniques which actually sequester carbon; further details are in the buildings section. In the case of cement, this can also be reduced through combining it with pulverised fuel ash.

We therefore assume that emissions from cement production fall by 90%.

Adipic and nitric acid production

Most nitrous oxide produced from industrial sources originates from adipic and nitric acid production. The former is used for the production of nylons and the latter is used primarily for fertiliser production. 2.8 million tonnes of CO_2e, or 0.5% of British emissions, arose from the production of these acids in 2007 (Jackson *et al.*, 2009; MacCarthy *et al.*, 2010).

By changing production processes, it is possible to reduce emissions from the production of these acids by 90–98% at a low cost of less than 5 dollars a tonne of CO_2e (Lucas et al., 2007). We assume that emissions are reduced by 97%.

Lime production

About 1 million tonnes, or 0.1% of British emissions were produced from lime production and use in the UK in 2007 (Jackson *et al.*, 2009; MacCarthy *et al.*, 2010). Lime is

Table 12.1 Summary of industrial, waste and residual emissions:

Source	% of 2007 quantity remaining in ZCB2030 scenario	Residual emissions (million tonnes CO_2e)
Industrial combustion	0	0
Landfill	22%	4.2
Other waste	100%	2.4
Cement production	10%	0.6
High greenhouse gas potential greenhouse gases	10%	2.4
Lime production	300%	3.1
Iron and steel production non-combustion emissions	100%	6.8
Nitric and adipic acid production	3%	0.08
Other chemical processes	100%	4.4
Land converted to settlements	70%	4
Emissions from disused coal mines	100%	1.2
Total residual emissions: Industrial, waste, land conversion to settlements and disused coal mines		**29.82**
Residual emissions from the land use and agriculture sector		**17**
Miscellaneous residual emissions from the other sectors		**20**
Residual emissions: Grand total		**67**
2007 emissions		**637**
Percentage of 2007 emissions remaining		**10%**

Industrial, waste and residual emissions in the ZCB2030, compared to 2007 (million tonnes CO_2e).
Source: 2007 emissions data from Jackson et al. *(2009) and MacCarthy* et al. *(2010).*

used as an agricultural soil amendment. In the **zero**carbon**britain**2030 scenario lime production and its associated emissions is trebled, due to the increased growing of biomass for energy production and carbon sequestration.

Iron and steel production

Much of the emissions from steelmaking come from chemical processes rather than from combustion. These occur during the production of iron from iron ore, which is an iron oxide. To separate the iron and the oxygen, it is customary to use carbon in the form of coal or coke. The oxygen combines with the carbon and is released as carbon dioxide in a process known as "reduction".

It is possible to reduce iron ore using either hydrogen or electrolysis instead of carbon and the processes have been demonstrated at a small scale (Ultra–Low Carbon Dioxide Steelmaking [ULCOS], 2010). Assuming the electricity is renewably produced, producing steel using electrolysis should be able to reduce greenhouse gas emissions to close to zero.

Sadly, the reduction of iron ore by these methods is considered to be decades away from commercialisation (Weddige, 2008). For this reason we have not included these methods in the scenario, but it is useful to note that in the longer term it should be possible to almost entirely decarbonise iron and steel production.

Other industrial processes

There are a number of other greenhouse gases produced from industrial processes such as glass and chemicals manufacture, which each produce less than 0.1% of British emissions (Jackson et al., 2009; MacCarthy et al., 2010). These remain unchanged in the scenario although it may be possible to reduce some or all of them. Further work would be necessary to establish where reductions could be made.

Land use change: land converted to settlements

Land conversion to settlements generated 5.7 million tonnes of CO_2e in 2007, 0.9 percent of British greenhouse gas emissions. In the **zero**carbon**britain**2030 scenario, town planning is adapted with the aim of increasing the density of existing settlements rather than encouraging continued outward urban sprawl, as detailed in the transport section. For this reason we assume that 2007 emissions from land conversion to settlements are reduced by 30% in the scenario, to 4 million tonnes.

Conclusion

The 67 million tonnes of CO_2e. residual emissions which will need to be matched by sequestration.